ARMORED CAR

A HISTORY OF AMERICAN WHEELED COMBAT VEHICLES

by

R.P. Hunnicutt

Line Drawings
by
Michael Duplessis

FOREWORD
by
General Gordon R. Sullivan, U.S. Army (Retired)

ECHO POINT BOOKS & MEDIA, LLC

Published by Echo Point Books & Media
Brattleboro, Vermont
www.EchoPointBooks.com

Copyright © 2002, 2015 R. P. Hunnicutt
ISBN: 978-1-62654-155-9

Cover image by Deisel Division, General Motors of Canada Limited

Cover design by Adrienne Núñez,
Echo Point Books & Media

Editorial and proofreading assistance by Christine Schultz,
Echo Point Books & Media

Printed and bound in the United States of America

CONTENTS

ACKNOWLEDGEMENTS

The vehicles described in this volume covered a period of over a century. As a result, information had to be sought from a wide variety of sources ranging from the late 1890s to the present day. I would like to express my gratitude to the many people who helped with this research and to particularly thank General Gordon R. Sullivan who was kind enough to write the Foreword.

John Purdy, Charles Lemons and Candace Fuller at the Patton Museum were especially helpful. A lot of material came from the collection of my old friend the late Colonel Robert J. Icks that is now in the Museum Library. Also at Fort Knox, Jon Clemens of Armor Magazine located many of the photographs included in the book.

The Marine Corps Museum at Quantico, Virginia was the source of most of the photographs and data on the Marine Corps light armored vehicles. These were located by Ordnance Specialist Dieter Stenger who also arranged an opportunity to photograph some of the vehicles.

The Ordnance Museum and Library at Aberdeen Proving Ground provided much valuable information thanks to the Director Dr. William F. Atwater.

The U. S. Army Transportation Museum was the major source of information and photographs of the vehicles armed and armored for use as gun trucks during the fighting in Vietnam.

Dr. Richard E. McClelland of the U. S. Army Tank Automotive Research, Development and Engineering Center found drawings, photographs and other material essential to the research project.

David Fletcher of the Tank Museum at Bovington, England supplied photographs and the answers to many questions regarding the armored cars built in the United States for Britain during World War II.

Hal Johnson produced many of the photographs in the book from his superb collection. His help was essential to the early part of the story.

As usual, my friend Fred Pernell, formerly with the National Archives, guided me in locating many old records and photographs, particularly of the World War II period.

Jeff McKaughan of Darlington Productions supplied material from his publication "Journal of Military Ordnance".

At Textron Marine & Land Systems, Paige Eaton provided photographs and data on the Armored Security Vehicle.

When locating vehicle photographs, a visit to Fred Crismon's home ranks almost on par with the National Archives. His excellent books also provided much valuable information.

Michael Green and Greg Stewart were the source of many photographs, particularly those of the Marine Corps light armored vehicles.

I am indebted to Steve Zaloga for his help with some of the World War II vehicles. He is the undoubted expert on modifications and markings applied by the troops in the field.

Some of the best photographs of the Marine Corps light armored vehicles came from Wade Barttels. I only wish that there was room for all of them.

Other photographs were furnished by Jim Mesko, David Haugh, Todd Fitzgerald of General Motors Defense and Reg Hodgson of Army Motors. As usual, many problems were solved by examining the restored vehicles in the incredible collection of my friend Jacques Littlefield. Dean and Nancy Kleffman also were always ready to help track down photographs of some elusive vehicle.

Michael Duplessis prepared the five view drawings of the key armored cars. He also noticed many variations and modifications of these vehicles that frequently escaped my notice.

My first book on American armor was published 31 years ago in early 1971. This is the tenth and final volume of the series. Since this is my last book, I would like, once again, to thank everyone who supplied the research material, photographs and valuable advice that made these books possible.

R. P. Hunnicutt
Granite Bay, California
April 2002

FOREWORD
by
General Gordon R. Sullivan, U. S. Army (Retired)

I can think of no better time for Dick Hunnicutt to publish "A History of American Wheeled Combat Vehicles." General Eric Shinseki, Army Chief of Staff, decided correctly, in my view, to acquire a number of modern, functionally designed, wheeled combat vehicles. These modern vehicles, unlike the original ones are designed primarily for strategic deployability and use in low to mid intensity environments; however, as a reading of this historical survey will indicate, once again, there is very little new in the experience of the United States Army.

In March 2000, Major General James Dubik, Deputy Commanding General, U. S. Army Training and Doctrine Command, noted in remarks related to wheeled vehicles, "What we are trying to do is provide the nation with a capability that does not exist and to provide our soldiers with the kind of equipment that they need to succeed in a new environment."

It is noteworthy and probably news to most that Colonel Royal P. Davidson, Illinois National Guard, as a major in 1898 installed a Colt .30 caliber machine gun on a Duryea light three wheeled car. From this small beginning over a century ago, the Army has come full circle and Dick Hunnicutt enables students and professionals to learn, and from this learning, shape the future.

Throughout World War II, a lot of emphasis was devoted to the development of wheeled combat vehicles. Much of the early work resulted from the British experience in the Desert and many of the vehicles were built for them. The M8 was the most produced lightly armored vehicle. Over 8,500 were built by Ford between 1943 and 1945. I think the most interesting aspect of this program is found in the British and U. S. conclusion that this vehicle was capable of crossing Class 9 bridges which apparently was the class of replacement bridges used to replace those destroyed by enemy action. Tactical, operational and strategic mobility has challenged the leadership of the Army for years as they attempt to balance the lethality, survivability and mobility equation against affordability.

The time for armored wheeled combat vehicles has returned. Dick Hunnicutt's well-researched and documented historical treatment of the ups and downs of wheeled vehicles is important and timely. Ground forces have always required a wide variety of equipment designed to satisfy functional demands.

One hundred years from today, this excellent compilation of facts will provide analysts what they need to learn about the realities of ground force use of wheeled combat vehicles.

INTRODUCTION

Wheeled combat vehicles in the armed forces of the United States have had a history of intermittent employment. Despite the efforts of early pioneers such as Colonel Royal P. Davidson, only a few experimental armored cars were built prior to World War I. The lack of employment of such vehicles by the U. S. Army during that war resulted in a lack of interest during the early postwar period. An exception to this was the use of armored cars by the U. S. Marine Corps during their operations in the 1920s. The Army did evaluate some light automobiles during this period to determine their value as "cross-country" cars. However, they were not armed or armored.

In 1928, the Army procured two T1 light armored cars based upon a Pontiac chassis beginning a development series that continued until the armored car was deleted from the list of U. S. Army requirements in 1937. During this period, the armored car M1 had been standardized and 20 produced. At that time, it was believed that the light, open top, scout cars being produced for the Cavalry would meet all requirements.

With opening of World War II the situation changed. The experience of the British in the desert had shown the value of armored cars and they requested large numbers to be produced for their use. The U. S. Army considered that the role of the armored car was as a reconnaissance vehicle and it should be light enough to cross any bridges likely to be encountered in the area of operation. As a result, the weight was limited to about eight tons. This eliminated the medium and heavy armored cars then under development. Some of these were produced for use by Britain. The U. S. Army adopted the light armored car M8 and its later derivative, the light armored utility car M20. Just before the end of the war, the new M38 armored car was standardized, but its production was canceled by the end of hostilities. The M38 was a far superior vehicle weighing a little less than the M8 and equipped with a fully independent suspension giving it excellent cross-country mobility.

The Army Ground Forces Equipment Review Board recommended that an armored car based upon the M38 be retained in the postwar army. However, doctrine now gave the reconnaissance role to the light tank and the later Stilwell Board dropped any requirement for an armored car. Thus the state of the art M38 was never produced and the M8 and M20 armored cars continued in service until after the Korean War.

When the United States became involved in Vietnam, an armored car was required for truck convoy escort and military police work. Except for a few proposals, armored car development had ceased and the Army had to turn to a commercial source to meet the new requirement. The need was met by a small four wheel armored car named the V-100 Commando produced by the Cadillac Gage Company. After field tests in Vietnam and some minor modification, it was standardized as the M706 and a modified version was designated as the XM706E1. Both types performed excellent service during the war in Vietnam. However, because of their limited numbers, other vehicles, including several types of trucks, were armored in the field to perform the escort role.

Experimental programs to improve the cross-country mobility of wheeled vehicles produced some interesting solutions. The Lockheed Twister consisted of two bodies joined by a yoke that permitted movement about the pitch, roll and yaw axes. Experience from this program was applied to the wheeled version of the Armored Reconnaissance Scout Vehicle (ARSV). However, the wheeled Scout lost out in competition with the tracked version. In the end, neither type was produced.

In September 1982, the U.S. Marine Corps adopted the eight wheel light armored vehicle (LAV) produced by General Motors of Canada. To equip the Marine LAV battalions, the vehicles were produced in several types. Initially, these consisted of the basic LAV-25 armed with a turret mounted 25mm M242 automatic gun and carrying a scout section of four to six marines, a command and control vehicle, a mortar carrier, an antitank vehicle, a logistics vehicle and a recovery vehicle. Later, an air defense version was produced armed with Stinger missiles. An assault gun armed with a 105mm gun was developed, but it never went into production.

The LAVs were successfully employed by the Marines during Operation Just Cause in Panama and in the Persian Gulf War. The scout platoon of the 3/73rd Armor in the 82nd Airborne Division also used LAVs on loan from the Marines.

With the Army transformation program announced by the Army Chief of Staff in October 1999, the wheeled combat vehicle was again under consideration. On 16 November 2000, the LAV III was selected as the interim armored vehicle for the new force and a contract was awarded for its production to General Motors and General Dynamics Land Systems.

Perhaps at long last, the wheeled combat vehicle will have a major role in the U.S. Army.

PART I

EARLY DEVELOPMENT

Above, the Duryea light three wheeled car armed by Colonel Davidson appears at the left. The later four wheel Duryea is at the right. The .30 caliber Colt Model 1895 "Potato Digger" machine gun can be seen on both vehicles.

THE APPEARANCE OF WHEELED FIGHTING VEHICLES

The advent of the automobile resulted in numerous efforts to apply the new mode of transportation to military use. These early efforts considered the automobile both as a means of transporting weapons to their point of use and as an actual fighting vehicle. As would be expected from the early interest in automotive development, a number of such applications were made in the United States. A name which appeared frequently during the early years of American fighting vehicle development was that of Colonel Royal P. Davidson. An officer in the Illinois National Guard, Colonel Davidson was Commandant of the Northwestern Military and Naval Academy. As a major in 1898, he was responsible for the installation of a Colt Model 1895 .30 caliber machine gun on the Duryea light three wheeled car. The armor on this vehicle was limited to a small shield on the machine gun. Later, the same weapon was installed on the four wheel Duryea. Under Colonel Davidson's leadership, additional fighting vehicles were produced. These included two steam powered cars. The armament was the Colt Model 1895 .30 caliber machine gun, the same as used on the earlier vehicles. Colonel Davidson was encouraged by Major General Nelson A. Miles who recommended that the Army convert some cavalry units

The 37mm automatic cannon installed on the truck bed by Samuel M. McClean is being demonstrated at the right.

to an automobile corps. Unfortunately, in 1905 there was no support for such a project.

During this period, other people were showing interest in fitting weapons to mobile mounts. In the Summer of 1904, Samuel M. McClean demonstrated his 37mm automatic cannon mounted on a truck bed. Designated as a one pounder at the time, it was a gas operated, fully automatic, weapon fed by clips holding either five or ten cartridges. Although over 1,000 rounds of ammunition were fired during the tests, the gun was considered to be unsatisfactory. Numerous breakages and difficulties with the sights and gun mount were responsible. Other one pounder truck mounts were tested during this same period, but none were adopted for service.

Above, steam powered cars numbers 1 and 2 can be seen at the left and Colonel Davidson's 1909 semi-armored Cadillac is at the right. On the latter, the Colt machine guns have been fitted with high angle mounts for use as a balloon destroyer. No doubt, this was the first American antiaircraft vehicle. Colonel Davidson was definitely ahead of his time.

Colonel Davidson continued his work during the period prior to the entry of the United States into World War I and produced a number of interesting vehicles. These included special purpose cars for radio communication and reconnaissance work, a field kitchen, and a vehicle for medical use. Beginning in 1910, he constructed several partially armored cars using a Cadillac chassis. Although the first Cadillac carried its .30 caliber machine gun mounted on the dash, two later such vehicles were fitted with high angle mounts for anti-balloon use. The first fully armored car was completed in 1914 using, once again, a Cadillac chassis. In the Spring of 1915, Colonel Davidson led a convoy of eight cars from Chicago to San Francisco to evaluate their performance on the roads of that period. They arrived in San Francisco during the Panama-Pacific Exposition.

Above at the right is the fully armored Cadillac assembled in 1914. The vehicles of the 1915 convoy to San Francisco are shown below ready for their long cross-country trip.

The fully armored Davidson Cadillac can be seen in the views above and below at the left. Note the Colt machine guns still provide the armament. Colonel Davidson also was aware of the need for improved communications and the Cadillac below at the right was converted into a radio car for use in reconnaissance.

During the same year, the Jeffrey Motor Company built a fully armored car based upon its quad truck chassis. This vehicle, known as Armored Car Number 1, was equipped with four wheel drive, dual controls, and four wheel steering. First used by the New York National Guard in 1915, it was armed with two Colt .30 caliber machine guns protected by shields. The Canadian Russell armored car also utilized the Jeffrey quad truck chassis at about the same time.

The Jeffrey Quad truck chassis appears in the two photographs below. The various components are identified in the drawing at the right. Note the two driver's seats and steering wheels in the photographs that would permit rapid movement in either direction.

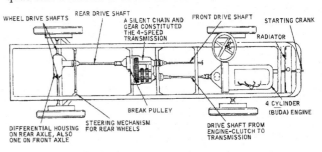

WHEEL DRIVE SHAFTS   REAR DRIVE SHAFT   A SILENT CHAIN AND GEAR CONSTITUTED THE 4-SPEED TRANSMISSION   FRONT DRIVE SHAFT   STARTING CRANK   RADIATOR   4 CYLINDER (BUDA) ENGINE   DRIVE SHAFT FROM ENGINE-CLUTCH TO TRANSMISSION   STEERING MECHANISM FOR REAR WHEELS   BREAK PULLEY   DIFFERENTIAL HOUSING ON REAR AXLE, ALSO ONE ON FRONT AXLE

Armored Car Number 1 appears in the views above and at the left. Below is another armored body also installed on the Jeffrey four wheel drive chassis.

At the left, Armored Car Number 1 is serving with the troops on the Mexican border during 1916. Below are views of the Canadian Russell armored car utilizing the Jeffrey Quad chassis.

In 1916, these cars were in use by regular army units serving on the Mexican border and at that time, the armament was the .30 caliber Benet-Mercie Model 1909 machine gun. During this same period, a vehicle designated as Armored Car Number 2 was produced by the White Motor Company. Like the Jeffrey vehicle, the armor was limited to a maximum thickness of $\frac{1}{5}$ inch and the armament still consisted of rifle caliber machine guns. Armored Car Number 2 also was used to equip troops serving on the Mexican border.

Armored Car Number 2 can be seen in the two photographs above. The view at the top left shows the vehicle during its service on the Mexican border. No armament is visible in these views.

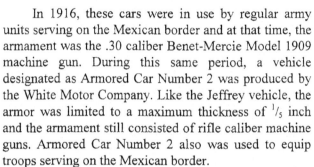

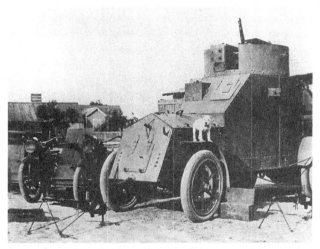

The .30 caliber Benet-Mercie machine gun used to arm these vehicles is shown above at the left. This weapon can be seen with Armored Car Number 2 on the Mexican border above at the right. Two additional views of Armored Car Number 2 appear below in these photographs dated June 1916.

Above, the Mack truck chassis used as the basis for an armored car is at the left. At the top right, it is fitted with the armored hull and shields for two machine guns on the open top vehicle.

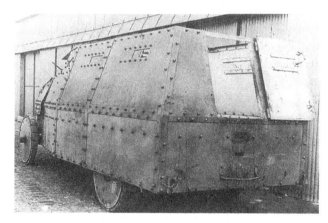

Later photographs of the Mack armored car dated 1 March 1920 are shown above. Note the slots provided in the front armor to increase the flow of cooling air to the radiator. The general arrangement and dimensions of the armored car can be seen in the contemporary sketch below.

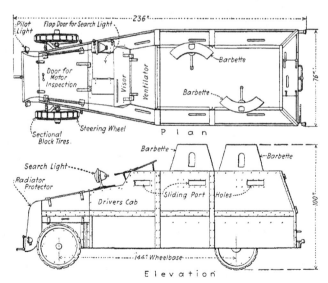

The Mack armored car consisted of an open top box-like hull installed on the chassis of a Mack 2 ton truck. Weighing over 9,000 pounds, it was driven by a four cylinder, 45 horsepower, engine. The hull was a bolted assembly of $\frac{1}{5}$ inch thick steel armor plate. Armament on the open top vehicle consisted of two .30 caliber machine guns with shields on swivel mounts. Hulls of a similar design also were installed on Locomobile and White chassis for use by the New York National Guard in 1916. The three vehicles served on the Mexican border that same year.

At the right, all three armored cars are operating together during 1920. From front to rear are the White, Mack and Locomobile vehicles.

14

Above are two early views of the Mack armored car. The front armor over the radiator has not yet been installed and a sheet metal cover is fitted in its place. Below are two photographs of the White armored car with an early view at the left. Like the Mack above, a sheet metal cover is installed over the front in place of armor. The right photograph, dated 2 March 1920, shows the armored front.

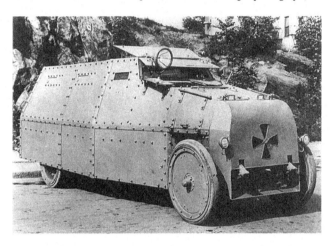

The Locomobile armored car appears above. All three of the armored cars served as training vehicles and were used in parades for morale purposes and to sell Liberty bonds. Although, like the other armored cars, they were deployed to the Mexican border in 1916, they never saw combat.

 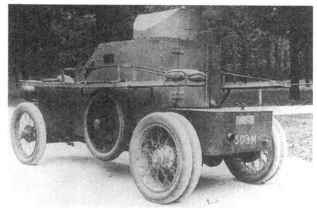

The original configuration of the King armored car can be seen in the photographs above and below dated September 1916. At the lower right, the vehicle is operating off the road in reasonably rough terrain. Note the dual tires on the rear.

In 1917, two additional cars were designed and built. The first was a product of the King Motor Car Company and the second was another design by the White Company and the Van Dorn Iron Works. Once again, armament was limited to rifle caliber machine guns and protection was provided only against small arms fire. With the limited employment of armored cars in France during the latter part of World War I, none of these designs created enough interest to ensure production in large numbers. However, the King armored car was employed by the United States Marine Corps during operations in the Caribbean after World War I.

A modified version of the King vehicle also referred to as the King-Eight armored car appears below. These photographs taken at Rock Island Arsenal were dated 1 March 1920. Note the new sloped configuration of the armor on the rear of the vehicle.

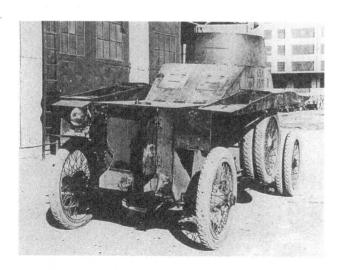 

The 1917 White armored car on this page was fitted with an armored body produced by the Van Dorn Iron Works. The rear hatch and the radiator armor are shown in both the open and closed positions.

Below are side views of the 1917 White armored car with the armored body by the Van Dorn Iron Works. Note the sign in the background indicating its travel on the Lincoln Highway.

 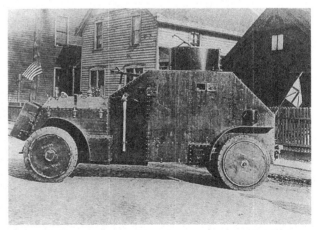

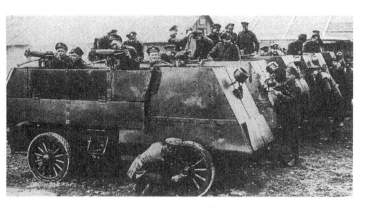

The armored Autocar vehicles employed by the 1st Canadian Motor Machine Gun Brigade can be seen above and at the right. Note the Vickers machine guns on these cars.

Although the American Expeditionary Force did not employ armored cars in France, American car and truck chassis provided the basis for several vehicles used by the British and Canadian forces. The 1st Canadian Motor Machine Gun Brigade organized by Lieutenant Colonel Raymond Brutinel was equipped with Autocar vehicles fitted with an armored cab and folding armor panels on the sides and rear. The open top cars were armed with Vickers machine guns although Colt machine guns were originally installed. Twenty of these armored cars were shipped to France and they were particularly effective in helping to halt the German offensive of March 1918.

Other Canadian armored cars were based upon the Packard motor car and, as mentioned earlier, the Russell armored car made use of the Jeffrey quad chassis.

Seabrook (Standard) and Pierce-Arrow chassis were armored and armed with 3 pounder guns to provide fire support to armored car units in British service. Some of the Pierce-Arrow vehicles were assigned to the Russian Armored Car Division of the British Royal

Naval Air Service. This unit, under the leadership of Commander Oliver Locker-Lampson, served on the Eastern Front starting in early 1916. During this period, it was noted that the Ford Model T used as a tender had fairly good off road mobility because of its high ground clearance and light weight. As a result, Commander Locker-Lampson requested that a number of the Model Ts be fitted with armor plate and shipped out to Russia. Nine of the vehicles had heavier rear springs installed and were armored with 5mm thick steel plate according to the design prepared by Chief Petty Officer L. Gutteridge. The driver's cab was armored on the top and all sides and the armament consisted of a single Maxim or Vickers machine gun in the open top rear compartment. Shipped out to Russia, the armored Model Ts served the Royal Navy until the collapse of the imperial regime during the Russian revolution. The ubiquitous Model T also was armed in its normal unarmored state on several occasions with Vickers or Lewis machine guns.

The British made use of the Pierce-Arrow chassis to carry some heavy armament with armor protection. Below at the left, the Antiaircraft Brigade of the Royal Marine Artillery is equipped with a 2 pounder Pom-Pom gun installed on an armored Pierce-Arrow. Note the attachments to the wheels in an effort to improve traction on the soft ground. At the bottom right, a 1 pounder Pom-Pom is mounted on a Pierce-Arrow armored by Vickers.

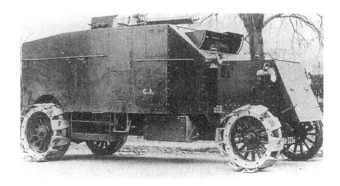

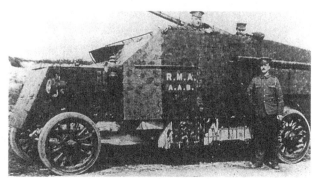

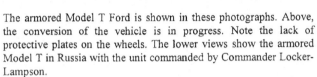

The armored Model T Ford is shown in these photographs. Above, the conversion of the vehicle is in progress. Note the lack of protective plates on the wheels. The lower views show the armored Model T in Russia with the unit commanded by Commander Locker-Lampson.

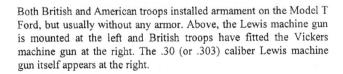

Both British and American troops installed armament on the Model T Ford, but usually without any armor. Above, the Lewis machine gun is mounted at the left and British troops have fitted the Vickers machine gun at the right. The .30 (or .303) caliber Lewis machine gun itself appears at the right.

Photographs of the 75mm antiaircraft truck mount model 1917 are above and at the right. A top view drawing of this weapon in firing position is at the bottom of the page.

European experience had shown the need for highly mobile antiaircraft weapons prior to the entry of the United States into World War I. To meet this requirement, the 75mm gun Model 1916 was adapted to the White 2 ton truck chassis. Weapon and mount were installed at the rear of the chassis over the rear axle. With a maximum elevation of 82 degrees and a total traverse of 240 degrees, the weapon fired a 15 pound high explosive shell with a muzzle velocity of 1,830 feet per second. The chassis was equipped with jacks to support the firing platform thus relieving the load on the truck springs. The complete weapon was designated as the 75mm antiaircraft truck mount Model 1917.

J. Walter Christie also built five, four wheel drive (4x4), chassis armed with the 3 inch antiaircraft gun M1917. This was a more powerful weapon with a muzzle velocity of 2,600 feet per second.

The Christie chassis armed with the 3 inch gun M1917 is above.

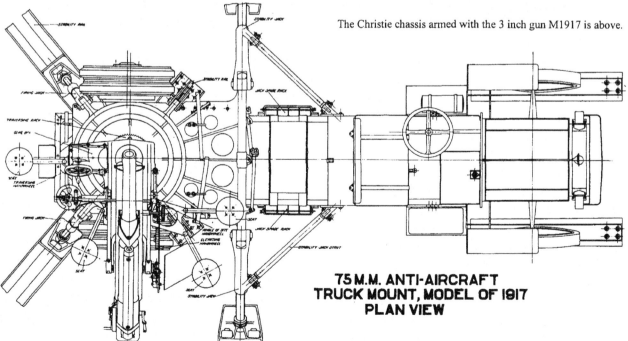

75 M.M. ANTI-AIRCRAFT
TRUCK MOUNT, MODEL OF 1917
PLAN VIEW

20

Above is a lineup of Ford cross-country cars at Aberdeen Proving Ground on 6 October 1925.

DEVELOPMENT PRIOR TO WORLD WAR II

At the end of World War I and the subsequent reduction in armaments, armored car development essentially ceased in the United States. However, during the 1920s, the Army evaluated a series of vehicles referred to as "cross-country cars". These were commercial vehicles stripped down to bare essentials and frequently fitted with oversize tires to improve their mobility over soft terrain.

Above, Ford cross-country car Number 50 appears at the left and Chevrolet cross-country car number 71 is at the right. Note the different stowage for the spare tire. Below at the left, Secretary of War Dwight Davis and former Chief of Staff General Hines get a ride in a Ford cross-country car. At the bottom right, Chevrolet cross-country car number 71 is operating on a slope. Note the chains on the rear wheels for better traction.

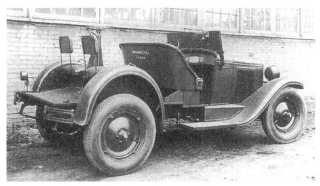

Above, the Pontiac chassis that became the light armored car T1 is shown at the left without any armor, but two .30 caliber machine guns have been mounted. At the top right, the windshield armor has been installed, but the machine guns are omitted.

The light armored car T1 on the Pontiac chassis appears above with the windshield and radiator armor installed and the two .30 caliber machine guns mounted. These photographs taken at Aberdeen Proving Ground were dated 12 October 1928.

In 1928, the Ordnance Department built two T1 light armored cars based upon a Pontiac chassis. The term armored car was rather optimistic since the only protection was that from a $\frac{1}{4}$ inch thick steel plate replacing the windshield. Pedestal mounts were provided for two .30 caliber machine guns. At the same time, the Cadillac Company built the armored car T2. Four of these vehicles were produced based upon the commercial La Salle chassis and the armament was still limited to a .30 caliber machine gun. The armor now covered the front, sides and rear, but the thickness was reduced to $\frac{1}{8}$ inch. Powered by an 86 horsepower V8 engine, the T2 had a maximum road speed of 70 miles per hour. The T2 was subsequently developed into the T2E1, T2E2, T2E3, and T2E4 with the latter four having a turret added.

The armored car T3 was a modified Pontiac touring car. It also was designated as the scout car T1 and it is described under that designation.

Details of the front machine gun mount and the driver's controls on the light armored car T1 are visible above.

The medium armored car T2 based upon the LaSalle chassis is shown in the two photographs above. Below, a medium armored car T2E1 is at the left and a T2E1(left) and T2E2(right) are at the right. Note that the lowered rear hull on the T2E2 permits higher turret walls and greater protection for the gunner without increasing the height of the vehicle.

Above, the medium armored car T2E2 is at the left and the medium armored car T2E3 is at the right. Details of the .30 caliber machine gun and mount on the T2E2 can be seen at the right.

The Armored car T4 is shown on this page prior to its standardization as the armored car M1. The upper photographs taken at Aberdeen Proving Ground were dated 30 June 1931. The windshields are lowered and replaced by the armor plate in the views above.

The armor plate is raised and the windshields are in place in the photographs of the armored car T4 above. The rear pistol port is open in the view at the left. The spare wheels were mounted so that they could carry a load and roll to help the vehicle cross obstacles on rough terrain.

The first American armored car to be standardized started out as the T4 designed by the Ordnance Department. Two were built by James Cunningham, Son and Company in 1931. After tests at Aberdeen Proving Ground, they were standardized as the armored car M1. A total of 20 of these cars were produced up to March 1938. The M1 armored car weighed over 10,000 pounds and was armed with one .50 caliber and two .30 caliber machine guns. The maximum armor plate thickness was $3/8$ inches. Driven by a 133 horsepower V8 engine, the M1 had a maximum road speed of about 55 miles per hour.

The armored car T5 was a designation originally applied to the combat car T2 before the latter name was selected for use by the Cavalry. It was a convertible wheel or track vehicle.

At the right, the armored car T4 is at Rock Island Arsenal on 19 May 1932. Note that the armored louvers over the radiator are fully open.

Above, the armored car T4 is under test at Aberdeen Proving Ground. In the view at the top right, the T4 is stuck in the mud despite the installation of tracks around the rear wheels.

At the right, the vehicle, now standardized as the armored car M1, is serving with Troop A, 1st Cavalry at Fort Knox, Kentucky during 1938.

The M1 armored cars above and below at the left carry the markings of the 1st Cavalry. The armament of one .50 caliber and two .30 caliber machine guns can be seen in the turret. The M1 at the upper right is on Governor's Island, New York during 1938. New York City is in the background. Note that the armored radiator louvers are closed.

Above, the Franklin 1¼ ton truck chassis is at the left and the armored car T6-4WD is at the right. Note that it carries the marking of A Troop, 1st Cavalry. The turret and machine gun mount are similar to that on the armored car T2E2.

The armored car T6 appears above. This is the vehicle converted from the armored car T7. As its markings indicate, it was in service with the 1st Cavalry at Fort Knox in this photograph dated 1934. Note the dual tires on the rear wheels.

Starting about 1925, the Quartermaster Depot at Fort Holabird, Maryland began the design and assembly of a series of trucks utilizing commercially available parts. These vehicles were referred to as the Standard Fleet. The lightest vehicle in the series was the 1¼ ton 4x4 powered by the Franklin 95 horsepower air-cooled engine. The basic chassis was designed to carry either a cargo or an armored body. The first example of the latter was the armored car T6-4WD with the designation indicating its four wheel drive. Protected by 3/16 inch thick armor plate, it weighed about 7,200 pounds. The vehicle was armed with a single, turret mounted, .30 caliber machine gun.

At the right is another view of the armored car T6 (formerly T7)

The armored car T7, sometimes referred to as the Franklin armored car, appears in all of these photographs. Note the turret mounted water cooled .50 caliber machine gun and the two air cooled .30 caliber machine guns.

The second armored vehicle based upon the Quartermaster $1\frac{1}{4}$ ton standard truck was designated as the armored car T7. Armament on the T7 consisted of a water-cooled .50 caliber machine gun in the cylindrical rotating turret and two .30 caliber air-cooled machine guns. One of the latter was mounted in the right front and one in the rear of the crew compartment. The T7 hull was assembled from $\frac{3}{16}$ inch thick armor plate and

was designed to be interchangeable with the cargo body on the $1\frac{1}{4}$ ton 4x4 truck. A total of six T7 armored cars were built at Fort Holabird. One of these was later modified with a new armor configuration and fitted with an angular turret with flat sides similar to that on the original T6. The modified vehicle was redesignated as the armored car T6 and it was armed with a single .30 caliber machine gun.

27

One of the two T8 light armored cars based upon the Chevrolet chassis is shown in these three photographs. The armament consisting of a single, turret mounted, .30 caliber air cooled machine gun is clearly visible.

In an effort to obtain a low cost, lightweight, armored car, the Quartermaster Depot at Fort Holabird built six light armored cars using commercial 4x2 chassis. This work extended from 1928 to 1930. The first of these was designated as the light armored car T8 utilizing a Chevrolet chassis powered by a six cylinder engine. Two T8s were completed. The armored car T9 was similar in appearance, but it was based upon a Plymouth chassis powered by a four cylinder engine. Only one T9 was completed. The armored car T10 was based upon a Willys-Overland Whippet chassis with a four cylinder engine. Three T10 armored cars were completed. Armor on these vehicles ranged from $1/8$ to $3/16$ inches thick. All three types were armed with a single air-cooled .30 caliber machine gun in a cylindrical turret and they all weighed about two tons. One T10 was later modified with flotation extensions installed on all four wheels. Large rubber grousers were on the rear flotation extensions to improve traction on soft ground or mud. These extensions did not touch the surface on a hard road.

J. Walter Christie produced a small four wheel (4x2) armored car dubbed the M1933 Airborne Combat Car. It was a two man vehicle with a single .30 caliber machine gun and armor 14mm thick. The M1933 had pneumatic tires on all four wheels and was powered by a four cylinder engine. A maximum road speed of 110 miles/hour was claimed. Only one M1933 was built.

The single T9 light armored car, based upon the Plymouth chassis, is in the photographs below. Like the T8, it is armed with a single .30 caliber air cooled machine gun.

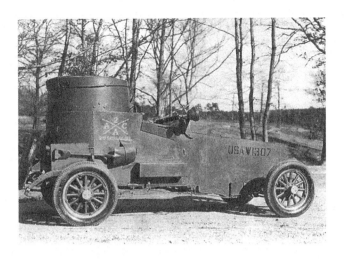

One of the three T10 armored cars based upon the Willys-Overland Whippet chassis appears in these photographs. The original configuration of the T10 can be seen in the two top views. At the right and below, the vehicle has been fitted with the large flotation extensions with grousers on the rear wheels.

The M1933 Airborne Combat Car produced by J. Walter Christie can be seen below with Mr. Christie himself manning the vehicle in the left photograph. The armored shield for the single .30 caliber air cooled machine gun is at the front.

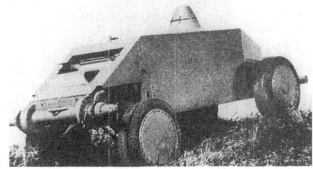

The original version of the armored car T11 appears above and below at the left. At the top left, the driver's front armor has been raised and the windshield is in place. The driver's front armor is in place at the top right and below. The full armament is installed consisting of the coaxial .30 and .50 caliber air cooled machine guns in the turret and the single .30 caliber machine gun in the bow mount.

The next armored car development was the T11 built by the Four Wheel Drive Auto Company. The general design of the T11 was considered superior to the standard M1 and the vehicle would probably have been standardized except for some mechanical failures which proved to be difficult to correct. In particular, the engine failed to cool properly and the suspension system was unsatisfactory. With a maximum armor thickness of $\frac{1}{4}$ inch, the T11 had a loaded weight of 11,250 pounds. With a 115 horsepower Cadillac V8 engine, it had a maximum road speed of almost 70 miles per hour. The T11E1 was an effort to correct the problems with the T11 and make it suitable for production. The maximum armor thickness was increased to $\frac{3}{8}$ inches and a new

Below, the prototype of the armored car T11 has been modified. Note that spare tires on rotating mounts at each side have replaced the steel rollers in the same location in the views above.

Above at the left, armored car T11E1 (No. 1143) is at Aberdeen Proving Ground on 18 December 1934. The driver's front armor is raised in both photographs above and the windshield is in place. A lineup of T11E1 armored cars can be seen below at the right.

cooling system was installed. Tire size was increased from 8.25 x 20 to 9.00 x 20 and the tires were filled with sponge rubber in place of inner tubes. Six T11E1s were built by Marmon-Herrington and five were assigned to the Mechanized Cavalry for service tests. A single T11E2 was built with additional modifications. In this vehicle, the Cadillac engine was replaced with a Hercules WXLC3 which produced 115 horsepower. The rear shutters were replaced with a solid steel plate changing the air flow to the radiator. The most obvious change was the modification of the armor to simplify production. However, the improvements were not considered sufficient and there was no further development of the T11 series.

The pilot armored car T11E2 below is at Aberdeen Proving Ground on 11 May 1936. Note the changes in the armor configuration on both hull and turret compared to the earlier vehicles.

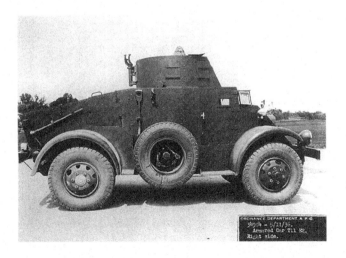

Above are the two heavy armored cars built for the Persian government. The left view shows the vehicle manufactured by American LaFrance. At the top right, the Marmon-Herrington car is fitted with a Swedish designed turret.

The armored car T12 was a design study only and was the last T designation assigned before the intensive development which resulted from the opening of World War II. However, in addition to these cars, there were several privately constructed vehicles during the same period. Two heavy armored cars were built for the Persian government. The first by American LaFrance in 1933 and the second by the Marmon-Herrington Company in 1934. Both of these carried a 37mm gun as main armament.

In 1938, Preston Tucker constructed a four wheeled armored car with the unlikely name of the "Tucker Tiger Tank". It also carried a 37mm automatic gun mounted in what was described as a bullet proof glass turret. Powered by a V12 Packard special engine, the car easily attained a speed of 74 miles per hour during tests at Aberdeen. Firing tests against the $2\frac{3}{4}$ inch thick laminated glass windows were inconclusive, but indicated that further consideration should be given to bullet resisting glass in future designs.

The armored car produced by Preston Tucker is shown above and at the left. A view under the 37mm gun turret looking into the driver's compartment is at the lower left.

In 1937, the armored car as a standard item was deleted from the list of U. S. Army requirements. It was then assumed that all needs for a light, wheeled, armored reconnaissance vehicle would be met by the scout car then under development.

The armored car T3 (scout car T1) appears above at the left. At the right and below, it has been modified and is now designated as the scout car T1. The photograph at the top right at Aberdeen Proving Ground, dated 17 June 1932, shows the .30 caliber machine gun mounted above the front armor plate. Below, the scout car has been fitted with a radio at Aberdeen on 12 August 1932.

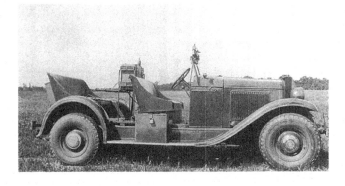 

In 1932, armored car development had split into two separate lines with the introduction of the armored car T3. As mentioned previously, this vehicle also was designated as the scout car T1. It was the first of a line of lightweight reconnaissance vehicles designed with a minimum of armor protection and good cross-country mobility. The only frontal protection added to the commercial Pontiac touring car chassis was a $\frac{1}{4}$ inch thick steel armor plate in place of the windshield and similar armored louvers in front of the radiator. Armor also was placed around the back of the rear seat. Armament was a single .30 caliber machine gun. The T1 had a loaded weight of 2,700 pounds and the six cylinder Pontiac engine developed 57 horsepower giving the vehicle a maximum road speed of 45 miles per hour. It did not have front wheel drive, but the 7.50 x 15 tires provided increased flotation improving off road operation.

The scout car T2 was tested at Aberdeen Proving Ground from May to September 1932. It was based upon

At the right is the scout car T2 after modification at Aberdeen Proving Ground on 8 September 1932. Armament consists of a single .30 caliber machine gun.

a Chevrolet Phaeton modified by the addition of soft steel louvers over the radiator and a similar plate over the lower part of the windshield. It was armed with a single .30 caliber machine gun. Like the T1, only the rear wheels were driven. To improve cross-country mobility, the car was fitted with 7.00 x 16 tires.

The scout car designations T3 and T4 were assigned to design studies and the vehicles were never built. The scout car T5 was a proposed modification of the half-track truck T1, but it was never completed. Another proposed variation of the half-track truck T1 was the scout car T6. It was to have two "swivel chair" type turrets. It also died on the drawing board.

Above, the scout car T7 has the driver's front armor down and the windshield installed. No armament has been installed, but the mounts are in place.

The scout car T7 above is fitted with its full armament consisting of one .50 caliber machine gun and two .30 caliber machine guns. At the left is a new scout car T7 at the Truck Division of the White Motor Company.

The first design to be standardized was the scout car T7 built by the Indiana Motortruck Company, a subsidiary of the White Motor Company. It was based upon the chassis of a $1\frac{1}{2}$ ton four wheel drive truck. Assembled in 1934, this vehicle was armed with two .30 caliber and two .50 caliber machine guns with frontal armor protection ½ inch thick. Armor on the sides and rear was $\frac{1}{4}$ inch and $\frac{5}{16}$ inches respectively. It weighed 7,700 pounds and was powered by a six cylinder, 75 horsepower, Hercules gasoline engine. Tests at Aberdeen Proving Ground from July to November 1934 indicated that it would be a satisfactory reconnaissance vehicle after some minor modifications and it was standardized as the scout car M1. A total of 76 vehicles were produced.

The T7 scout car at the left is operating in rough terrain during its test program.

34

Now standardized, the scout car M1 is operating with the troops in these photographs. The canvas top is removed and the armament is installed. Below, the scout car M1 belonging to the Communications Officer of Headquarters Troop, 1st Cavalry is armed with a single .30 caliber machine gun. Note the radio antennas.

In August 1934, a scout car built be the Marmon-Herrington Company was briefly tested at Aberdeen for comparison with the scout car T7. Although the tests were too short for a complete evaluation, several features were noted that were superior to the T7. These included a lower silhouette and center of gravity, a higher top speed and power to weight ratio, and better riding characteristics.

The scout car T8 was another design study and the vehicle was never built.

Below are two views of the Marmon-Herrington scout car. The windshield is installed, the driver's front armor is raised and the side door armor is folded down. No armament has been mounted.

The scout car T9 appears above at the left. At the right above and below is the standardized scout car M2 now serving with the troops. Details of the machine gun mount can be seen in the lower photograph. At the bottom of the page are two views of the scout car M2A1 at Aberdeen on 22 September 1937. Note the changes in the side armor compared to the M2.

In 1938, another vehicle, the scout car T9, was standardized as the scout car M2. Based upon the Corbitt $1^{1}/_{2}$ ton truck chassis, it was driven by the eight cylinder, 94 horsepower, Lycoming engine referred to as the "Corbitt Eight". Weighing 7,900 pounds, the M2 had a maximum road speed of 50 miles per hour. The armor protection was $^{1}/_{2}$ inch thick in front and $^{1}/_{4}$ inch thick on the sides and rear. The pilot was assembled with soft steel plate. The pilot and one production vehicle were tested from March to November 1935 at Aberdeen Proving Ground. It was considered to be superior to the T7 and the cross-country performance was exceptionally good. A total of 22 vehicles (T9 and M2) were produced by 28 March 1938.

A modified version of the M2 was designated as the scout car M2E1. It was fitted with heavier axles and the driver's seat was lowered. A track for skate mounted machine guns was installed around the top of the crew compartment. This was referred to as a Tourelle mount. During September 1937, the M2E1 was tested in comparison with the scout cars M2A1 and T13 at Aberdeen Proving Ground. It was considered to be inferior to the M2A1, but it was superior to the T13. Only two M2E1s were built.

Further development of the M2 had led to improvements in crew protection, comfort, and visibility as well as a greater cruising range. These changes resulted in a new standard designation as the scout car

M2A1 (later changed to M3). It was produced by the White Motor Company. This was a four wheel car with all wheels driven (4x4) weighing almost four tons. Armor protection was $^{1}/_{2}$ inch thick on the windshield cover and $^{1}/_{4}$ inch thick on the other surfaces. As with the other scout cars, the top was open. The vehicle was normally armed with three machine guns skate mounted on the steel track rail which encircled the interior of the body flush with the top of the armor plate. With a six cylinder, 95 horsepower, Hercules gasoline engine, a top speed of approximately 60 miles per hour was attained on a hard surface road. Total production of the scout car M3 was 36 in Fiscal Year 1937, 39 in Fiscal Year 1938, and 25 in Fiscal Year 1939. It was followed in 1939 by the improved scout car M3A1.

A new M3 (M2A1) scout car is shown above and below. The canvas top and the windshield are installed. The armor flap on the door is down in the view above and it is raised at the lower left.

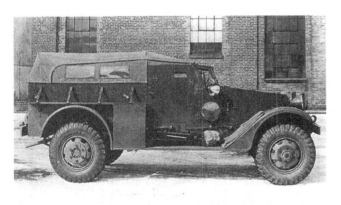

The armament is mounted on the scout car M3 in the two photographs below. Note the stowage on these vehicles.

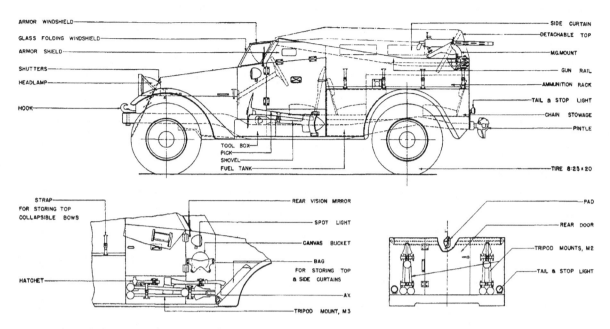

ARMOR WINDSHIELD
GLASS FOLDING WINDSHIELD
ARMOR SHIELD
SHUTTERS
HEADLAMP
HOOK
TOOL BOX
PICK
SHOVEL
FUEL TANK

SIDE CURTAIN
DETACHABLE TOP
M.G. MOUNT
GUN RAIL
AMMUNITION RACK
TAIL & STOP LIGHT
CHAIN STOWAGE
PINTLE
TIRE 8:25 x 20

STRAP
FOR STORING TOP
COLLAPSIBLE BOWS
HATCHET
TRIPOD MOUNT, M3

REAR VISION MIRROR
SPOT LIGHT
CANVAS BUCKET
BAG
FOR STORING TOP
& SIDE CURTAINS
AX

PAD
REAR DOOR
TRIPOD MOUNTS, M2
TAIL & STOP LIGHT

The arrangement of stowage items on the scout car M3 can be seen in the drawing above. Below, the various components on the chassis of the scout car M3 are identified.

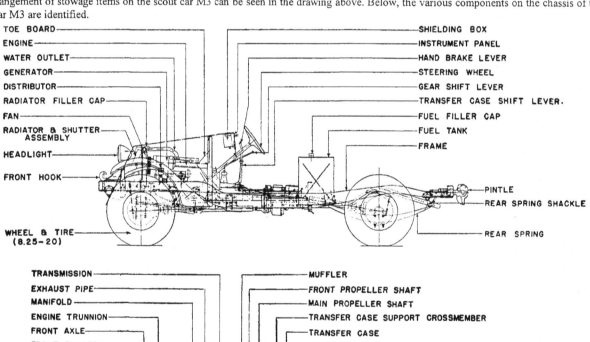

TOE BOARD
ENGINE
WATER OUTLET
GENERATOR
DISTRIBUTOR
RADIATOR FILLER CAP
FAN
RADIATOR & SHUTTER ASSEMBLY
HEADLIGHT
FRONT HOOK
WHEEL & TIRE (8.25-20)

SHIELDING BOX
INSTRUMENT PANEL
HAND BRAKE LEVER
STEERING WHEEL
GEAR SHIFT LEVER
TRANSFER CASE SHIFT LEVER.
FUEL FILLER CAP
FUEL TANK
FRAME
PINTLE
REAR SPRING SHACKLE
REAR SPRING

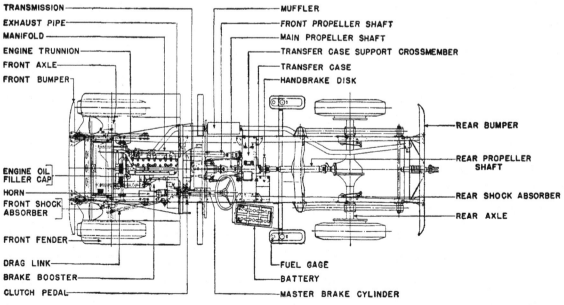

TRANSMISSION
EXHAUST PIPE
MANIFOLD
ENGINE TRUNNION
FRONT AXLE
FRONT BUMPER
ENGINE OIL FILLER CAP
HORN
FRONT SHOCK ABSORBER
FRONT FENDER
DRAG LINK
BRAKE BOOSTER
CLUTCH PEDAL

MUFFLER
FRONT PROPELLER SHAFT
MAIN PROPELLER SHAFT
TRANSFER CASE SUPPORT CROSSMEMBER
TRANSFER CASE
HANDBRAKE DISK
REAR BUMPER
REAR PROPELLER SHAFT
REAR SHOCK ABSORBER
REAR AXLE
FUEL GAGE
BATTERY
MASTER BRAKE CYLINDER

A fully stowed scout car M3 appears above. At the left below, Major General John K. Herr, the Chief of Cavalry (left), stands in front of a scout car M3 with Brigadier General Adna R. Chaffee, the first commander of the Armored Force.

Above at the right, Lieutenant Colonel Jack Heard, Major C. H. Ungar, Brigadier General Adna R. Chaffee and Major J. J. B. Williams (left to right) are in an M3 scout car. Below are two M3 scout cars operating with the troops during the early training of the new Armored Force.

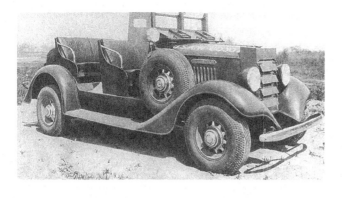 

The scout car T12 built by International Harvester is shown in the two views above. At the top right, the front bumper has been replaced by a very heavy duty brush guard. Below, the Marmon-Herrington scout car T13 is serving with the National Guard during 1937.

The designations scout car T10 and scout car T11 were assigned to design studies and were never built.

The scout car T12 was based upon a standard $\frac{1}{2}$ ton truck chassis Model C-1 produced by the International Harvester Company. It was tested at Aberdeen Proving Ground during April and May 1935. Armor was provided only for the radiator and the windshield. Since the vehicle had only rear wheel drive, the cross-country mobility was limited. Only the one pilot was built.

In 1937, Marmon-Herrington produced the scout car T13 based upon the Ford/Marmon-Herrington $1\frac{1}{2}$ ton commercial chassis. It utilized the 85 horsepower Ford V8 engine and weighed a little under four tons. Armor $\frac{1}{4}$ inch thick was provided on the front, sides and rear and the armament consisted of a skate mounted .50 caliber machine gun. As mentioned earlier, it was tested in comparison with the scout cars M2A1 and M2E1 and was considered satisfactory as a training vehicle. Procured for the National Guard , 38 vehicles were built.

During 1935 and early 1936, two vehicles powered by the 83 horsepower Ford V8 engine were evaluated for the Infantry. Designated as the squad cars T1 and T2, they were protected only by armored radiator louvers and armor plate over the windshield. On the T1, only the rear wheels were driven, but the T2 was a 4x4 vehicle with a Marmon-Herrington front wheel drive to improve the cross-country mobility. Neither vehicle went into production.

Below, the squad car T1 is at the left and the squad car T2 is at the right. Note the limited protection provided by the armored radiator louvers and the windshield cover.

The 3 inch antiaircraft gun mount T1 based upon the Garford 6x4 truck is at the top left. At the top right, it is now the 75mm truck mount T3. Below at the right, the 75mm truck mount T6 is based upon the White 620 S.W.

In early 1931, a 3 inch antiaircraft gun was installed on a 7½ ton Garford 6x4 truck. Designated as the 3 inch antiaircraft gun mount T1, it was tested at Aberdeen Proving Ground. Later the 3 inch weapon was replaced by a 75mm gun and the designation became the 75mm truck mount T3. However, the mount was unstable with both weapons and the project was ended.

A large truck with a 173 inch wheelbase was built by White in 1930. Designated as the Model 620 S.W., it was converted into the 75mm truck mount T6 by the installation of the 75mm gun M1897. The total weight of the truck mount was 14,170 pounds. The weapon was mounted firing toward the rear with a traverse of 30 degrees left and 30 degrees right. The elevation was limited to +19 degrees. An armored cab was fitted to protect the crew when traveling.

During the early 1930s, a number of antiaircraft multiple machine gun mounts were evaluated by the Army. In the Summer and Fall of 1930, the multiple machine gun motor mount T1 was under test at Aberdeen Proving Ground. Armed with four .50 caliber machine guns, for which it carried 5,000 rounds of ammunition, the mount was installed on a 10 ton Diamond T 6x4 truck. It was followed a short time later by the multiple machine gun truck mount T2 installed on a White truck chassis. The latter was armed with two .50 caliber machine guns. In 1932, the multiple machine gun truck mount T5 was at Aberdeen using a White four wheel drive truck. This mount was armed with four .50 caliber machine guns.

At the upper right is the multiple machine gun mount T1. The multiple machine gun mount T2 is shown below and the multiple machine gun mount T5 appears at the bottom right.

41

Above, the 4.2 inch mortar motor carriage T5 is at the left and the 4.2 inch mortar motor carriage M2 (T5E1) is at the right. The T5 has the mortar emplaced for firing. Note that the machine gun track rail has been eliminated on the M2

The 4.2 inch mortar motor carriage M2 is shown above with the mortar emplaced for firing on the left and stowed in the vehicle for travel on the right.

With the adoption of the scout car as the major vehicle in the Cavalry regiment, its importance greatly increased. This led to the development of the 4.2 inch mortar motor carriage T5 with the weapon installed on a Marmon-Herrington four wheel drive chassis. Later, the mortar was mounted on the M3 scout car and designated as the 4.2 inch mortar motor carriage T5E1. It was briefly standardized as the M2. This vehicle was a modification of the scout car M3 with the circular machine gun rail eliminated and the body interior rearranged. A 4.2 inch chemical mortar was mounted in the center of the vehicle aimed forward. The mortar also could be removed for emplacement on the ground where a greater range of elevation was obtainable.

In 1935, the Chief of Cavalry had recommended that a vehicle be developed to carry the 81mm mortar as an accompanying weapon for mechanized cavalry. Studies of a suitable carrier were based upon the experimental scout cars then available as well as full tracked chassis. In 1937, the 81mm mortar was mounted on the scout car as well as on a $^1\!/_2$ ton four wheel drive truck chassis. The truck mount proved to be unsuitable, but the tests on the scout car M3 showed it to be a satisfactory carrier for the mortar. When armed with the mortar, the scout car was designated as the 81mm mortar motor carriage T1. The mount was designed to permit the mortar to be fired from the vehicle or on the ground. On 16 May 1940, OCM 15805 recommended that the later scout car M3A1 be used for the mortar carrier. The same action also recommended that it be standardized as the 81mm mortar carrier M2. However the subsequent standardization of the half-track mortar carrier M4 resulted in the termination of the project.

When the desert battle experience of the British became available in 1940 and early 1941, interest in the armored car sharply increased. This experience had shown the value of such cars in the flat desert areas where wheeled vehicles could operate effectively. Their relatively high speed, long range, and good reliability made them particularly attractive under these conditions. By this time, the rearmament program was in full swing and money was available for development.

PART II

THE WORLD WAR II

DEVELOPMENT PROGRAM

On the scout car M3A1 above, the canvas top is installed and the armor plate over the windshield has been raised. The armor flap on the side door has been folded down. Note the roller on the front and the Cavalry insignia on the side door.

SCOUT CARS

The scout car M3A1 was essentially an improved version of the M3 described earlier. The interior space was increased by widening the body and the circular machine gun track rail was lowered below the top edge of the armor. The rear door was eliminated and the interior stowage and the seating were rearranged. To improve the cross-country mobility in rough terrain, a spring loaded roller replaced the front bumper. Except for minor modifications, this was the vehicle that remained in production through March 1944 for a total run of 20,894 cars. They served with both the United States and Allied Forces in every theater of operation. As of 1 February 1945, 11,440 M3A1s had been allocated to foreign aid under the Lend-Lease Program. These included 6,987 to the United Kingdom, 3,310 to the Soviet Union, and 104 to China. No further shipments were expected at that time.

At the upper right, the door armor flap is down and the side curtain is installed on this M3A1 scout car. At the lower right, the side curtain is removed and the top rolled up to provide visibility for the crew.

The M3A1 scout car above and at the right below have an interesting combination of weapons. Note the .50 caliber water cooled machine gun, a .30 caliber Lewis air cooled machine gun and a water cooled .30 caliber machine gun. At the left below, the M3A1 is fitted with the early standard armament of one .50 caliber air cooled machine gun and two .30 caliber water cooled machine guns.

The machine gun armament on the M3A1 scout car can be seen in the photographs above. Note the padding around the machine gun rail above the doors. A lot of bruises must have resulted prior to its installation.

At the right, during its last days, the horse cavalry is operating with the M3A1 scout cars.

The change in standard armament of the M3A1 scout car can be seen in these photographs. At the top left, it consists of .30 caliber water cooled machine guns and a .50 caliber air cooled machine gun. At the top right, a single .30 caliber air cooled machine gun is mounted with the one .50 caliber air cooled machine gun. At the left, a second .30 caliber machine gun has been added. Below, the machine guns are not mounted and we have, once again, the pads on the rails over the doors.

Further details of the scout car M3A1 can be seen in the photographs at the left and below. Note the two radio antennas on the vehicle below.

47

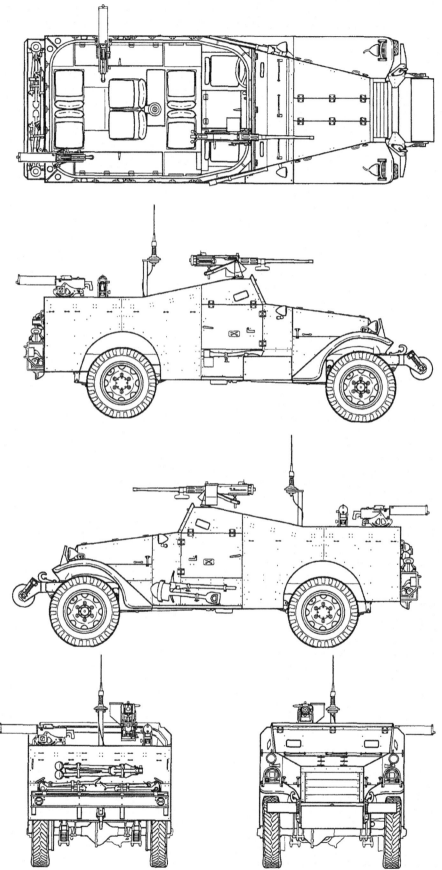

Scale 1:48

Scout Car M3A1, early production

© M. Duplessis

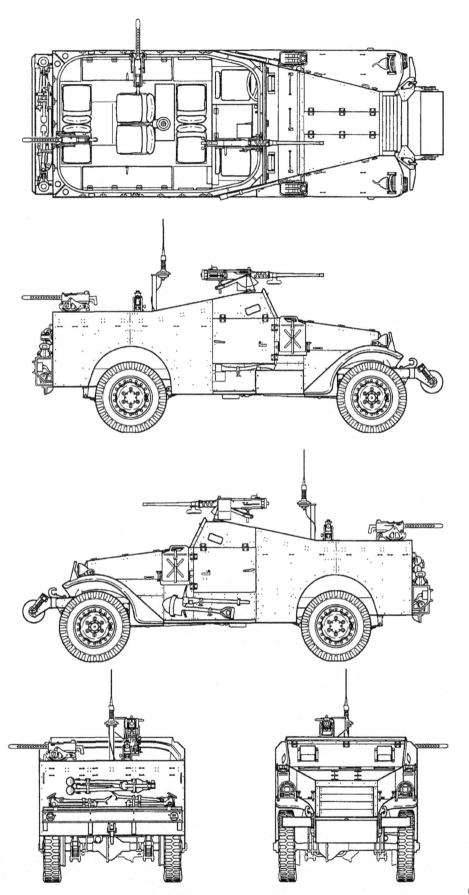

© M. Duplessis

Scout Car M3A1, late production

49

The scout car M3A1 above is fitted with the canvas top and the windshield armor is raised. The side door armor is folded down and the side curtains are installed. Below, the interior arrangement of the M3A1 is shown at the left and the driver's controls and instruments are at the right.

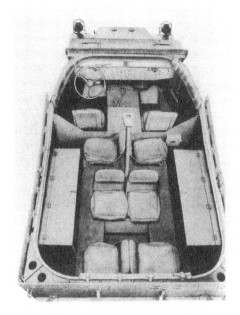

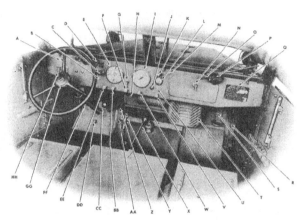

A. TROUBLE LIGHT RECEPTACLE, B. STOP LIGHT SWITCH, C. BLACKOUT AND SERVICE LIGHT SWITCH, D. FUEL TANK SELECTOR, E. INSTRUMENT CLUSTER, F. THROTTLE, G. IGNITION, H. STARTER, I. SPEEDOMETER, J. HEATER, K. DASH LIGHT, L. VOLTMETER, M. SCREW, N. MAP COMPARTMENT, O. WINDSHIELD WIPER TUBE, P. WINDSHIELD WIPER ASSEMBLY, Q. RESISTRATION PLATE, R. RADIATOR SHUTTER LEVER, S. FIRE EXTINGUISHER BRACKET, T. HEATER, U. VOLTMETER SWITCH, V. R. H. VENTILATOR CONTROL, W. CHOKE, X. TRANSFER CASE SHIFT LEVER, Y. HAND BRAKE, Z. TRANSMISSION GEAR SHIFT, AA. ACCELERATOR, BB. SPARK, CC. BRAKE, DD. DIMMER SWITCH, EE. L. H. VENTILATOR CONTROL, FF. CLUTCH, GG. HORN, HH. GEARSHIFT INSTRUCTION PLATE.

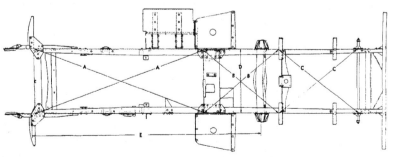

The chassis for the scout car M3A1 is shown in the two photographs above and in the drawing at the left. The letters in the latter indicate the measurements to be taken when checking the alignment of the frame.

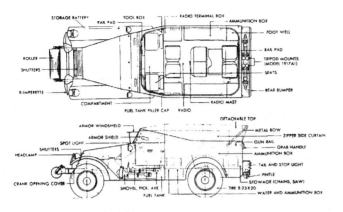

Components and stowage on the M3A1 scout car are identified above. At the top right, an M3A1 scout car on the Gafsa road in Tunisia makes the first contact with the British Eighth Army. Below and at the right, a specially modified M3A1 scout car is the mount for Lieutenant General George S. Patton Jr. in North Africa.

At the right is a heavily loaded M3A1 scout car of the British 11th Hussars. Below, the gun rail has been removed from this M3A1 belonging to the British 23rd Hussars. At the bottom right is another M3A1 scout car in British service.

The United States Marine Corps also made use of the M3A1 scout car. In the photograph above, an M3A1 is leaving a landing craft during a practice landing.

A front view of a Marine Corps M3A1 scout car is at the right. Note that these vehicles retain the water cooled .30 caliber machine guns in addition to the .50 caliber air cooled machine gun.

Below, the Marine Corps M3A1 scout cars participate in the welcoming parade in Melbourne, Australia on 4 May 1943.

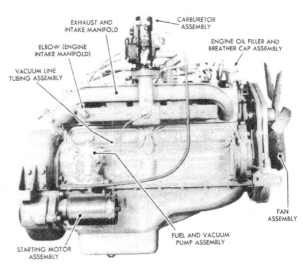

Above, the left and right sides of the Hercules JXD gasoline engine that powered the scout car M3A1 are at the left and right respectively. Below are views of the Hercules DJXD diesel engine (left) and the Buda-Lanova 6DT-317 diesel engine (right) that were installed in the diesel versions of the M3A1 scout car.

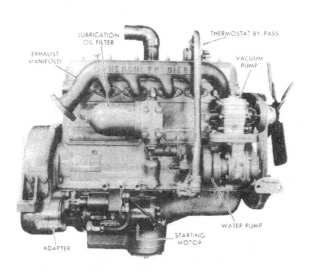
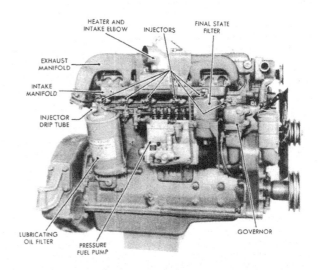

The basic scout car M3A1 was used for a number of experimental modifications. Item 15403 of the Ordnance Committee Minutes (OCM), dated 13 October 1939, authorized the evaluation of automotive type diesel engines in vehicles procured by the Ordnance Department. The Buda-Lanova Company offered to install their 6DT-317 diesel engine in an M3A1 scout car without cost to the government. The second M3A1 off the production line at the White Motor Company in Cleveland, Ohio was driven to the Buda-Lanova plant at Harvey, Illinois for the conversion. It was then driven to Aberdeen Proving Ground for testing. OCM 15471, dated 9 November 1939, designated the converted vehicle as the scout car M3A1E1. Another M3A1 scout car fitted with a Hercules DJXD diesel engine also was submitted for test at Aberdeen, but it retained its original designation.

The tests of the diesel powered scout cars were successful and OCM 15948, dated 3 July 1940, authorized the installation of diesel engines in 100 new production M3A1 scout cars. They included both Hercules and Buda-Lanova engines. These vehicles retained the M3A1 designation and were submitted for service test during operations of the Third Army.

The high torque and speed required to start the diesel engines required changes to the 12 volt electrical system of the M3A1. Two 12 volt batteries were installed with a series-parallel switch. When the starter button was pushed, this switch connected the two batteries in series to provide 24 volts. When the button was released, the batteries were connected in parallel providing the normal 12 volt system. The two batteries required a compartment on each side of the vehicle providing an obvious identification point for the diesel

These photographs show the chassis of the scout car M3A1E1 driven by the Buda-Lanova diesel engine. Note that there is a battery on each side of the vehicle to provide the necessary power for the 12/24 volt electrical system.

powered scout car. Since these vehicles were improvised modifications of the standard M3A1 scout car, OCM 15948 also authorized the development of a properly designed diesel powered scout car and designated it as the scout car M3A2. It was intended to power this vehicle with the heavier, more powerful, Hercules DWXD diesel engine. However, this program was delayed by higher priority projects and on 12 March 1942, OCM 17919 recorded a new policy that all U. S. Army wheeled vehicles be powered by gasoline engines. About this time, the M3A2 had come to the attention of Brigadier General G. M. Barnes who noted that it was improperly classified as a standard vehicle. He directed that the M3A2 designation be canceled and the vehicle be redesignated as the scout car M3A1E5. This action was recorded as OCM 18134 on 20 April 1942. Despite the decision to drop the diesel engine, the M3A1E5 (M3A2) project continued and a single pilot vehicle was completed and evaluated at the Studebaker Proving Ground in early 1944. The M3A1E5(M3A2) included various late production features such as a new canvas cover and demountable headlights.

After their evaluation, the original 100 M3A1 diesel scout cars were turned in and components were salvaged that could be used in M3A1 production. The remaining parts were scrapped.

The single pilot scout car M3A1E5 (M3A2), Registration Number 609926, appears in the photographs on this page. It is fitted with a new design canvas top and demountable headlights. The view at the right shows the vehicle at Aberdeen during the postwar period. Note that there is no battery box on the left side.

The mockup in the two photographs above is an early attempt to provide a roof for the scout car M3A1. Below at the right is the final mockup for the scout car M3A1E2 with the flaps on the top cover down and the machine guns at maximum depression.

Concern over the vulnerability of the open top vehicle to air attack resulted in the design of an armor plate roof. Several wooden and sheet metal mockups were constructed at Aberdeen Proving Ground. With the armor roof, the vehicle was designated as the scout car M3A1E2 by OCM 16161 dated 3 October 1940. The protection of $\frac{1}{4}$ inch thick face hardened steel plate was specified and a final wooden mock-up was prepared for test at Aberdeen during the first six months of 1941. These tests indicated that the roof and its supports interfered with the operation and traverse of the machine guns and made access to and from the vehicle more difficult. The roof also greatly reduced the view from the vehicle and it was noted that the car tended to weave when it was being driven. The test report concluded that these disadvantages far outweighed the slight additional protection gained from the $\frac{1}{4}$ inch thick armor plate roof and further work on the project was terminated by OCM 17611 on 8 January 1942. However, this did not prevent some of the troops in the field from improvising armored covers for their scout cars.

Below at the left, the scout car M3A1E2 appears with the flaps on the mockup of the armor cover raised. Note the maximum elevation of the machine guns in this position. Below is a view of the .30 caliber machine gun and mount.

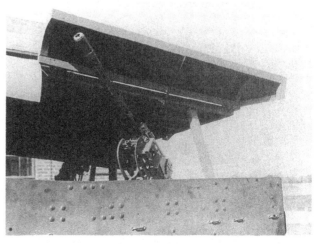

Additional views of the scout car M3A1E2 are shown here with the flaps on the mockup of the armor top in various positions.

The scout car M3A1E3 armed with the 37mm gun M3 on mount T6 appears in the photographs on this page. The mount is installed on scout car number 130, Registration Number W-60653. These photographs were taken at Aberdeen Proving Ground on 27 June 1941 and it still has the Cavalry insignia on the door.

The use of the scout car as the main cavalry vehicle resulted in its consideration as a mount for the 37mm antitank gun. OCM 15865, dated 6 June 1940 authorized the installation of the 37mm gun M3 on the scout car. On 14 November 1940, OCM 16261 assigned the designation scout car M3A1E3 to the vehicle and the mount became the 37mm gun mount T6. The weapon was mounted just to the rear of the front seats in vehicle number 130. The gun barrel extended forward past the windshield. Later, the vehicle was fitted with a modified mount standardized as the 37mm gun mount M25. Firing tests were conducted at Aberdeen Proving Ground, but it was concluded that the scout car was unsatisfactory as a mount for this weapon because of its excessive weight and the high silhouette. Once again, the project was terminated without any further production.

These views of scout car M3A1E3 were dated 1 August 1942 at Aberdeen. The 37mm gun M3 is now installed on the M25 mount. This is the same mount used on the 37mm gun motor carriage M6. Even at this late date, W60653 retains it Cavalry insignia on the door.

The observation post tender T2 appears in the two photographs at the top of the page. The sections of folding armor including the view ports with the sliding covers are shown in up position. They could fold down on top of the hull.

During late 1941, another light, wheeled, armored vehicle was evaluated at Aberdeen Proving Ground. Designated as the observation post tender T2, it was a four wheel, four wheel drive (4x4) vehicle manufactured by the Ford Motor Company. With an empty weight of 5,800 pounds, it was manned by a crew of three. Powered by a 90 horsepower, six cylinder, gasoline engine, the T2 had a maximum road speed of 55 miles per hour. The open top vehicle was protected by steel armor $^3/_8$ inches thick on the front and $^1/_4$ inch thick on the sides and rear. No armament was specified. Although the T2 had good cross-country performance with its 9.00 x 20 tires, it did not go into production.

In April 1942, the Tank Destroyer Command initiated the development of a light armored reconnaissance vehicle designated as the scout car T24. The vehicle was constructed on the same chassis as the 37mm gun motor carriage T14. The latter vehicle was a six wheeled chassis with all wheels powered (6x6). Manufactured by Willys-Overland Motors, Inc., it was based upon the $^1/_4$ ton truck and referred to as the "Super Jeep". The open top armored body carried a crew of three. The armor was well sloped and was $^1/_4$ inch thick on the front, sides, and rear. However, the pilot was constructed from soft steel plate. Because of the large number of Jeep parts used, the manufacturer estimated that quantity production could start in 12 weeks after authorization. A production level of 150 cars per day was intended. The pilot was tested by the Tank Destroyer Board and later by the Special Armored Vehicle Board. The latter, often referred to as the Palmer Board after the name of its President, Brigadier General Williston B. Palmer, was convened on 14 October 1942 by order of the Secretary of War. Its purpose was to sort through the wide variety of armored vehicles then under development, particularly armored

Below, the scout car T24 is shown at the left with the front armor sections folded down. At the bottom right, the folding armor sections are in the up position. The T24 was photographed at Aberdeen Proving Ground on 4 November 1942

The top view of the scout car T24 above shows the interior arrangement and some of the stowage on this vehicle. Here, once again, the upper front armor sections are folded down.

cars, and determine which projects should be continued and which should be terminated. Both Boards recommended standardization of the T24 after minor changes. However, higher authority disapproved the recommendation since only the Tank Destroyer Command had use for such a vehicle and the scout car T24 project was ended without further production.

A similar fate awaited the Chrysler scout cars. Both were private ventures of Chrysler Corporation. The first was a 4x4 armored vehicle tested at Aberdeen Proving Ground during 1941. The second was based upon the Fargo six wheel drive $1\frac{1}{2}$ ton truck. Equipped with a lightly armored body, a pilot was submitted to Aberdeen for test. However, the using arms were no longer interested in this type of vehicle. The Special Armored Vehicle Board considered the 6x6 to be a well built vehicle and recommended it for use by the Infantry or the Field Artillery. However, neither car was adopted.

The Chrysler 4x4 scout car can be seen in the view above. The Chrysler 6x6 scout car is shown below. Note that it also was referred to as the Model T230 gun carrier.

The Jeep armored by the Smart Engineering Company is shown above and below at the right. Note the vision slots and gun ports in the folding front armor plate. This plate could fold down on top of the hood. There was no armor on the rear of the vehicle.

The wide use of the $^1/_4$ ton truck or Jeep as a reconnaissance vehicle resulted in many field modifications which attempted to provide some degree of armor protection. The need for such protection had been considered by the Ordnance Department prior to the entry of the United States into the war. In 1941, a Jeep was tested at Aberdeen Proving Ground which had been fitted with armor by the Smart Engineering Company. The adverse effect of the weight on the vehicle handling characteristics and maintenance problems resulted in an unfavorable report at that time. Under continued pressure from the using arms, the project was reopened in June 1942 and a number of experimental vehicles were

The two photographs below show the scout car T25 during its evaluation at Fort knox. The front vision port is open and the side vision ports are closed. There was provision for the installation of a gun mount in the front armor. There was no armor on the rear of the T25. Note the exposed fuel tank.

constructed. All of these were modified $\frac{1}{4}$ ton trucks and they were designated as the scout cars T25, T25E1, T25E2, and T25E3. They differed essentially in the amount of armor installed with the T25 having the least and the T25E3 having the greatest armor protection. The original T25 also was equipped to carry a machine gun in a ball mount in the armored windshield. The three other vehicles eliminated this feature. Tests by the Armored Board indicated that the four vehicles were overloaded from 785 pounds to 1,265 pounds above the normal rated load for the $\frac{1}{4}$ ton truck. The poor weight distribution on the T25E1, the T25E2, and the T25E3 emphasized the overloaded condition. All of the vehicles were more difficult to handle and were generally unsatisfactory for cross-country operation. The Board concluded that all four scout cars were unsatisfactory for use by the Armored Force and the project was terminated without further development. This decision did not deter the troops who continued to improvise armor protection for the Jeep throughout the war.

The scout car T25E1 can be seen above and below at Aberdeen Proving Ground on 2 December 1943. Note the armor on the rear of the vehicle.

Below, the scout car T25E2 appears at the left and the T25E3 is at the right. The rear armor on the latter vehicle has been folded down.

63

Despite the unfavorable reports from the testing agencies, the troops did not hesitate to add armor to their Jeeps. Above, the 82nd Airborne Division is operating near La Gleize, Belgium on 18 January 1945 and their armored Jeep is painted white to blend with the snow. No doubt the test people would consider the Jeeps below to be heavily overloaded, but it did not deter the troops.

Above at the left, the final pilot of the Ford amphibious Jeep is afloat during its evaluation. At the top right is the Marmon-Herrington amphibious Jeep pilot.

WHEELED AMPHIBIANS

During the Summer of 1940, the Quartermaster Corps suggested the development of an amphibious version of the $\frac{1}{4}$ ton truck (Jeep) to the National Defense Research Committee (NDRC) which had just been established by President Roosevelt. The NDRC later became part of the Office of Scientific Research and Development (OSRD). General Marshall and other high ranking officers believed that an amphibious version of the highly mobile Jeep would be extremely valuable to a fast moving mechanized army, particularly to reconnaissance units.

Preliminary studies by Sparkman & Stephens, Inc., under OSRD contract OEMsr-154 indicated that the best approach to the problem would be a permanent conversion of the standard $\frac{1}{4}$ ton 4x4 vehicle. Originally, consideration had been given to detachable pontons and glider wings. Contracts for the construction of pilot vehicles were awarded to the Marmon-Herrington Company and the Ford Motor Company. These pilots were to be based upon specifications resulting from scale model tests. The pilot vehicles from both manufacturers were completed and submitted for evaluation between February and April 1942. Both entries retained the standard Jeep engine and power train as well as the wheels. A single propeller was located at the rear and a bilge pump was installed. The Marmon-Herrington vehicle measured $179\frac{1}{2}$ inches in length, 64 inches in width and weighed about 3,500 pounds empty. The Ford pilot was $179\frac{1}{2}$ inches long, 61 inches wide with an empty weight of 3,150 pounds.

After a series of tests, the Ford design was selected and a production contract was awarded for 6,000 vehicles. This was later increased to 12,774. At this point, the NDRC left the project and this proved to be a major mistake. The design engineer at Ford also was transferred to a glider project and the production was assigned to personnel unfamiliar with the program. This resulted in inadequate quality control with defective welds and excessive clearances on some components causing leakage. Many of the first thousand vehicles delivered sank after a few hours or days of operation. This did not help its reputation with the troops who had no instruction manuals or training to introduce the new amphibious Jeep. Tests of the early production vehicles also revealed the need for numerous modifications. For example, it was obvious that the engine should be waterproofed. However, the introduction of waterproofing into production was delayed and it was applied only to the last 420 vehicles. Modification kits were prepared for the earlier production, but they rarely reached the vehicles for which they were intended. As a result, the amphibious Jeep was considered to be a failure by most of the troops and its full potential was never realized.

Despite the various problems, the amphibious Jeep was standardized in February 1943 as the $\frac{1}{4}$ ton amphibian truck. Manned by a crew of four, it had a gross weight of 4,300 pounds. The production vehicle was slightly larger than the pilot with an overall length of $181\frac{3}{4}$ inches and a width of 64 inches. A 3,500 pound direct pull capstan was installed on the bow. The maximum speed was 55 miles/hour on roads and $5\frac{1}{2}$ miles/hour in water. The vehicle could tow a $\frac{1}{4}$ ton trailer that would float with its rated load.

The production version of the amphibious Jeep can be seen in the two photographs above.

In the Spring of 1942, the NDRC launched a new amphibian truck program without the prior approval of the Armed Forces. The objective this time was to produce an amphibious version of the General Motors $2^{1}/_{2}$ ton, 6x6 truck. The cab over engine version of the CCKW-353 truck was chosen for the initial conversion after a series of tests with scale models. Once again, this initial research was performed at the Stevens Institute of Technology under the direction of Sparkman & Stephens, Inc. The first pilot also was fitted with dual tires on the rear four wheels (4DT). Later pilots and all production vehicles located the cab behind the engine. This arrangement lengthened the bow deck, provided better access to the engine, and improved water protection. The GMC Model 270 engine drove the vehicle through the standard truck transmission and two speed transfer case. Power for the 25 inch diameter propeller was taken from the water propeller transfer case located in the drive train between the transmission and the two speed truck transfer case. Single tires were mounted on all six wheels of the production vehicles. The welded steel hull varied in thickness from about 0.1046 inches at the bow to 0.0938 inches at the bottom to 0.0625 inches at the sides. It was reinforced inside by transverse "hat section" channel frames and on the outside by similar longitudinal rub rails. The springs and axles were attached to the hull and suspended in the water when the vehicle was afloat. An open top driver's compartment with a folding windshield was installed on the earlier production vehicles. The was replaced later by a heavier sloping windshield with side wings to withstand the impact of heavy surf. A tire inflation system was fitted to allow the tire pressure to be reduced for crossing soft sand and to be increased for normal road operation. An M36 mount for a .50 caliber machine gun could be installed over the right side of the cab. A 10,000 pound capacity winch was mounted at the rear with cable guides to permit operation toward the front or rear. The cargo compartment could hold about 25 men and their equipment or approximately 5,000 pounds of cargo for operation on land.

Standardized in October 1942 as the $2^{1}/_{2}$ ton 6x6 amphibian truck, it was designated as the DUKW-353. This resulted in the instant nickname of the "Duck". First operational use of the Duck was at Noumea in March 1943 and it was deployed to the Pacific and Mediterranean theaters of operation that Summer. The Duck initially received an unfavorable reception from some untrained users. However, having learned from their experience with the amphibious jeep, trained

The pilot model of the DUKW appears below at the left. Note that it has dual tires on the rear four wheels. The basic vehicle from which it was developed is at the bottom right.

The DUKW above shows its versatility by carrying a 105mm howitzer ashore. At the right below, the bottom of the production DUKW can be seen. Note that these production vehicles all have only single tires on the rear wheels.

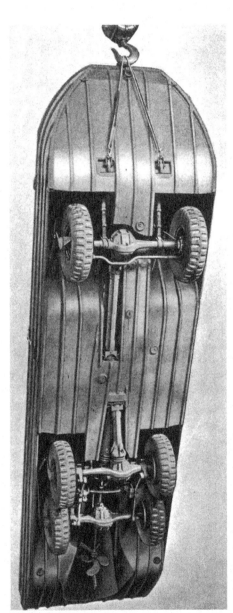

amphibian truck companies were dispatched and the NDRC assigned support groups of consultants to train the troops in the proper employment of the new amphibian. As a result, they were an outstanding success and were employed in every theater for the remainder of the war. By the time production ended in August 1945, 21,147 Ducks had been produced.

Beginning in October 1942, NDRC studied the installation of rocket launchers on a variety of vehicles. Initially, it was intended to mount the launchers on both the standard and the amphibious $\frac{1}{4}$ ton Jeep. Later, the DUKW was chosen because of its greater load carrying capacity. An improvised launcher for the Navy 4.5 inch barrage rocket was installed in a DUKW and it was shipped out to Australia with the 2nd Engineer Special Brigade in early 1943. Further development produced the Scorpion launcher carrying 144 4.5 inch rockets. After tests, the number of rockets was reduced to 120 in the improved Scorpion. Four DUKWs were armed with the improved launcher and shipped to the 2nd Engineer Special Brigade where they were employed during the 15 December 1943 landing at Arawe on the island of New Britain. This was the first use of the barrage rockets in an amphibious landing in the Pacific. They were subsequently employed during the next six months at Cape Gloucester, the Hollandia operation, and the invasion of Biak. For later operations, the DUKWs were replace by LVTs to carry the rocket launchers.

A later launcher was developed to carry the 7.2 inch rocket. Installed in the DUKW it was demonstrated at Fort Pierce, Florida during February 1944. Although approximately 100 were produced, they were never used in action.

The power train of the production DUKW is illustrated at the left.

Above is the improved Scorpion rocket launcher capable of firing 120 4.5 inch barrage rockets. Below at the left, a DUKW is landing on the beach during the invasion of Sicily. At the bottom left, the DUKWs are working with the LVTs to bring in the assault troops on Guam. At the lower right, a DUKW is leaving the ramp of an LST to carry marines ashore on Iwo Jima.

A model of the eight wheel Baker jumping vehicle is shown in the two photographs on this page.

NDRC ARMORED CAR PROJECTS

In the Spring of 1941, the National Defense Research Committee studied the development of a new series of armored vehicles. Referred to as the Turtle series, it included not only medium and heavy equipment, but also a highly mobile, lightly armored, vehicle suitable for air transport. A wheeled vehicle was considered to be necessary to meet the latter requirement and it was studied in two basic models. The larger, eight wheel, version was intended to carry a 3 inch gun while the smaller, four wheel, design was to be armed with a lighter weapon. The weapons under consideration included the British 17 pounder (3 inch gun) and the 40mm gun M1. All wheels were powered on these vehicles and an hydraulic anti-recoil system was a feature of both designs. However, the most interesting aspect of the new vehicles was the method used to overcome obstacles and achieve good cross-country mobility. This was accomplished by a new independent suspension system which was designed to permit the vehicle to jump over ditches, fences, and similar obstructions. This suspension was capable of very high energy absorption and was designed to permit the

chassis to squat and then be accelerated upward. The wheels would then be accelerated upward and the entire vehicle would leave the ground. Although no actual vehicle was constructed, a full scale test unit consisting of one wheel with its suspension drive, associated frame members, and hydraulic jumping apparatus was completed. Tests performed with this equipment indicated that a full scale vehicle using this design could clear a height of 49 inches or a ditch 47 feet wide at a speed of 40 miles per hour. However, under estimating the

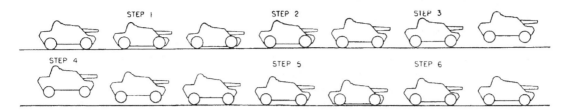

The jumping cycle of the Baker vehicle is illustrated above in the following steps: 1. Chassis squats, 2. Chassis accelerates upward, 3. Wheels accelerated upward, 4. Vehicle in air, 5. Chassis decelerated upward, and 6. Chassis rises to normal road clearance.

Above is the model of the four wheel Baker jumping vehicle. The view at the right shows the turret removed with the driver in his position. Note the different weapons illustrated in the models. The right view obviously shows a 40mm gun.

dimensions of the obstacle might have been disastrous. Although a variety of armament was considered, preliminary designs were based upon the use of the 3 inch gun for the eight wheel vehicle and the 40mm weapon for the four wheel design. The eight wheel car was designed with a wheel base of 189 inches, a width of 121 inches, and an estimated weight of approximately 20,000 pounds. The four wheel vehicle had a wheel base of 137 inches, a width of 121 inches, and an estimated weight of about 10,000 pounds. Except for the test apparatus, the program did not progress beyond the model stage. Design work on the jumping vehicle program was carried out by the Baker Manufacturing Company of Evansville, Wisconsin under OSRD contract OEMsr-524. As a result, these vehicles were frequently referred to as the Baker tank.

Below at the left is another view of the four wheel model without the turret. At the right is a bottom view of the four wheel model.

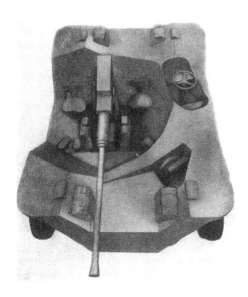

The eight wheel Trackless Tank shown here is at Aberdeen Proving Ground on 22 January 1941. Additional views of the vehicle can be seen below.

MEDIUM AND HEAVY ARMORED CARS

In January 1941, an eight wheeled vehicle constructed as a commercial venture by the Trackless Tank Corporation was tested at Aberdeen Proving Ground. Although considered unsatisfactory as a tank, the performance of the eight wheel, pneumatic strut, independent suspension was very impressive. Further tests at Fort Knox confirmed the desirability of such a suspension for use in an armored car. The Armored Force Board reported that in many respects, the cross-country mobility exceeded that of any other Armored Force vehicle. Following these tests, a contract was negotiated with the Trackless Tank Corporation for seventeen test vehicles. The new vehicle was to consist of an eight wheel armored chassis with independently sprung wheels. The rear six wheels were chain driven with power supplied by a Guiberson T-1020 diesel engine. Thirteen of the cars were to be fitted with a light tank type turret mounting a 37mm gun and a .30 caliber machine gun. These were to be designated as the armored car T13. The four remaining chassis were to be finished as the 3 inch gun motor carriage T7. In December 1941, authority also was received to procure two 105mm howitzer motor carriages T39 based upon

The Trackless Tank crosses an obstacle at the top left and is operating at high speed at the top right during its test program at Fort Knox on 19 March 1941. Note the improvised turret and gun mount.

the T13 chassis. After the attack on Pearl Harbor, the Ordnance Committee recommended that contracts be placed for 1,000 of these chassis prior to standardization.

Two modified pilots, designated as the armored car T13E1, were authorized in April 1942. The chassis of these vehicles were lengthened permitting the installation of wheels with 12 x 20 combat tires and the diesel engine was replaced by a Continental W670-9A gasoline engine. At that time, 500 of the authorized 1,000 vehicles were suspended from procurement pending the development of the armored car T20 which was being carried out by Reo Motors Incorporated.

The Trackless Tank Corporation had executed a subcontract with Reo Motors Incorporated for the manufacture of the T13. After numerous delays, the first pilot car was demonstrated at the subcontractor's plant in May 1942 and on 7 June, two vehicles were shipped to Fort Knox for tests. Many components were experimental, having been designed particularly for these vehicles and numerous failures occurred during the tests. This resulted in an order to the subcontractor to temporarily cease manufacture of the other pilot vehicles. After further review, the entire T13 project was canceled including the 3 inch gun motor carriage T7 and the 105mm howitzer motor carriage T39. One pilot T13 was modified by the manufacturer to correct defects noted in the early testing. The car was then sent to Aberdeen Proving Ground for evaluation by the Special

Armored Vehicle Board. As mentioned earlier, this board had been convened in October 1942 and among its tasks was the specification of the armored car requirements for the Army. Although the cross-country performance of the T13 was outstanding, its weight was almost double that considered desirable in an armored reconnaissance vehicle. Both the steering and the chain drive were felt to be inherent sources of weakness in the design and the many pneumatic and hydraulic devices made it particularly vulnerable to mechanical failure. As a result of these considerations, it was recommended that the project be dropped entirely.

As originally proposed, the armored car T20 was an eight wheel vehicle with each wheel independently sprung and power applied to each wheel by a separate electric motor. The car was designed by Mr. O. F. Quartello for construction by Reo Motors. A gasoline engine drove a generator which supplied power to the electric motors on each wheel. In general, the vehicle was similar to the T13 with a gross weight estimated to be about 26,000 pounds. Procurement of four chassis was approved in March 1942 with two to be completed as armored cars and two to be used as the basis for a 105mm howitzer motor carriage. However, the T20 did not progress beyond the mock-up stage. Further design studies indicated excessive weight over the original estimates and performance well below that which was desired. For these reasons, the project was terminated in August 1942.

Below are additional views of the Trackless Tank during its test program.

The armored car T13 (Son of Trackless Tank) appears in these photographs taken during its evaluation at Aberdeen Proving Ground on 14 November 1942. The armament consists of the 37mm gun and coaxial .30 caliber machine gun in the turret and the .30 caliber machine gun in the bow mount.

Details of the turret and rear deck on the armored car T13 can be seen above and in the views below. Note the stowage boxes on the fender at the lower right.

Stowage boxes are installed on both fenders of the armored car T13 in the views below and at the right at Fort Knox.

Additional views of armored car T13 are above and at the right. The driver's compartment on the T13 can be seen below.

The hatches of the armored car T13 at the right are open. Note the stowage boxes on the fenders of this vehicle at Fort Knox.

75

The pilot medium armored car T17 appears above with its full armament installed. This consists of the turret mounted 37mm gun with a .30 caliber coaxial machine gun and a .30 caliber machine gun in the bow mount.

In the Spring of 1941, the British Purchasing Commission submitted specifications for medium and heavy armored cars which it wished to procure as rapidly as possible. At the same time, the Armored Force Board, after observing the British battle experience in the desert, recommended the early procurement of a wheeled, turreted, reconnaissance vehicle for which it submitted a specification. The two specifications were combined and it was recommended that both medium and heavy armored cars be designed in addition to the T13 already under consideration. The medium and heavy armored cars were designated as the T17 and T18 respectively and, according to the original proposal, one pilot was to be built of each after approval of the design. However, both the Ford Motor Company and the Chevrolet Division of General Motors submitted satisfactory designs for the medium armored car. The Ford design was a six wheel vehicle designated as the armored car T17. The Chevrolet had four wheels and was designated as the armored car T17E1. All wheels were powered in both designs. Authorization was obtained to construct two pilots of each type. The original T17 proposal used two Ford six cylinder engines of 90 horsepower each. In the final design, the power was increased by changing to two Hercules JXD 110 horsepower engines. The twin engines mounted at the rear of the hull had individual transmissions connected to a common transfer case. This system provided eight speeds forward and two in reverse. The suspension used conventional leaf springs and power steering was applied to the front wheels. The turret assembly was manufactured at Rock Island Arsenal. The

advantage of using many standard components was readily apparent in the rapid completion of the first pilot when compared to the many delays on the T13 project. The first pilot arrived at Aberdeen Proving Ground in March 1942, approximately six months after authorization. The second pilot, fitted with a new three man turret, was shipped to the Armored Force Board at Fort Knox. Testing revealed numerous mechanical defects and was finally halted by extensive failures in axles and transmissions. A variety of changes were required for the production model resulting in stronger, heavier components with a different type of transmission and a change in the gear ratio. The Special Armored Vehicle Board evaluated the armored car T17 and reported that both its dimensions and weight were far in excess of those desired for a reconnaissance vehicle. At that time, the Board considered the only use of an armored car to be as a reconnaissance vehicle. The contract for the T17 was cut to 250 production vehicles, all of which originally were allocated to the British who designated it as the Deerhound. However, none of the T17s were shipped overseas and they were used by military police units in the United States after removal of the 37mm gun.

The rear of the pilot T17 armored car can be seen at the right. Note the air intake and exhaust configuration unique to the pilot vehicle.

The production version of the T17 armored car is shown here at Aberdeen Proving Ground on 4 December 1942. Note the changes to the engine deck and the rear of the vehicle. The stowage boxes also have been modified.

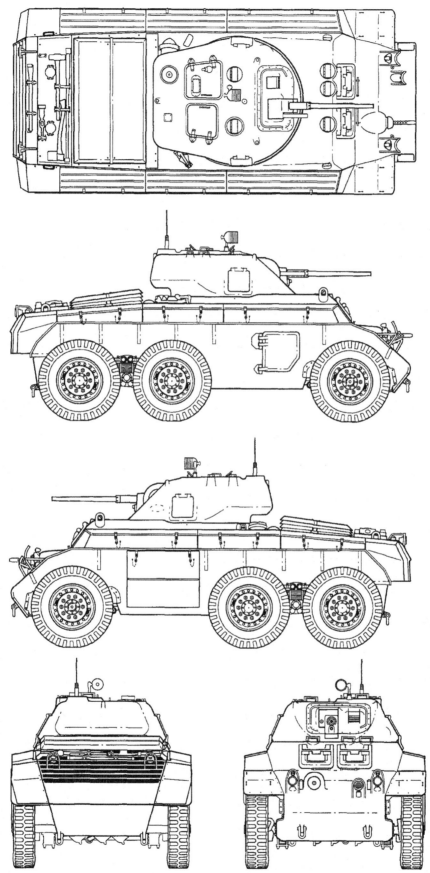

Scale 1:48

Medium Armored Car T17

© M. Duplessis

The production model of the armored car T17, Registration Number W-6025151, above is at Aberdeen on 4 December 1942. The three photographs at the left and below show T17 armored car, Registration Number W-6025172, during tests of the production vehicle at Fort Knox. Note that the protectoscope viewing device has been eliminated from the pistol port covers on the production cars.

79

Above and at the left below are additional photographs of T17 armored car, Registration Number W-6025172, at Fort Knox. The armor type and thickness on the T17 is shown in the view below at the right.

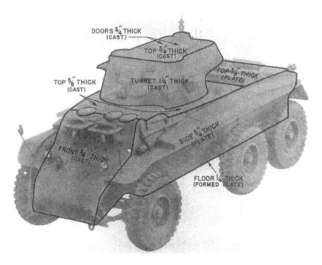

The bogie assembly of the T17 armored car is at the left. The power train of the vehicle appears below and one of the Hercules JXD engines is at the bottom left. The numbers in the latter photograph indicate various engine components in the vehicle manual.

The mockup of the medium armored car T17E1 appears above at the left. At the top right is an early production T17E1. The turret installed on the early T17E1 medium armored car is below at the right. This was the same turret used on the early medium armored car T17 and the heavy armored car T18.

Chevrolet's fortune with the T17E1 was much brighter. The first pilot vehicle also was delivered to Aberdeen Proving Ground in March 1942. After inspection, it was sent along with the second pilot to the General Motors Proving Ground for tests. Although many mechanical failures occurred, they appeared to be easily corrected. The changes involved the gear box, differential, universal joints, and splines. A wooden mock-up of the production model was completed on 16 June 1942 and the final stowage was approved. The production vehicle carried a crew of five, two men in the hull and three in the turret, with a gross weight of 32,000 pounds. The hull itself was a main structural element so no frame was required. The springs, steering gear, and transfer case were attached directly to the hull.

The production medium armored car T17E1, Registration Number W-6024839, below is at Aberdeen Proving Ground on 4 December 1942. The jettison fuel tanks and stowage boxes have been installed on each side of the vehicle.

Above is another view of T17E1, Registration Number W-6024839, at Aberdeen. Details of the production turret can be seen in this view. Note that the protectoscope viewing device has been removed from the pistol port covers.

The turret was similar to that designed for the light tank T7, but the thickness was reduced to 1¼ inches at the front, sides, and rear and ¾ inches at the top. The hull armor ranged from $^7/_8$ inches at the front to $^3/_8$ inches at the rear. The frontal armor of the hull and turret was angled at 45 degrees from the vertical. Turret armament consisted of a 37mm gun M6 and a .30 caliber machine gun in a coaxial mount. A .30 caliber machine gun was on the turret roof and another such weapon was mounted in the right front hull. The cruising range was extended by jettisonable fuel tanks installed on each side of the vehicle. Two 97 horsepower, six cylinder, GMC engines were mounted in the rear hull. The engines could be operated simultaneously or individually. A Hydramatic

transmission for each engine transmitted its power to a single, two speed, transfer case. From there, drive shafts powered the front and rear axles. Named the Staghound I, the T17E1 was authorized for production to fill British requirements. A total of 2,844 T17E1s were built from October 1942 through December 1943. The T17E1 was never standardized, although standardization as the armored car M6 was proposed at one time and some of the name plates bear that designation in anticipation of standardization.

The T17E1 medium armored car at the right is under test at the Desert Proving Ground at British request. Note that all of the hatches are open in the hot weather.

82

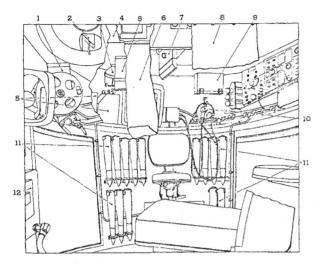

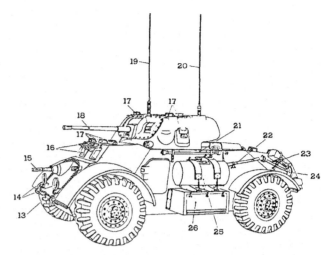

1. 37MM GUN MOUNT, 2. PERISCOPE M2, 3. CANTEEN, 4. CALIBER .30 MACHINE GUN MOUNT, 5. CALIBER .30 AMMUNITION BOXES, 6. CALIBER .30 EMPTY CARTRIDGE BAG, 7. PERISCOPE M6, 8. 37MM EMPTY CARTRIDGE BAG, 9. SPARE PERISCOPE M6, 10. PHONE, 11. 37MM AMMUNITION H.E. M63, 12. PERISCOPE M2, 13. TOWING CABLE, 14. HEADLIGHT SOCKET PLUGS, 15. CALIBER .30 MACHINE GUN AND MUZZLE COVER, 16. FRONT VISION DOORS, 17. PERISCOPES M6, 18. 37MM GUN M6 AND MUZZLE COVER, 19. ANTENNA MP 48, 20. ANTENNA MP 37, 21. RAMMER STAFF, 22. PICK, 23. TRIPOD WITH PINTLE, 24. SHOVEL, 25. JETTISON TANK, 26. LUGGAGE BOX, 27. AXLE, 28. CROWBAR, 29. CAMOUFLAGE NET AND TARPAULIN.

30. CALIBER .30 MACHINE GUN AND MUZZLE COVER, 31. ANTENNA SECTIONS, 32. JETTISON TANK, 33. LUGGAGE BOX, 34. 37MM CANNISTER M2 AMMUNITION, 35. SPARE PERISCOPE HEADS, 36. RADIO SCR-506 OR SCR-508, 37. SPOTLIGHT HANDLE AND REEL, 38. PERISCOPES M6, 39. CALIBER .30 AND 37MM SMALL PARTS, 40. PHONE, 41. SPARE PERISCOPE M6, 42. BINOCULARS, 43. CANTEENS, 44. MAP, 45. COMPASS, 46. FLASHLIGHT, 47. 37MM AMMUNITION A.P. M51, 48. HAND GRENADE BOXES, 49. SPOT LIGHT SHAFT, 50. SPOT LIGHT, 51. SIGNAL FLAGS, 52. 37MM SPARE PARTS, 53. RADIO SCR-510.

Components and stowage on the exterior and the turret interior of the medium armored car T17E1 are identified in the four drawings here. The right side of the turret interior is at the left above and the left side is at the right below.

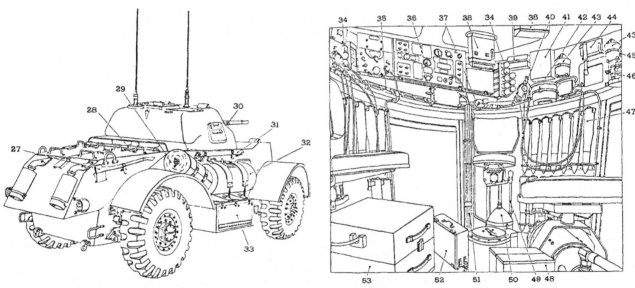

Below, the right side of the hull interior is at the left and the left side of the hull interior is at the right.

54. WINDSHIELD AND WIPER, 55. CALIBER .45 AMMUNITION BOXES, 56. CANTEENS, 57. CALIBER .45 SUBMACHINE GUN, 58. 37MM AMMUNITION A.P. M51, 59. 37MM AMMUNITION H.E. M63, 60. CREW SUPPLY COMPARTMENT: FIXED FIRE EXTINGUISHERS, 61. CALIBER .30 AMMUNITION BOXES, 62. CALIBER .30 AND CALIBER .45 SPARE PARTS, 63. PORTABLE FIRE EXTINGUISHER, 64. INTERPHONE AMPLIFIER BC-667, 65. CALIBER .30 AND SMALL PARTS, 66. FIRST AID KIT, 67. SPARE BARRELS FOR CALIBER .30 MACHINE GUN.

68. OIL CAN, 69. BOOK, FORM 7255, 70. CALIBER .30 EMPTY CARTRIDGE BAG, 71. CALIBER .30 MACHINE GUN, 72. COMPASS, 73. SPARE PERISCOPE HEADS M6, 74. PERISCOPE M6, 75. PHONE, 76. 37MM AMMUNITION A.P. M51, 77. CALIBER .30 AMMUNITION BOXES, 78. FLASHLIGHTS, 79. SPARE PERISCOPE HEADS M6, 80. WINDSHIELD AND WIPER, 81. LUBRICATION GUIDE, 82. PERISCOPE M6, 83. MAP, 84. SPARE PERISCOPES M6, 85. SPARE PEEP HOLE PROTECTORS, 86. LIGHT TOOLS, 87. HAND GRENADE BOXES.

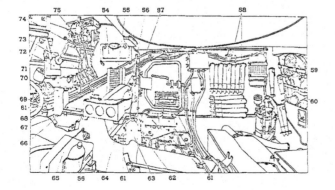

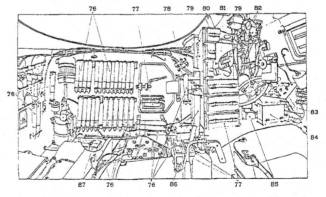

This production medium armored car T17E1 serial number 902, Registration Number W-6023735, is under test at the General Motors Proving Ground on 10 June 1943. Note that the pistol ports have been eliminated from the turret.

This medium armored car T17E1, Registration Number W-6024950, represents the latest production version. It is shown here completely stowed.

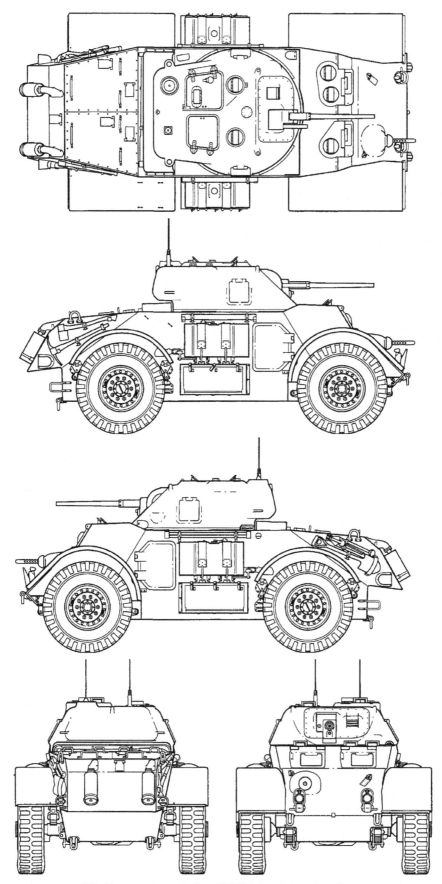

Scale 1:48

Medium Armored Car T17E1, early production

© M. Duplessis

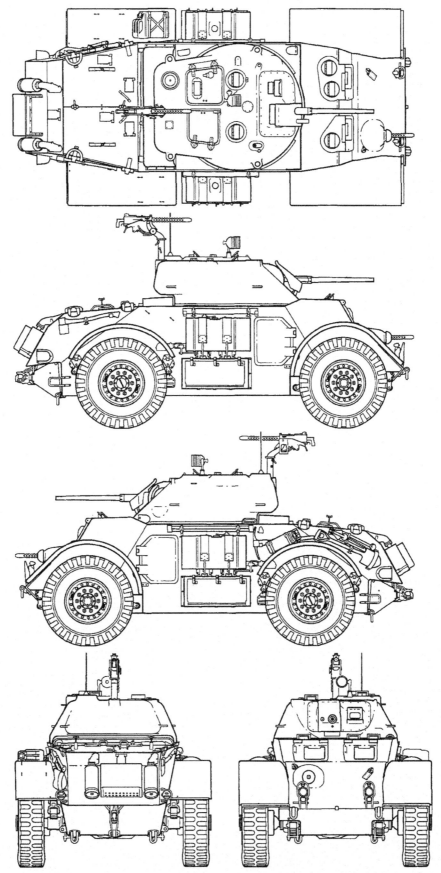

Scale 1:48

Medium Armored Car T17E1, late production

© M. Duplessis

87

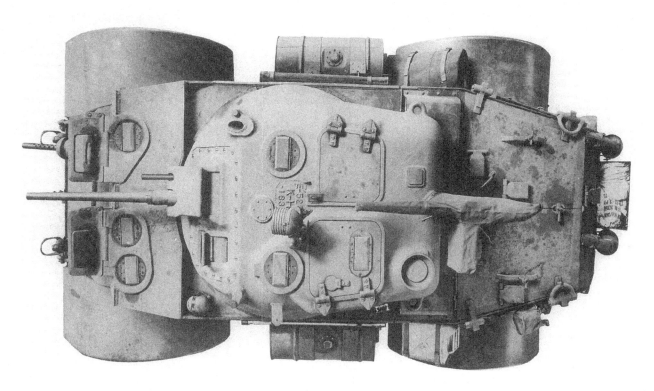

These additional views of medium armored car T17E1 show features of the final production version. Note the 2 inch smoke mortar in the right front of the turret roof.

1. TRANSMISSION CONTROL, 2. TRANSFER CASE SHIFT LEVER, 3 TRANSFER CASE SHIFT LEVER GATE PLATE, 4. ENGINE SELECTOR, 5. CHOKE, 6. HAND THROTTLES, 7. HAND BRAKE, 8. TRANSFER CASE FRONT AXLE LEVER, 10. HEAD LAMP RELEASE, 11. BRAKE PEDAL, 12. ACCELERATOR, 13. STEERING GEAR MOTOR SWITCH, 14. SIREN CONTROL, 15. FIRE EXTINGUISHER, 16. FIRE EXTINGUISHING SYSTEM CONTROL, 17. PERISCOPES, 18. HAND BRAKE ASSIST PEDAL, 19. CHOKE LEVERS CLAMP BOLT, 20. THROTTLE LEVERS CLAMP BOLT, 21. COMPASS.

The driver's compartment in the T17E1 is above and the engine compartment is below. At the right are views of the left side of the left engine (upper) and the right side of the right engine (lower).

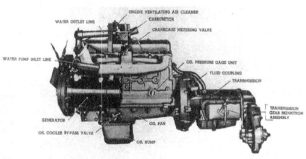

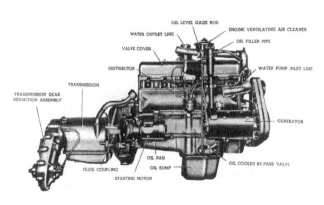

The Staghound I is shown above in British service. Note the stowage in the field. In the left photograph, ammunition boxes have been attached to the front fenders to provide stowage space. In the right view, the jettison fuel tanks have been replaced by stowage bins on this Canadian vehicle in Italy during August 1944.

Although the Staghound was widely used by the British forces, it was not a popular vehicle. Designed for the desert, it was considered to be too large and heavy for operations in Italy and France. The following comments were taken from the history of the 11th Hussars entitled "The Eleventh at War" by Brigadier Dudley Clarke.

"The Staghound was an American product intended to replace the Daimlers at the squadron and regimental headquarters. It was a huge vehicle, 8 feet broad and 13 tons in weight carrying a crew of five with a 37mm gun and a .3 Browning machine gun. The 11th Hussars found it unwieldy and it never earned their affection."

Above at the right, a Staghound I is serving as a command car for the Royal Dragoons near Epene, Normandy. Below at the left, this Staghound I is on parade and at the bottom right, a Staghound I has been armed with aircraft rockets. Both vehicles have eliminated the jettison fuel tanks.

Above are two views of the armored car T17E2 pilot vehicle at Aberdeen Proving Ground on 20 March 1943. It is armed with the early twin .50 caliber machine gun Frazier-Nash turret with the flat sides.

In February 1943, the United Kingdom requested that the armored car T17E1 be modified as an antiaircraft vehicle. These cars were to be fitted with a Frazer-Nash machine gun turret replacing the standard 37mm gun turret. The new vehicle was designated as the armored car T17E2. Chevrolet assembled a pilot vehicle using the Norge N80 twin .50 caliber machine gun turret. This was essentially the British designed Frazer-Nash turret consisting of a power driven gun mount with the gunner seated in the center. The turret was driven by an electro-hydraulic power system with a traverse rate of 55 to 60 degrees per second. Twin hydraulic cylinders elevated the guns at rates up to 38 degrees per second. The gunner used handlebar type controls which could be turned in both the horizontal and vertical positions. The amount of movement in either plane determined the speed and direction of the turret movement. Triggers were just forward of the handlebar controls in a position to be actuated by the index fingers. The pilot vehicle was shipped to Aberdeen Proving Ground for extensive firing tests and then returned to the manufacturer in April 1943 for modification.

Additional photographs of the T17E2 armored car pilot vehicle at Aberdeen are shown above and below. This vehicle, converted from a T17E1, has the port for the bow machine gun blanked off.

As modified for production, a General Electric ammunition booster feed was installed. The production turret was protected by $1\frac{1}{4}$ inches of armor on all sides and the front plate was angled at 45 degrees to the vertical. The two .50 caliber machine guns were supplied with 2,610 rounds of ammunition.

Since there was no room in the new turret for the British Number 19 radio, it was installed in the right front hull eliminating the bow machine gun. The crew was reduced to three men compared to the five in the T17E1. Production of the T17E2 began in October 1943 and ended in April 1944 with all 1,000 vehicles produced going to the British where they were named the Staghound AA.

Above is an early armored car T17E2. Note the flat sides on this welded turret. Below, the late production welded turret can be seen with the rounded sides. These vehicles are fully stowed with the jettison fuel tanks installed.

The armored car T17E2 below is under test at Fort Knox. Details of the stowage and the turret interior can be seen in the left photograph.

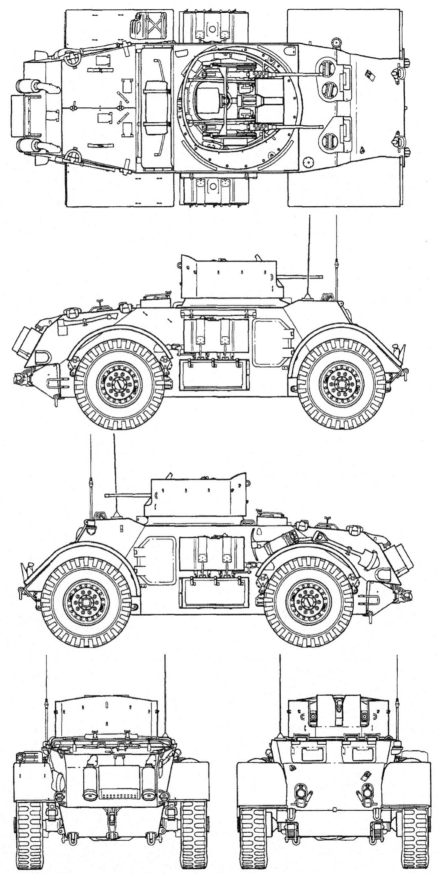

Scale 1:48

© M. Duplessis

Medium Armored Car T17E2

93

The medium armored car T17E3 armed with the 75mm howitzer is shown on this page. This is the pilot vehicle. Note that it was converted from the T17E1, Registration Number U.S.A. 6024950, on page 85.

British requirements in November 1943 included 100 medium armored cars equipped with the 75mm howitzer and turret of the 75mm howitzer motor carriage M8. This vehicle was designated as the armored car T17E3 and the pilot was assembled by Chevrolet. Firing tests were successfully performed at the Erie Proving Ground on 9 December 1943. However, by the end of the month, information had been received that the requirement for the T17E3 had been dropped. Development was terminated and the project officially canceled in late 1944.

The turret interior with the 75mm howitzer and mount on the T17E3 can be seen at the right and below. The antiaircraft machine gun has not been mounted on the vehicle.

The first and third cars in the lineup above are Staghound IIs. Note the shorter, thicker, barrel on the 3 inch tank howitzer. At the right is a Staghound III fitted with the Crusader turret armed with a 75mm gun. Note the large stowage bin replacing the jettison fuel tanks.

Although the British never received the T17E3, they met the requirement for a close support vehicle by converting some of the T17E1s. The 37mm gun in the turret was replaced by the British 3 inch tank howitzer and the converted vehicles were dubbed the Staghound II. The bow machine gun was eliminated and the assistant driver's space was filled with 3 inch ammunition. The 2 inch smoke mortar in the turret roof was replaced by 4 inch smoke dischargers externally mounted on the turret.

Another British conversion was the replacement of the Staghound turret with the turret from the Crusader tank. These turrets became available after the conversion of the Crusader chassis to special purpose vehicles. The turrets were armed with the British 75mm gun Mark V which fired the same ammunition as the U.S. 75mm gun M3. The converted vehicles were named the Staghound III.

A top view of the Staghound III is at the right.

95

The Staghound Command appears above and the Bantu mine detector is installed on a Staghound I at the right. Neither vehicle carries the jettison fuel tanks.

The Staghound also was used as a command vehicle with the turret removed. Frequently a wind screen was installed across the front of the turret ring. Appropriately, this vehicle was named the Staghound Command.

A British experimental application of the T17E1 was the installation of electric mine detection equipment. Named the Bantu, the mine detection apparatus was mounted in two large wooden rollers in front of the wheels and one large roller at the center in the rear. The was the same equipment mounted on the Sherman tank and named Lulu. Like Lulu, Bantu proved to be impractical and the project was dropped.

Another device evaluated on the T17E1 was the anti-mine reconnaissance caster roller (AMRCR). Also tested on the Sherman and Churchill tanks, it consisted of four rollers with two trailed in line in front of the wheels on each side. Each was assembled from four $^{1}/_{2}$ inch thick, 26 inch diameter steel discs separated by pairs of 22 inch diameter cast iron spacer discs. Bolted together, the complete roller was about 17 inches in width. The AMRCR program was terminated in favor of more promising mine exploders.

At the upper right, a Staghound I is fitted with the AMRCR and at the lower right, a Staghound I is armed with two rocket launchers. One rocket has just been fired.

96

At the top left is the mockup for the heavy armored car T18. Above and below at the right are photographs of the pilot heavy armored car T18 at the General Motors Proving Ground on 25 November 1942. The armament has not been installed.

The procurement of two heavy armored car T18 pilot vehicles was recommended by the same Ordnance Committee action in July 1941 that authorized the T17 series of medium armored cars. The T18 originally was intended to be a similar vehicle, but with a heavier armor basis. The front armor was increased to a 2 inch basis compared to $1^{1}/_{4}$ inches for the T17 series vehicles. General Motors Truck and Coach Division received the contract and completed a wooden mock-up of the T18 early in December 1941. Originally, the design weight was optimistically estimated to be about 36,000 pounds. The T18 was an eight wheel vehicle with the wheels suspended by leaf springs in two four wheel bogies. The four wheels in the front bogie were steerable. Power was supplied by two GMC truck engines each providing 145 horsepower at 3,000 rpm. The power from each engine was transmitted through a Spicer torque converter with a direct drive clutch, a three forward and one reverse speed transmission with blocking type synchronizers, and a single speed transfer case. Each transfer case had a solid drive to one of the axles in the rear bogie and an automatic pick-up drive to one of the axles in the front bogie. The drives to the front bogie were automatically engaged whenever the rear bogie wheels slipped and

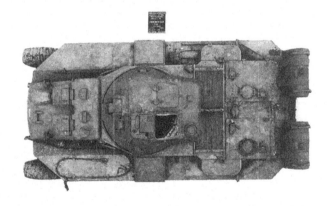

Below and at the upper right are additional views of the heavy armored car T18 at the General Motors Proving Ground. This was the only T18 completed and it carried serial number 1, Registration Number W-6032224.

97

Front and rear views of the pilot heavy armored car T18 can be seen in the two photographs above.

their speed exceeded that of the wheels on the front bogie. The right engine was connected to the rear wheels on each bogie and the left engine was connected to the front wheels on each bogie. As on the T17 series vehicles, the turret was based upon that of the light tank T7 with a thickness of 2 inches. This turret, designed and built at Rock Island Arsenal, was armed with a 37mm gun M6 and a coaxial .30 caliber machine gun. The first pilot T18, Registration Number W-6032224, was delivered to General Motors Proving Ground in July 1942. By this time, battle experience had indicated the need for a more powerful weapon than the 37mm gun. The British Tank Mission and the United States Tank Committee agreed that a 57mm gun would be suitable

and instructions were issued to modify the second pilot to mount this weapon. A turret mounting the 6 pounder Mark III (57mm) was obtained from the light tank T7E2 program and installed on the second pilot. This vehicle, Registration Number W-6032225, was designated as the heavy armored car T18E2. This particular turret was fitted with roof hatches that were tapered in width unlike the rectangular hatches selected for the production cars. After initial tests, the T18E2 pilot was shipped to Britain for further evaluation.

At the time the original T18 mock-up was constructed, General Motors submitted a new design for a heavy armored car using a six wheel independent suspension with power applied to all six wheels. This

The pilot heavy armored car T18E2, serial number 2 (Registration Number W-6032225), is shown below at Aberdeen Proving Ground on 5 November 1942. Note the heavy barrel of the 6 pounder Mark III gun installed in the pilot vehicle.

The photographs on this page show additional views of the heavy armored car T18E2 pilot. The top view at the bottom left was taken after the vehicle was shipped to Britain for evaluation. Note the tapered hatch doors on the turret.

vehicle was to be powered by two Cadillac engines with each driving through its own Hydramatic transmission. The Ordnance Committee approved the construction of two pilots and designated the six wheel vehicle as the heavy armored car T18E1. However, the development of the medium armored car T19 was initiated shortly thereafter in January 1942 and it was considered unnecessary to develop two six wheel armored cars with independent suspensions. The project for the T18E1 was canceled without any construction.

After flotation tests at the General Motors Proving Ground, the pilot T18 was returned to the manufacturer for use in the development of the T18E2. The production T18E2 was considerably heavier than originally expected with a gross weight of about 53,000 pounds. The production turret carried the 57mm gun M1 and a coaxial .30 caliber machine gun in the combination mount T63. The 57mm gun M1 had a longer, thinner barrel than the 6 pounder Mark III and it was lighter in weight. This was the version of the 6

pounder produced in the United States. A 2 inch smoke mortar was fitted in the turret and a .30 caliber machine gun was installed in a bow mount in the right front hull. The armor plate varied in thickness from $1\frac{1}{4}$ to 2 inches in front and from $1\frac{1}{4}$ to 1 inch along the sides.

The seating arrangement in the T18E2 was similar to that in other armored vehicles with the driver and assistant driver in the front hull and the gunner, loader, and car commander in the turret. A British Number 19 radio set was installed in the turret bustle. Production of the T18E2 began during December 1942 and was completed in May 1943 with the total limited to 30 vehicles, all of which were transferred to the United Kingdom. Named the Boarhound, the T18E2 had been designed for the desert war which was now ending. The British Army staff required no further procurement of spare parts for the T18E2 after January 1944 and the Ordnance Committee declared the T18E2 obsolete. This action also closed the projects for the T18 and the T18E1.

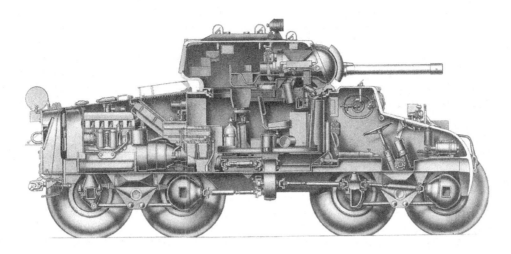

Sectional views of the pilot heavy armored car T18E2 appear above and below. The internal components and stowage are clearly visible. Note the shorter barrel of the 6 pounder Mark III gun installed in the turret.

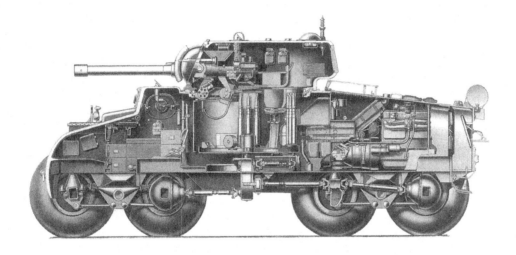

The power train for the pilot heavy armored car T18E2 can be seen below. This view of the power train can be compared with those in the sectional views above.

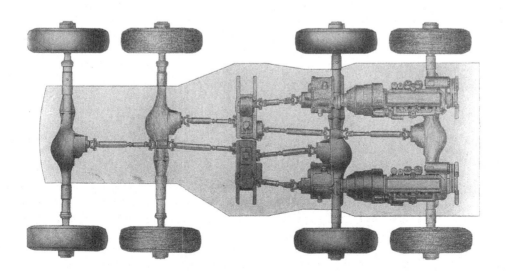

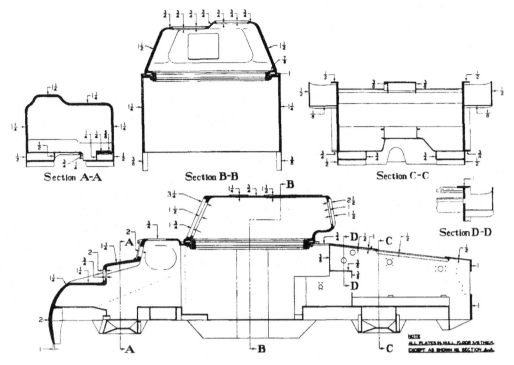

Section A-A   Section B-B   Section C-C

Section D-D

The armor thickness on the heavy armored car T18E2 is shown in the drawing above.

Details of the driver's vision door and pistol port can be seen in the two photographs above. The interior of the driver's compartment is at the left below with the vision and escape doors closed. The design of the production turret for the heavy armored car T18E2 is illustrated at the bottom right. Note the rectangular hatch doors. The production vehicle also had a 2 inch smoke mortar in the right front of the turret roof.

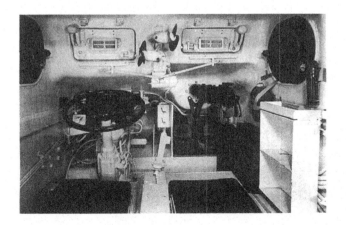

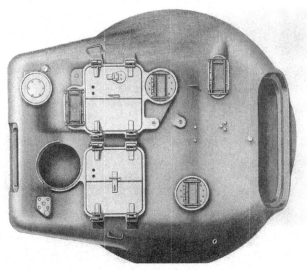

The production heavy armored car T18E2 in these photographs, serial number 4 (Registration Number U.S.A. 6030413), is at the General Motors Proving Ground on 19 January 1943. The longer slim barrel of the 57mm gun M1 is obvious.

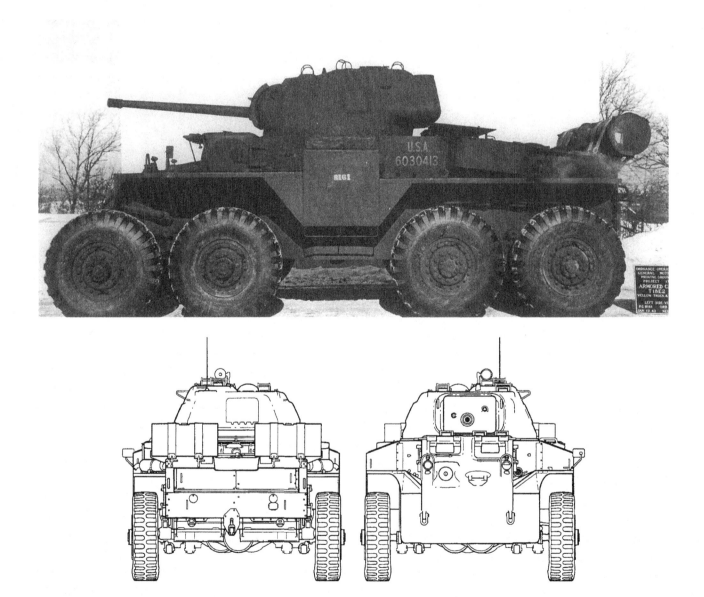

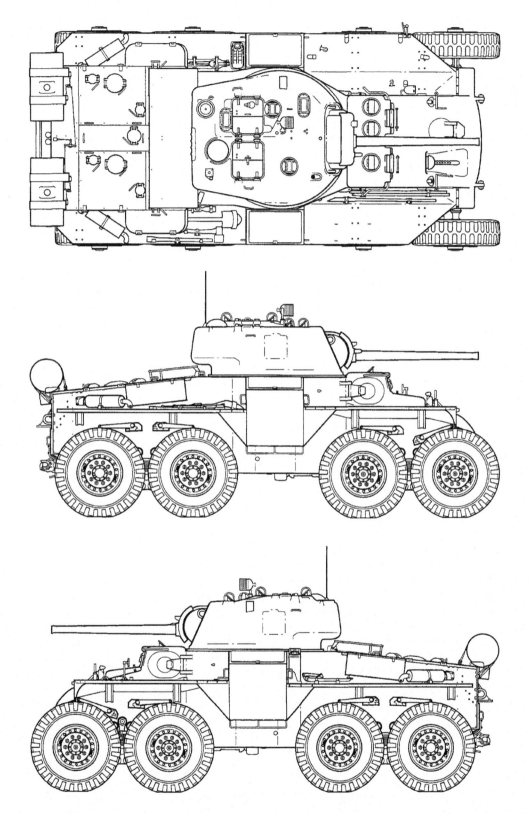

Scale 1:48

Heavy Armored Car T18E2

Above, the pilot medium armored car T19, built by the Chevrolet Division of General Motors, is at Aberdeen Proving Ground on 5 November 1942. Note the independent coil spring suspension on this six wheel vehicle. The turret is without armament and appears to be the same as on the early T17E1 and T18.

In January 1942, the Ordnance Committee authorized the procurement of two pilot medium armored cars with independently sprung wheels for comparison with the T17 and T17E1 which had conventional truck type suspensions. The new vehicles were designated as the medium armored car T19 and were equipped with six wheels, all of which were driven. The first pilot was completed by Chevrolet and delivered to the General Motors Proving Ground in July 1942. Except for its suspension, it was quite similar to the T17 and T17E1. Each wheel had approximately 13 inches of vertical movement with the independent swing arm suspension. Coil springs, fitted around a direct action shock absorber, were attached between the hull and the swing arm suspension mechanism. The car was driven by two GMC truck engines. After fitting with a T17 turret, the T19 was shipped to Aberdeen Proving Ground in October 1942.

Shortly after the construction of the first pilot T19, the project was brought under the jurisdiction of the Development Branch of the Tank Automotive Center in Detroit. A meeting was held on 20 August 1942 which modified the specifications for the second pilot. The modified design was designated as the medium armored car T19E1. The GMC truck engines were replaced by two Cadillac engines and the turret was redesigned to reduce the weight. The 12 x 20 tires on the T19 were replaced with 14 x 20 tires. The vehicle had the power train of the light tank M5 with the two Cadillac engines driving through two Hydramatic transmissions. Power from the transmissions was delivered to a two speed transfer case and then to a special differential that provided $\frac{1}{3}$ of the total power to the front axle and the remaining $\frac{2}{3}$ was equally distributed to the intermediate and rear axles. The vehicle could be operated, if necessary, on only one engine.

The pilot medium armored car T19E1 is shown below. Note the new, lighter weight, turret armed with the 37mm gun.

The exterior configuration of the medium armored car T19E1 can be seen in the two views above. Details of the new, lighter weight, turret are visible at the right below in this photograph taken at Aberdeen Proving Ground on 5 February 1943.

Prior to the completion of the T19E1, the original T19 had been evaluated by the Special Armored Vehicle Board. As mentioned earlier, the Board defined the role of the armored car as that of a reconnaissance vehicle. For this purpose, both the T19 and the T19E1 were too large, heavy, and expensive and the Board unanimously recommended that their development be ended. It did consider the independent suspension a desirable feature which should be incorporated in future armored car design. To evaluate the suspension further, the pilot T19E1 was tested at Aberdeen Proving Ground from 31 January to 5 February 1943. These tests confirmed the previous conclusions of the T19 tests that the vehicle was too heavy and large for a reconnaissance vehicle.

Below, the medium armored car T19E1 is plowing through the mud during its evaluation program. These tests showed the clear advantage of the fully independent six wheel suspension on the T19E1.

105

The 75mm gun motor carriage T66, based upon the medium armored car T19E1, is at Aberdeen Proving Ground on 5 February 1943. The 75mm gun M3 is installed in a modified version of the M34 mount without a coaxial machine gun.

On 5 November 1942, the Ordnance Committee had recommended the procurement of a pilot vehicle based upon the T19E1 chassis, but armed with a 75mm gun in the turret. The new vehicle was designated as the 75mm gun motor carriage T66. The project for the T66 was closed along with the T19E1 in March 1943. However, by that time, the pilot had been completed and was shipped along with the T19E1 to the Desert Warfare Board at the request of the British Army. Both vehicles were tested in comparison with the armored car T17E1 over all types of desert terrain. The results indicated that the T19E1 was superior to the T17E1 in that the independent suspension provided a smoother, faster ride. The gun mount and turret arrangement were an improvement over the T17E1 and the light tank type hatch openings were easier to use than the T17E1's side doors. However, with the end of the desert war, a vehicle of that size and weight was no longer considered suitable for operations.

The 75mm gun motor carriage T66 was proposed for use as a tank destroyer. However, a prime requirement for a tank destroyer was cross-country mobility equal or superior to that of a tank and it was considered that only a full track vehicle could provide such mobility.

Details of the turret and rear deck on the 75mm gun motor carriage T66 are visible in the view at the right. Built by the Chevrolet Division of General Motors, the T66 was photographed at Aberdeen on 5 February 1943.

Above are artist's concept drawings of the light armored car T22 (left) and the light armored car T22E1 (right). Both of these are armed with a .30 caliber bow machine gun in addition to the turret mounted 37mm gun and coaxial .30 caliber machine gun.

LIGHT ARMORED CARS

In July 1941, a requirement was presented for the development of a light, highly mobile, self-propelled gun carriage. At that time, the 37mm gun was considered to be an effective antitank weapon and the new mount was to be suitable for use by the Tank Destroyer Command. With this in mind, a low silhouette vehicle adaptable to low cost mass production was required. It also was desirable that the basic design be suitable for carrying a multiple .50 caliber machine gun mount, a dual 20mm antiaircraft mount, or an 81mm mortar and be adaptable for use as a cargo carrier. Shortly after the declaration of war, four pilot vehicles were authorized in place of the two specified in the original requirement. These were to be built by the Ford Motor Company and the Fargo Division of Chrysler

The pilot light armored car T22 built by the Ford Motor Company appears above at the right. Below, the light armored car T23 is at the left and the light armored car T23E1 is at the right. Both of these were built by the Fargo Division of Chrysler Corporation.

Above, the light armored car T21 built by Studebaker is at Aberdeen Proving Ground on 16 November 1942. It is armed with the turret mounted 37mm gun and the coaxial .30 caliber machine gun, but it does not have a bow machine gun.

Corporation. The Ford cars were the six wheeled 37mm gun motor carriage T22 and the four wheeled 37mm gun motor carriage T22E1. The Fargo vehicles were the six wheeled 37mm gun motor carriage T23 and the four wheeled 37mm gun motor carriage T23E1. Power was supplied to all wheels in each vehicle. The Studebaker Corporation also offered to construct a pilot without cost to the Government and submit it for tests. The offer was accepted and it was designated as the 37mm gun motor carriage T43. It was similar to the T22 and T23 in that it was a six wheel drive vehicle.

On 12 March 1942, the designations of all five vehicles were changed to light armored cars. The Ford and Fargo vehicles retained the same T numbers, but the Studebaker pilot became the light armored car T21. Shortly thereafter, the armament specification was revised requiring only a 37mm gun M6 in a turret combination mount with a .30 caliber M1919A4 machine gun. This new specification eliminated the bow machine gun required in the original design, although this weapon was installed in some of the early pilots.

The pilot light armored car T22 was demonstrated at Aberdeen Proving Ground on 16 March 1942. Three days later, it was driven cross-country to Fort Knox for tests by the Armored Force Board. These tests indicated that, subject to some modifications, the T22 was suitable

for use as a reconnaissance vehicle for both the Armored Force and the Cavalry and would meet the requirements of the Tank Destroyer Command for a 37mm gun motor carriage. Since the chassis was conventional in design, no difficulties were expected in achieving rapid mass production. This same feature also limited its cross-country speed. It also was noted that only a four man crew could be carried when a minimum of five was considered desirable. Among the modifications requested was a mount for a .50 caliber machine gun on the rear of the turret and a change in the electrical system to increase the voltage from 6 to 12 volts. An auxiliary generator also was required to keep the battery charged for radio use when the vehicle was stopped with the engine off. As mentioned previously, the bow machine gun was eliminated and it was recommended that the T22 be standardized pending the availability of armored cars with independently sprung wheels. The vehicle incorporating all of the changes was designated as the light armored car T22E2 and this was the version standardized as the light armored car M8. When standardization was recommended for the T22E2, the projects for the T22E1, the T23, and the T23E1 were closed. Since little work remained to be done, these pilots were completed for use as proof facilities by the Ordnance Department.

Below, the pilot armored car T22 is at Aberdeen Proving Ground on 18 March 1942. In the left view, the driver's armor shields are erected and at the right they are folded down.

These photographs show the early light armored car M8 (T22E2). The view above was taken at the General Motors Proving Ground on 18 August 1942. Those below were dated 16 November 1942 during experiments to develop an antiaircraft machine gun mount. Note that the collapsible armor shields for the driver have been replaced by a fixed armor structure.

The light armored car T21 was completed by Studebaker and delivered to the General Motors Proving Ground on 22 May 1942. Numerous mechanical failures during endurance testing resulted in a recommendation for a redesign of the transmission and the addition of an engine tachometer to prevent over speeding. It also was recommended that the driver's compartment be enlarged. Since the M8 had now been standardized and was going into production, the project on the T21 was terminated with the recommendation that no further development be done on the vehicle.

Production of the M8 started at Ford in March 1943 and continued through May 1945 with a total run of 8,523 cars. Because of the light armor protection on the M8, a self-sealing fuel tank was desirable and it was directed that all M8 armored cars shipped overseas be equipped with self-sealing tanks.

The M8 also was evaluated by the British and given the name Greyhound. Like the Special Armored Vehicle Board, they considered its light weight an advantage as can be seen in the following excerpt from the " History of the XII Royal Lancers" by Captain P. F. Stewart, M.C.

"C Squadron experimented hastily with Greyhounds, a fast six-wheeled American armored car with magnificent cross-country performance, hard to reverse, and difficult to protect against mines, but - and this was the point - capable of crossing Class 9 bridges with which it was planned to replace those destroyed by the enemy."

The early production light armored car M8 is shown here. Details of the turret and the driver's armor protection can be seen above. A rack for three M1A1 antitank mines has been added to each side of the vehicle. The full armament consisting of the 37mm gun and the coaxial .30 caliber machine gun has been installed.

On 9 October 1942, the Tank Destroyer Board submitted the results of their tests on the M8 and recommended, with the usual list of modifications, that it be adopted as the standard mount for the 37mm gun in all tank destroyer battalions. The modifications included changes in the elevation and traversing mechanisms, some redesign of the driver's controls, and stowage changes. The gunner's telescope on the late production vehicle was shifted to the left to allow more room for the gunner when using the sight and a two speed traverse mechanism was installed. The Board also requested early consideration of the M8 as a command car and as a personnel and cargo carrier. On 17 December 1942, development was authorized for three vehicles based upon the M8. They were designated as the multiple gun motor carriage T69, the armored command car T26, and the personnel cargo carrier T20.

The turret interior of the early production light armored car M8 is shown in the two views below. Details of the armament, turret controls and ammunition stowage are clearly visible.

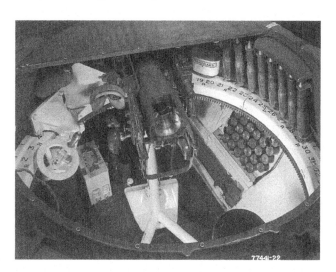 

110

Light armored car M8, serial number 2940, on this and the next three pages was photographed at the Engineering Standards Vehicle Laboratory in Detroit, Michigan on 25 February 1944. The stowage details are those for a mid production vehicle.

M8 light armored car, serial number 2940, is fitted with a canvas cover for the turret and guns in the views above and below.

Stowage details without the canvas turret cover can be seen on light armored car M8, serial number 2940. Note that this vehicle is not armed with an antiaircraft machine gun. Although painted out, close examination of the original photographs reveal the Registration Number, U.S.A. 6035164.

Above are front and rear views of light armored car M8, serial number 2940, at the Engineering Standards Vehicle Laboratory on 25 February 1944. The driver's station in the light armored car M8 appears below at the left. Components on the driver's instrument panel are identified in the view below at the right.

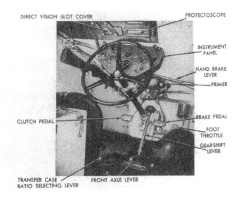 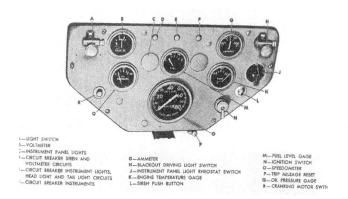

Both sides of the Hercules JXD engine installed in the light armored car M8 are illustrated below and the various components are identified.

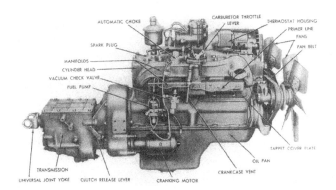 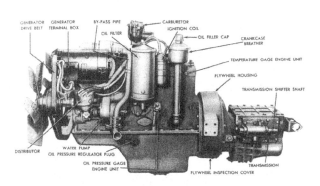

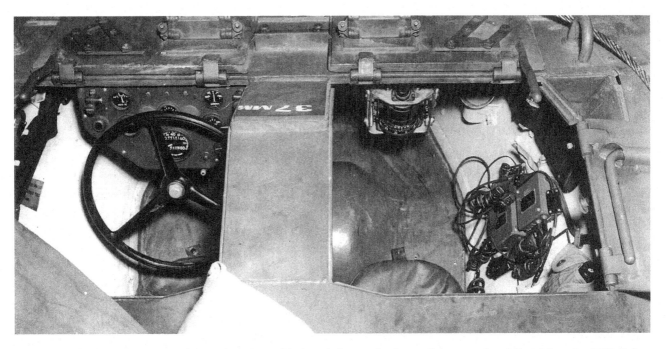

Above, the driver's compartment can be seen from the outside through the open hatches on light armored car M8, serial number 2940. Below, the early single speed turret traversing mechanism on the left can be compared with the later two speed mechanism installed on the later production M8 light armored cars.

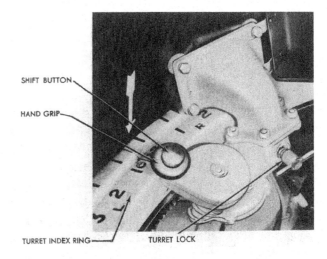

Top front and rear deck components on the light armored car M8 are shown below. In the right photograph, the antenna base MP-48 is on the left and the antenna base MP-57 is on the right.

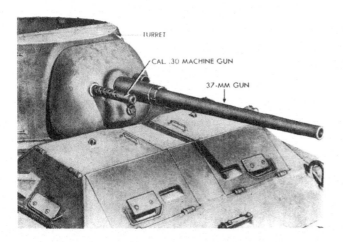

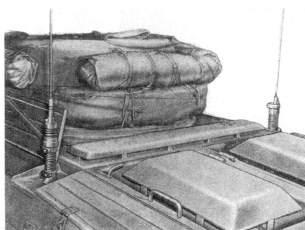

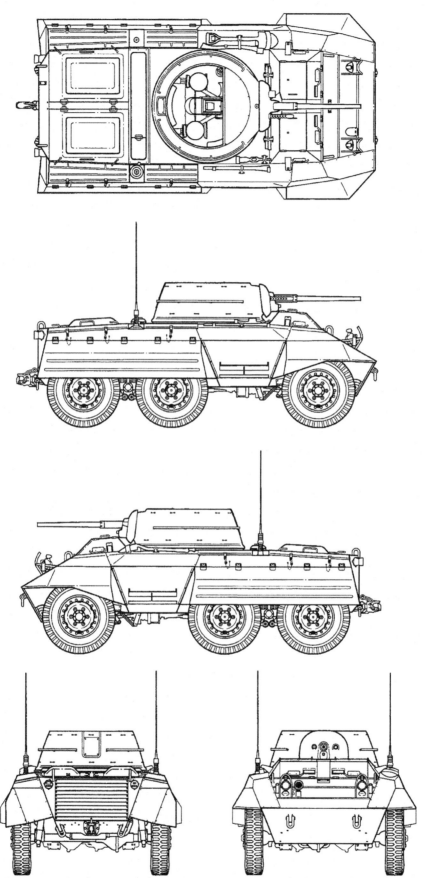

Scale 1:48

Light Armored Car M8, early production

© M. Duplessis

Above are views of the M49C ring mount installed on the light armored car M8 at Aberdeen prior to the development of the folding .50 caliber machine gun mount at Ford. These photographs were dated 16 November 1943.

Tests of the M8 by the using arms had indicated a need for a .50 caliber machine gun mount on the turret and the Ford Motor Company designed and constructed a folding type mount which was supported by a socket casting at the rear of the turret. This socket casting was designed so that it could be installed in the vehicle by removing the plate at the rear of the turret which normally provided access for the removal of the 37mm gun. When this plate was replaced by the socket casting, the only changes required were the drilling of two holes in the turret wall. At the same time that this development was taking place, the using arms had authorized the addition of an M49C ring mount for a .50 caliber machine gun on top of the turret. Since the folding mount appeared to meet all of the requirements for antiaircraft use and was much lighter, it was immediately shipped to the Cavalry Board for evaluation. Tests at the Cavalry Board confirmed the superiority of the lighter mount and the earlier standardization of the M49C ring mount was rescinded and the folding mount was approved for all M8 armored cars. However, it is noted that on many armored cars in service, ring mounts were installed as field modifications. They were frequently seen on armored cars operating in Europe.

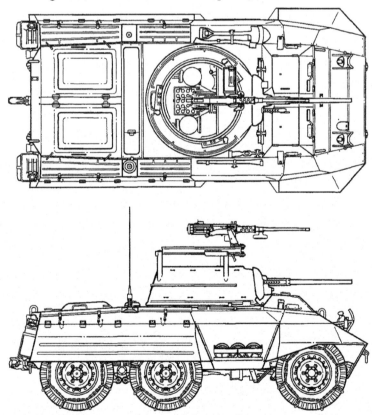

Scale 1:48

© M. Duplessis

Light Armored Car M8 w/M49C Ring Mount

The early production vehicles were fitted with a rack on each side capable of holding three M1A1 antitank mines. These racks were replaced in later production by two closed stowage bins welded to the side armor.

Leakage of rainwater along the inner, hinged side, of the engine compartment cover doors frequently wet the spark plugs and distributor. To correct this on later production vehicles, troughs were installed along the inner sides of the cover door openings to collect and divert the water. Instructions also were issued to fabricate and install such troughs on the earlier vehicles in the field.

The tests by the Special Armored Vehicle Board had indicated that a major point of inferiority for the armored car M8 was its lack of an independent suspension. Cross-country operation also revealed a serious problem of front spring breakage. The 11 leaf front springs were replaced by stronger 13 leaf springs in later production. This change improved the durability, but it decreased the riding comfort and made the front axle more vulnerable to failure. In an effort to correct this problem, two M8s were diverted from production in September 1943 and fitted with independently sprung front wheels. These vehicles were designated as the light armored car M8E1. The independently sprung front wheels employed a torsion bar parallelogram suspension. Tests at Aberdeen Proving Ground indicated that the ride characteristics were considerably improved over the standard M8, but numerous structural failures occurred in the suspension components. Modifications were recommended to correct these problems, but the end of the war closed the project before they could be put into effect. At best, the M8E1 was only a stopgap measure and far superior designs with completely independent suspensions were now available for production.

Late production light armored car M8, serial number 8325, is at the Engineering Standards Vehicle Laboratory in Detroit, Michigan on 10 August 1944. Other photographs of this vehicle are on pages 120 through 123.

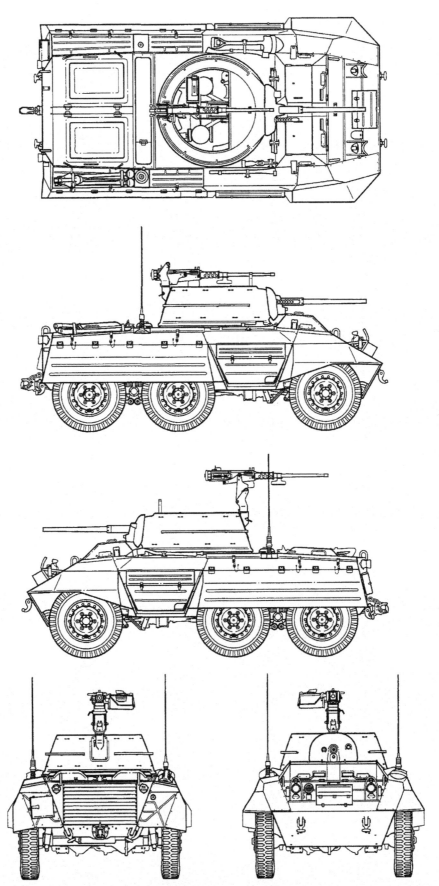

Scale 1:48

Light Armored Car M8, late production

This late production light armored car M8, serial number 8325, included several new features. The folding .50 caliber machine gun mount on the turret is shown in the stowed position above and extended for action below.

Above, the .50 caliber machine gun is protected by a canvas cover in the photograph of light armored car M8, serial number 8325. A new stowage box for the removable windshields is located on the front armor of this same vehicle below.

The new side stowage bins replacing the mine racks are clearly visible in these views of light armored car M8, serial number 8325. Although it has been painted out, close examination of the original photograph shows the Registration Number U.S.A. 6041228.

Light armored car M8, serial number 8325, is shown in the top view above and in the photographs below. The left front and right front of the turret interior can be seen below. Note the late type traversing mechanism and the radio installation.

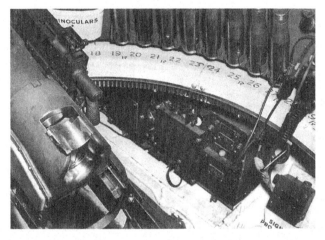

Below, the new side stowage bins are shown open and closed. Note that the M1A1 antitank mines can still be carried along with just about anything else.

Above, the armored utility car M20 is at Fort Knox in the left photograph. At the top right, M20, serial number 85, is at the General Motors Proving Ground on 9 August 1943.

The request of the Tank Destroyer Command for the development of an armored command car and an armored personnel-ammunition-cargo carrier based upon the light armored car M8 chassis resulted in the Ordnance Committee recommendation that pilot vehicles be procured of both types. As mentioned before, the command vehicle was designated as the armored command car T26 and the cargo version as the personnel cargo carrier T20. Design studies at the Ford Motor Company indicated that the two vehicles were sufficiently similar that a single design could meet both requirements. This new car was designated as the armored utility car T26 and the two previous designations were canceled.

The pilot T26 was completed in February 1943 and tested in early March at Aberdeen Proving Ground. During the latter part of the month, the vehicle was driven overland to Camp Hood, Texas for evaluation by the Tank Destroyer Board. Based upon the Aberdeen tests, the T26 was standardized in April 1943 as the armored utility car M10. This caused considerable confusion in the tank destroyer units where the new car

was expected to operate alongside the 3 inch gun motor carriage M10. To solve the problem, the armored car was assigned the new designation armored utility car M20. The M20 was quite similar to the standard M8, but the turret was eliminated and the armament consisted of a .50 caliber machine gun on a ring mount over the open top crew compartment. Tests by the Tank Destroyer Command, the Cavalry, the Armored Force, and the Desert Warfare Board resulted in some rearrangement of stowage and minor modifications. However, the performance and economy characteristics were all considered satisfactory and better than those of the similar, but heavier, M8 armored cars. Production of the M20 began at the Ford Motor Company in July 1943 and continued until a total of 3,791 cars had been produced through June 1945. During production, additional modifications were introduced and in August 1944, the M49 ring mount was replaced by the M66 ring mount. In November, a second generator and regulator were installed for all M20s equipped with two radios. Other modifications in late production M8 armored cars also were applied to the M20.

Below, the armored utility car M20 is at Fort Knox during studies to determine the appropriate stowage. The three M1A1 antitank mines are still carried in each of the two side racks as on the light armored car M8.

Photographs of the armored utility car M20, serial number 181 (Registration Number U.S.A. 60110953), from the Engineering Standards Vehicle Laboratory are shown on this and the four following pages. The vehicle is armed with a .50 caliber machine gun on the ring mount over the open top crew compartment. All of these photographs were dated 24 March 1944.

Details and stowage of the armored utility car M20, serial number 181, can be seen in these photographs.

Above is a top front view of the armored utility car M20, serial number 181, looking toward the rear. Note the details of the machine gun mount and the internal stowage. Below are front and rear views of the same vehicle.

The driver's compartment in the armored utility car M20, serial number 181, is above. Below, the fighting compartment of the armored utility car M20, serial number 181, can be seen looking toward the front of the vehicle. Note the stowage including the 2.36 inch rocket launcher and ammunition.

The left (above) and right (below) sides of the hull interior on the armored utility car M20, serial number 181, are shown on this page. The radios, M1 carbines for the crew and other stowage items are visible in these photographs from the Engineering Standards Vehicle Laboratory dated 24 March 1944.

A late production armored utility car M20, serial number 3038, is shown on this page with the hatches open and closed. The car was at the Engineering Standards Vehicle Laboratory on 16 February 1945. Other views of this vehicle appear on the next two pages.

Above, a canvas cover has been installed on armored utility car M20, serial number 3038. Note that this late production vehicle retains the antitank mine rack on each side. Details of the vehicle rear can be seen below.

The photograph of the armored utility car M20, serial number 3038, above provides a good view of the .50 caliber machine gun on its ring mount. The top of the vehicle can be seen below. Note that the late production M20 has the windshield stowage box on the front armor as on the light armored car M8.

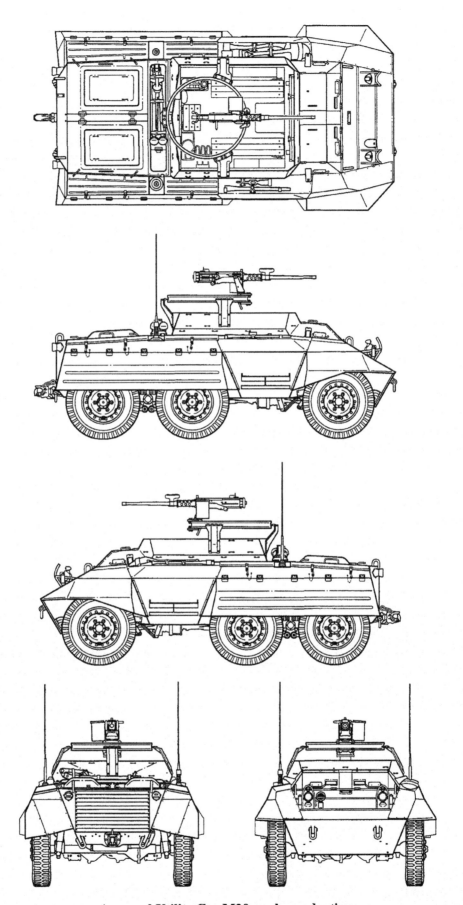

Scale 1:48

© M. Duplessis

Armored Utility Car M20, early production

133

The very late production armored utility cars M20 in the four photographs above and below are fitted with the side stowage bins replacing the mine racks.

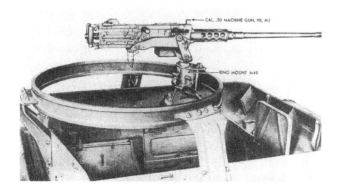

The two photographs above show a twin .50 caliber machine gun mount on the armored utility car M20. This mount was under evaluation at Aberdeen. The standard ring mount for the .50 caliber machine gun on the M20 appears at the left.

134

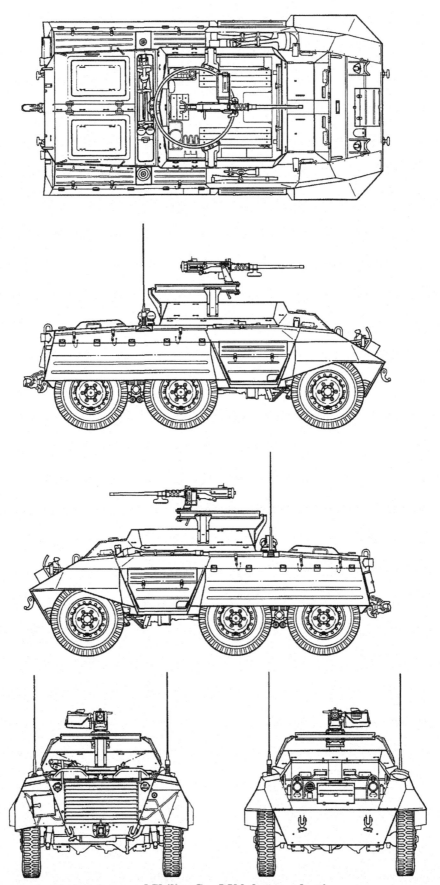

Scale 1:48

Armored Utility Car M20, late production

135

The multiple gun motor carriage T69 appears in the photographs on this page. The views at the bottom of the page show the gun mount at maximum depression (left) and maximum elevation (right). These photographs taken at Aberdeen Proving Ground were dated 29 April 1943.

As mentioned previously, the original light armored car specification included the requirement that the chassis be capable of mounting an antiaircraft turret. Such a vehicle mounting four .50 caliber machine guns in a power operated turret was developed at the W. L. Maxson Corporation and shipped to Aberdeen Proving Ground in early May 1943. This was the multiple gun motor carriage T69. Firing tests showed the need for strengthening the gun mount trunnions and sight brackets. It also was necessary to modify the method of disposing of empty links and cartridge cases. Although considered satisfactory in the Aberdeen tests, the Antiaircraft Artillery Board did not agree, finding the T69 inferior to the existing multiple gun motor carriages M16 and M17 in weight carrying capacity, space limitations, mobility, and fire dispersion. As a result of these recommendations, the project was canceled in March 1944.

It is interesting to note that the Germans modified at least one captured M8 for antiaircraft applications.

This modification involved removing the turret and replacing it with a triple 20mm mount. No record is available to the author regarding its use.

Another interesting modification proposed for the M8 chassis was the armored chemical car T30. This vehicle was intended to meet the requirement of the Armored Force for a mobile chemical weapon. Based upon the M8, it was to be armed with ten rocket projectors, five on each side of the turret, to be controlled and fired by the operator. A gas cylinder with a pressurizing device and nozzle was to be available for attachment to the M8 turret if desired. The crew in this vehicle was limited to two, one driver and one operator. Ten 7 inch rockets were carried for the projectors and 100 gallons of non-persistent chemicals. Originally, six pilots were recommended for procurement, but work had not progressed very far before the changing strategic and tactical situation eliminated the requirement for this weapon. On 18 November 1943, the Ordnance Committee recommended termination of the project.

The multiple gun motor carriage T69 is shown here after modification at Aberdeen on 24 August 1943. The views below show the modified mount at maximum depression (left) and maximum elevation (right).

Below, the turret armor has been removed from the modified multiple gun motor carriage T69 at Aberdeen on 3 September 1943. Details of the multiple gun mount can be seen in this view.

Above, the light armored car T27 built by the Studebaker Corporation is at Aberdeen Proving Ground on 9 December 1943. The armament is installed in this vehicle. Note that only a .30 caliber machine gun is mounted on top of the turret.

The extensive tests sponsored by the Special Armored Vehicle Board had indicated that the light armored car M8 was the most suitable candidate to fill the requirement for an armored reconnaissance vehicle. These conclusions were based primarily upon the size and weight limitations that ruled out many of the heavier vehicles. The weight limit of 14,000 pounds effectively eliminated all of the heavy and medium armored cars under test. The most serious deficiency of the M8 and similar vehicles was the truck type suspension which limited cross-country mobility. The final report of the Special Armored Vehicle Board recommended the development of a new armored car meeting the weight and size limitations characteristic of the M8, but equipped with an independently sprung suspension such as that on the armored cars T13 or T19. Both the Chevrolet Division of General Motors and the Studebaker Corporation submitted proposals to meet this requirement. The Studebaker design was an eight wheel

car with six wheels driven (8x6), using a torsion bar independent suspension. It was designated as the light armored car T27. A V8 Cadillac engine producing 110 horsepower at 3,400 rpm drove the T27 through a special four speed Hydramatic transmission and a transfer case with two speeds forward and one in reverse. This provided the vehicle with a total of eight speeds forward and four in reverse. The 1st, 2nd, and 4th pairs of wheels were driven and the two forward pairs were steered.

The Chevrolet entry in the competition for a new armored car used an independent coil spring suspension

The Registration Number U.S.A. 60120506 can be seen on the turret bustle of the light armored car T27 at the right.

Above, the light armored car T28 is at Aberdeen Proving Ground on 20 December 1943. It carries Registration Number U.S.A. 60123295.

on six evenly spaced wheels, all of which were driven (6x6). Hydraulic power steering was provided on the front four wheels. The new vehicle was designated as the light armored car T28. The T28 used the same V8 Cadillac engine as the T27. However, the Hydramatic transmission now had four speeds forward and one in reverse. With a two speed transfer case, this resulted in a total of eight speeds forward and two in reverse. Both the T27 and the T28 weighed just slightly over seven tons and carried a four man crew. Each was fitted with an open top, lightweight, turret mounting the 37mm gun M6 and a .30 caliber coaxial machine gun in a modified

M23 combination mount. An additional .30 caliber machine gun was carried on a pedestal mount at the rear of the turret. Construction of one pilot of each type was authorized and both were completed in October 1943. After preliminary demonstrations at the General Motors Proving Ground, both cars were driven to Aberdeen Proving Ground for engineering tests. These tests, completed in mid 1944, concluded that the T27 was satisfactory, but not as maneuverable or as able to operate at high cross-country speeds as the T28. The difference was due to the fact that only six of its eight wheels were powered, limiting the T27's operation on some types of terrain. The lack of power steering also limited its maneuverability. It also was noted that the torsion bars were mounted on the outside of the hull bottom and were subject to damage in rough terrain. In contrast, there were no obstructions on the bottom of the boat-like T28 hull permitting it to slip easily over obstacles.

Like the T27, the light armored car T28 has only a .30 caliber machine gun on the turret mount as can be seen at the left.

139

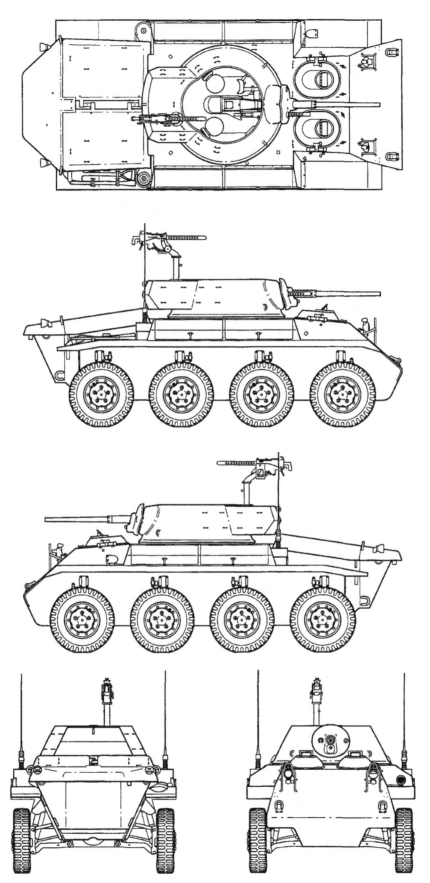

Light Armored Car T27

© M. Duplessis

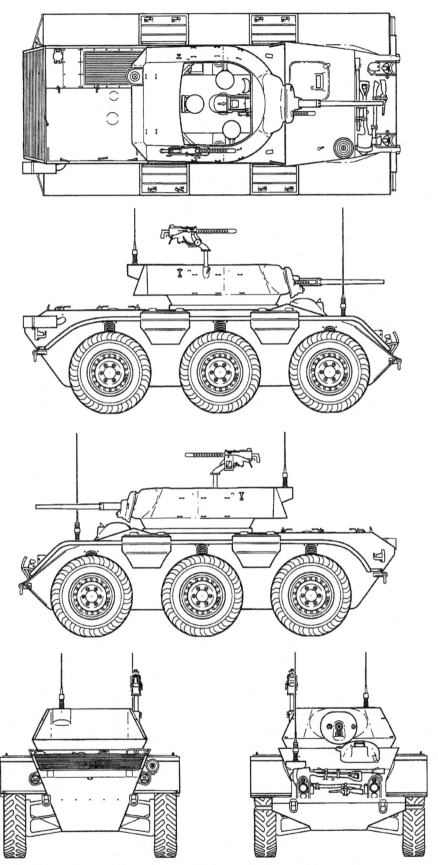

© M. Duplessis

Light Armored Car M38 (T28)

Above, the driver's hoods have been installed on the light armored car T27 at Aberdeen. In the top view below, the driver's hatches are closed. The full armament is mounted using a .30 caliber machine gun on the turret.

The light armored car T28 has been fitted with a canvas cover on the turret as well as muzzle covers on the 37mm gun and the coaxial machine gun. The driver's hatch cover has been opened to the right and the bad weather hood is installed.

Details and stowage on the light armored car T28 can be seen in these photographs of the vehicle taken during its evaluation at Fort knox.

After the tests were completed at Aberdeen, both cars were returned to Detroit for the installation of radio equipment. They were then shipped to Fort Riley, Kansas for tests by the Cavalry Board. These tests were intended to compare the T27 and the T28 with the standard light armored car M8. The Cavalry Board concurred with the findings at Aberdeen that the T28 was superior to the T27 in cross-country mobility and found that both vehicles were superior to the standard M8. On the basis of these reports, further development of the light armored car T27 was terminated. The T28 was recommended for standardization subject to modifications listed in the test reports. These modifications included a means for stopping the vehicle from the turret if the driver became a casualty, modifying the crew seats, and replacing the .30 caliber antiaircraft machine gun with a .50 caliber weapon. On 7 December 1944, it was recommended that the T28 be standardized as the light armored car M38. This action was approved in February 1945. In anticipation of future use, the British assigned the name Wolfhound to the M38.

Since the using arms recommended production of the M38 at the earliest possible date, it was not desirable to build a new pilot incorporating all of the recommended changes. Some of these changes could be checked out on the original pilot while others would be introduced directly into the production vehicles.

The pilot light armored car M38 (T28) above has been fitted with a turret from the light tank M24 armed with the 75mm gun M6. The photographs on this and the following page were taken at Aberdeen Proving Ground on 17 April 1946.

While preparations for production were underway, additional developments also were being considered. The American Bantam Car Company undertook a design study to develop a new turret for the M38 armed with a 75mm gun. The mount also was to be equipped for power slewing and provision was to be made for a coaxial .50 caliber machine gun. With the end of the war, the preparations for production were canceled, but development continued on the 75mm gun mount. However, the contract with the American Bantam Car Company was terminated and the M38 pilot was shipped back to Aberdeen Proving Ground. To check the firing stability of the M38 with a 75mm gun, a turret from a light tank M24 was fitted to the vehicle. Because of a 4 inch difference in the turret ring diameters, an adapter ring was bolted to the hull and the M24 turret, in turn, was bolted to the adapter ring. The turret, of course, could not be traversed. Firing tests were performed at 0 and maximum elevation and at 0 and 270 degrees

traverse. The traverse was achieved by unbolting the turret, lifting it with a crane, and bolting it into the new position. These tests showed that the vehicle was quite stable during firing. The hop was relatively large, but the recovery time was only about two seconds. In July 1946, the project for the 75mm gun turret on the M38 was discontinued ending the last World War II armored car development.

Since the M38 never reached production, the M8 and M20 were the only armored cars used in combat by the United States and they served in almost every theater of operations.

At the right is another view of the light armored car M38 with the 75mm gun turret from the light tank M24.

145

These photographs of the light armored car M38 with the 75mm gun turret from the light tank M24 show the turret fixed aiming forward. The difference in turret ring diameters requiring the adapter ring are obvious in the side view.

Above, an M8 light armored car from the 91st Cavalry Reconnaissance Squadron is operating near Cassino, Italy during 1944. Below, an M8 light armored car from the First Armored Division passes a knocked out American light tank on Route 7 in Italy during the drive toward Rome. This photograph was dated 4 June 1944.

Above, an M8 light armored car from a Fifth Army reconnaissance unit is in Norma, Italy on 30 May 1944. Below, M8 light armored cars from the 82nd Armored Reconnaissance Battalion, Second Armored Division are moving through St. Sever Calvados, France on 3 August 1944. The town is still under German artillery fire.

Above, Major General Lindsay M. Sylvester, Commanding General of the Seventh Armored Division, enters Chartres, France in his M8 light armored car on 16 August 1944. Below, M8 light armored cars and half-tracks of the Seventh Armored Division engage enemy forces near Epernay, France on 27 August 1944.

Above, an M8 light armored car from the 113the Cavalry Reconnaissance Squadron is almost to the border of Holland on 8 September 1944. Note the field installation of the ring mount for the .50 caliber machine gun. Below at the left, Lieutenant General George S. Patton Jr. tours the Third Army front with Ambassador Harriman (center) in his modified armored utility car M20 on 27 November 1944. Below at the right, this ring mount added to an M8 light armored car has been armed with two .50 caliber aircraft machine guns by the Fourth Infantry Division.

Above at the left, M8 light armored cars and a half-track operate behind the fortifications of the Maginot Line. Note the .50 caliber machine gun ring mount on the M8. At the top right, this M8 is in Gaeta, Italy during May 1944. The M8 below at the left is under new ownership after its capture by the Germans. The light armored car M8 at the right below is passing through Rongy, Belgium. Note the field installed ring mount for the .50 caliber machine gun.

Above at the left, this M8 from the Eleventh Armored Division is fitted with chains during its operation in the Winter of 1944-45. Above at the right, this M8 from the Fourth Infantry Division is in Luxembourg on 14 January 1945. Note the improvised .50 caliber machine gun mount. Below at the left, this M8 light armored car is on the island of Mindoro in the Philippines. At the bottom right, an M8 light armored car from the Seventh Infantry Division is in Kyongsong, Korea carrying a Japanese liaison officer after the Japanese surrender.

37 m/m Gun Motor Carriage T2
Weight - 2,910 lbs.   Height - 63"
Armament: 1 - 37 m/m
No. 37 m/m Rounds Carried: 40

Above are two photographs of the 37mm gun motor carriage T2 at Aberdeen Proving Ground on 5 August 1941.

WHEELED ANTITANK GUN MOTOR CARRIAGES

Early in 1941, an intensive effort began to develop a suitable self-propelled carriage for the 37mm antitank gun. The necessity for such a mobile weapon had been clearly demonstrated during the campaign in France the previous year. At that time, the 37mm antitank gun was still an effective weapon against the armor it was expected to defeat. Its firepower, combined with its relatively low weight, made it an attractive weapon for installation on various lightweight vehicles. Two such projects started simultaneously during May 1941. These were the 37mm gun motor carriage T2 series (T2 and T2E1) based upon the Bantam $\frac{1}{4}$ ton four wheel drive truck chassis (Jeep) and the 37mm gun motor carriage T8 on a special Ford chassis.

The T2 and T2E1 differed essentially in the mounting of the 37mm gun M3. On the T2, the weapon was installed to fire forward over the hood with the original traverse of 30 degrees to the right and 30 degrees to the left as on the M4 towed carriage. Since the muzzle of the forward firing gun was fairly close to the hood, the latter was strengthened by a $\frac{1}{8}$ inch thick steel plate to prevent a cave-in from the muzzle blast.

The original T2E1 mounted the gun on the bare Bantam chassis aimed toward the rear using a pedestal mount designed by Colonel B. Q. Jones of the Cavalry. Although this mount had a theoretical traverse of 360 degrees, this was actually available only at limited elevations because of interference from the driver's seat and the fuel tank. A modified version of the T2E1 replaced the Jones mount with the same 60 degree traverse mount found on the T2. This version retained the Bantam body. Since the gun was aimed to the rear, the windshield could be retained and the mount also was considered to be easier to manufacture.

Below, the first pilot of the 37mm gun motor carriage T2E1 appears at the left with the original Jones pedestal. At the bottom right, the modified version of the T2E1 is shown with the Bantam body. Both have the gun aimed to the rear.

37 m/m Gun Carriage T8
Weight: 4,940 lbs.   Crew 3
Description: 1-37 m/m gun M3
     mounted on Ford 4x4 chassis
Gun muzzle velocity: 26 F.S.
Gun traverse: 36°
Elevation: 10° to 15°
No. of 37 m/m rounds carried: 100
Maximum speed: 60 M.P.H.

The 37mm gun motor carriage T8 is above with pilot number 1 at the left and pilot number 2 at the right. These vehicles were photographed at Aberdeen with pilot number 1 on 11 August 1941 and pilot number 2 on 19 September 1941.

Tests of both the T2 and T2E1 showed that the vehicles were heavily overloaded. The $\frac{1}{4}$ ton Bantam truck chassis was designed for a maximum gross weight of 2,080 pounds. Both vehicles exceeded this weight by over 1,000 pounds. The tests also showed that the mount was unstable even when firing directly to the front or rear. The project was closed in January 1942 and it was recommended that further development of 37mm gun motor carriages be limited to vehicles of greater weight carrying capacity with a longer wheel base and a wider tread to insure greater stability when firing.

Developed parallel with the T2 series, the 37mm gun motor carriage T8 also was armed with the 37mm gun M3. The mount used the upper part of the M4 towed carriage fitted upon a special four wheel drive Ford chassis commonly called the Swamp Buggy. This chassis was constructed mainly from standard Ford 1½ ton truck components with a special frame and body. Two chassis were ordered in June 1941 and subse-

quently, an additional 15 were authorized. The carriage was powered by a Ford 6 cylinder, in line, engine developing 90 horsepower at 3,300 rpm. Loaded with 100 rounds of ammunition and a three man crew, the weight was approximately 5,430 pounds. Since the gun mount used the top portion of the M4 towed carriage, the 30 degrees left and 30 degrees right traverse was retained as well as a range of elevation from -10 to +15 degrees. The T8 was tested at Aberdeen in comparison with the 37mm gun motor carriage T21 and the cross-country performance of the two vehicles was quite similar. Modifications to the T8 permitted a 360 degree traverse, but the system was susceptible to clogging and binding from dirt in its exposed position. Although the T8 was considered to be satisfactory, the project was closed in April 1942 since the T21 had been standardized and was in full production. It was not considered desirable to produce another 37mm gun motor carriage of similar performance.

Pilot number 3 of the 37mm gun motor carriage T8 is below at the left. A modified version of the production model of the T8 can be seen below at the right. Pilot number 3 was photographed at Aberdeen on 2 December 1941 preceded by the modified production vehicle on 22 November.

Above, the ³/₄ ton weapons carrier armed with the pedestal mounted 37mm gun M3 is at Aberdeen Proving Ground on 12 September 1941. The gun mount retains the small shield of the towed antitank gun.

In June 1941, the Chrysler Corporation subsidiary, Fargo Motor Corporation, proposed the design of a 37mm gun motor carriage using the ³/₄ ton, four wheel drive, Fargo truck. This vehicle had the advantage of being in full production for the Quartermaster Corps and hence would simplify the supply of spare parts. A wooden mock-up of the proposed vehicle, designated as the 37mm gun motor carriage T21, was delivered to Aberdeen Proving Ground in August 1941 for evaluation. The 37mm gun M3 was mounted on the mock-up facing toward the front and toward the rear to determine the best arrangement. Although the weapon aimed toward the front produced the more even weight distribution, several disadvantages precluded its use. Among these were the necessity to discard the windshield and the effect on the driver from the muzzle blast. This arrangement also required a higher mount to provide adequate clearance over the hood.

With the gun aimed toward the rear, many of the problems were eliminated and the vehicle could move rapidly once it had fired without the necessity of turning around. A full 360 degrees of traverse also was available with a limited amount of depression to the front. This installation also permitted the use of the standard gun shield from the M4 towed carriage. However, tests at Aberdeen showed that some changes were necessary in this shield. The new version was designed to provide frontal, semi-overhead, and flank protection against .30 caliber ball ammunition at all ranges.

Although the T21 showed some disadvantages when compared to the 37mm gun motor carriage T8, it was recommended for standardization because of the rapid availability of the Fargo chassis. It must be remembered that these truck mounted gun carriages were expedients intended for use only until a properly designed armored vehicle was available. Standardization

The 37mm gun motor carriage T21 is shown below at Aberdeen Proving Ground on 17 November 1941. Note the new gun shield giving better protection to the gun crew.

154

The newly standardized, fully stowed, 37mm gun motor carriage M6 (T21, M4) above is at Aberdeen Proving Ground on 16 April 1942.

of the T21 as the 37mm gun motor carriage M4 was approved on 26 December 1941. To avoid confusion with other M4s such as the Sherman tank, a new designation as the 37mm gun motor carriage M6 was assigned in February 1942. Production of the M6 began in April 1942 and continued until October of the same year. A total of 5,380 vehicles were produced. Light platoons of the tank destroyer companies were equipped with the M6 and they first saw action in North Africa. With the development of the light armored car M8, the 37mm gun motor carriage M6 was reclassified as limited standard. Most of the carriages were reconverted into $^3/_4$ ton weapon carriers.

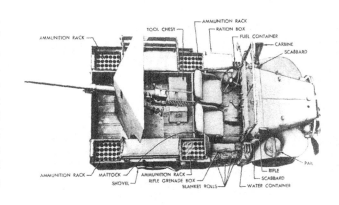

Components and various stowage items are identified in the illustrations above and below on the 37mm gun motor carriage M6.

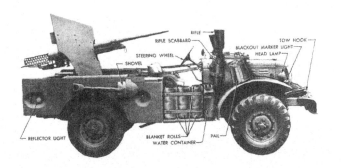

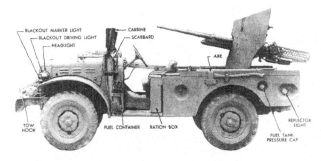

WINDSHIELD WIPERS
REAR VIEW MIRROR
REAR VIEW MIRROR
WINCH
HEAD LIGHT
FRONT MARKER LIGHT
BLACKOUT DRIVING LIGHT

The fully stowed 37mm gun motor carriage M6 is shown in these views. Below and at the left various items are identified.

RAMMER AND STAFF
TAILGATE CHAIN
REFLECTOR
SERVICE TAIL AND STOP LIGHT
BLACKOUT TAIL LIGHT
REAR BUMPER PINTLE HOOK
REAR BUMPER
TAILGATE CHAIN
REFLECTOR
BLACKOUT STOP LIGHT
BLACKOUT TAIL LIGHT

The driver's controls and instruments are identified in the two photographs below.

A. HEADLIGHT BEAM CONTROL SWITCH, B. CLUTCH, C. BRAKE PEDAL, D. WINCH CONTROL LEVER, E. COWL VENTILATOR HANDLE, F. STARTER PEDAL, G. ACCELERATOR PEDAL, H. HAND BRAKE LEVER, J. TRANSFER CASE CONTROL LEVER, K. MAP BOARD, L. FIRE EXTINGUISHER, M. SEAT LATCH, N. NEUTRAL POSITION SAFETY CATCH, O. GEARSHIFT LEVER.

A. COOLING SYSTEM DRAIN PLATE, B. SPEED CAUTION PLATE, C. HEADLIGHT BEAM INDICATOR, D. AMMETER, E. OIL PRESSURE GAGE, F. PANEL LIGHTS, G. SPEEDOMETER, H. FUEL GAGE, J. HEAT INDICATOR, K. SERIAL NUMBER PLATE, L. WINCH CAUTION PLATE, M. BLACKOUT DRIVING LIGHT, N. PANEL LIGHT SWITCH, O. THROTTLE CONTROL, P. CHOKE, R. IGNITION LOCK, S. MAIN LIGHT SWITCH, T. MAINTENANCE NUMBER PLATE, U. TRANSMISSION AND TRANSFER CASE SHIFT DIAGRAM PLATE.

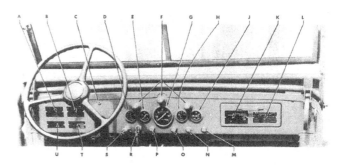

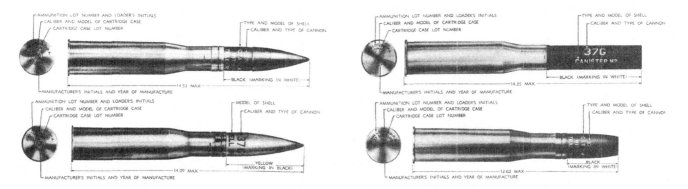

Various types of ammunition for the 37mm gun are illustrated above. At the left are armor piercing capped shot M51 (upper) and the shell high explosive M63 (lower). At the right are the canister M2 (upper) and the training projectile M51A1 (lower).

The views above and below show the 37mm gun motor carriage M6 during its short combat life in North Africa. Mud was frequently applied to the vehicles as camouflage.

The 37mm gun motor carriage T14 appears in these photographs taken at Aberdeen Proving Ground on 24 January 1942. Note that the shield from the towed gun mount is retained on this first pilot vehicle.

Studies during the Summer of 1941 showed that a six wheeled vehicle based upon the standard $\frac{1}{4}$ ton truck, the well known Jeep, might provide an excellent mount for the 37mm gun. In July, the procurement of two such chassis was authorized for the development of two 37mm gun motor carriages. The first was designated as the 37mm gun motor carriage T13 with the weapon firing toward the front. The second, with the gun aimed toward the rear, became the 37mm gun motor carriage T14. The using arms showed a strong preference for the gun aimed toward the rear so the T13 design was dropped and two T14s were constructed. Both pilots were built by the Willys-Overland Company and the first was delivered to Aberdeen Proving Ground in January 1942. The vehicle, the so-called Super Jeep, was essentially a six wheeled version of the Jeep with an additional axle at the rear and all wheels powered. It was unarmored except for the $\frac{1}{4}$ inch thick gun shield. Tests at Fort Benning as well as at Aberdeen indicated that the T14 was superior to the standardized 37mm gun motor carriage M6. However, by this time, the M6 was already in quantity production and, in any case, the need for expedient gun carriages was about over. Since the Tank Destroyer Board indicated a need for a lightly armored reconnaissance vehicle, the second pilot T14 was used as a basis for this new vehicle. This was designated as the scout car T24 and it has already been described in the section on scout cars.

The first pilot of the 37mm gun motor carriage T14 can be seen in the view at the right with the vehicle in position for firing.

The second pilot 37mm gun motor carriage T14 above and at the left is fitted with a new gun shield providing greater protection for the gun crew. These photographs at Aberdeen were dated 20 March 1942.

As mentioned previously, a requirement was submitted on 30 July 1941 for a lightweight, lightly armored, tank destroyer capable of mass production at minimum cost. Ford Motor Company submitted proposals for two designs. These were the six wheel (6x6) 37mm gun motor carriage T22 and the four wheel (4x4) 37mm gun motor carriage T22E1. Fargo submitted parallel designs with the six wheel (6x6) 37mm gun motor carriage T23 and the four wheel (4x4) 37mm gun motor carriage T23E1. At their own expense, Studebaker built and submitted for tests an additional vehicle (6x6) which was designated as the 37mm gun motor carriage T43. All of these vehicles were subsequently reclassified as armored cars and are discussed under that designation.

At the left and below, the height of the gun shield on the 37mm gun motor carriage has been reduced to lower the silhouette of the vehicle. These photographs were taken at Aberdeen on 23 April 1942.

The 37mm gun motor carriage T33 was being tested at Aberdeen Proving Ground on 16 January 1942 when these photographs were taken.

In November 1941, authorization was given for the modification of a four wheel drive, $^3/_4$ ton, Ford cargo carrier as a 37mm gun motor carriage. The resulting vehicle was somewhat similar to the T8 except that it had a front mounted engine with the driver alongside. The new vehicle was designated as the 37mm gun motor carriage T33. A pilot was completed by the end of January 1942 and tests indicated that it was superior to both the T8 and the T21. In particular, its low silhouette with the lighter and more rigid pedestal mount, as well as greater driver visibility, gave it a considerable tactical advantage. However, time had run out for this type of expedient weapon and already the need for increased firepower was becoming obvious. The project was closed and the vehicle was used as the basis for the 57mm gun motor carriage T44.

160

Here, the Ford chassis used for the 37mm gun motor carriage T33 is rearmed with the 57mm gun M1 and appears on this page as the 57mm gun motor carriage T44. These photographs taken at Aberdeen were dated 17 March 1942.

With more heavily armored tanks appearing on the battlefield, it became apparent by late 1941 that an antitank weapon more powerful than the standard 37mm gun would be required. The British developed 6 pounder weapon was adopted and standardized as the 57mm gun M1. It now was necessary to provide a self-propelled mount so that this weapon could be effectively used by the Tank Destroyer Command. The first effort to develop such a self-propelled mount utilized the $^3/_4$ ton, four wheel drive, Ford chassis previously part of the 37mm gun motor carriage T33. Armed with the new

weapon, the vehicle was designated as the 57mm gun motor carriage T44. The 57mm gun was installed on a pedestal mount at the rear of the carriage and test fired at Aberdeen Proving Ground during March 1942. The carriage proved to be too light for this heavier weapon and did not provide a stable gun platform. The project was canceled in April 1942.

A design study briefly considered mounting the 57mm gun on the modified chassis of the armored car T13. However, when the T13 was canceled, it was dropped without further development.

The 75mm gun motor carriage T27 assembled by Studebaker is shown here at Aberdeen Proving Ground on 18 October 1941. It used the shield from the towed 75mm gun.

During the development of the half-track gun motor carriage T12, a project was initiated at Aberdeen to compare the stability of a wheeled vehicle with that of a half-track when used as a mount for the 75mm gun. A low silhouette $1\frac{1}{2}$ ton, four wheel drive, truck chassis was obtained from the Quartermaster Corps. This vehicle was equipped with a dual steering apparatus and a reversible driver's seat that permitted it to be driven in either direction. The engine was mounted at one end of the chassis in the normal manner. A 75mm gun M1897A4 was installed on the chassis using a mount only slightly modified from that used on the 75mm gun motor carriage T12 with identical elevation and traverse. In appearance, the new vehicle, designated as the 75mm gun motor carriage T27, resembled the Swamp Buggy which was tested as the 37mm gun motor carriage T8, however, it was considerably larger. A second chassis was procured for this program and it was equipped with dual wheels instead of the single wheels on the first vehicle. It also had the dual steering apparatus, but the

engine was installed along the side of the frame halfway between the front and rear. Because of the limited time available, the gun was not mounted on the second chassis, but it was tested alone to determine its general operating characteristics. The first vehicle, complete with the 75mm gun, was tested at Aberdeen Proving Ground in October 1941. The tests concluded that the $1\frac{1}{2}$ ton four wheel drive chassis was not as stable as the half-track vehicle and that it would be overloaded when stowed with ammunition and carrying a full crew. Ordnance Committee action closed the project in April 1942. The gun was removed and the chassis returned to the Quartermaster Corps.

As mentioned before, the 75mm gun motor carriage T66 was considered for use as a tank destroyer. Based upon the medium armored car T19E1, it is described along with that vehicle. However, the Tank Destroyer Command preferred the superior cross-country mobility of a full track vehicle and the T66 was dropped from further consideration.

The 3 inch gun motor carriage T55, "The Cook Interceptor", was photographed at Aberdeen on 19 November 1942. The vehicle was fully stowed and armed with a .50 caliber machine gun in addition to the 3 inch gun.

The favorable performance of an eight wheel (8x8) vehicle developed by the Cook Brothers of Los Angeles, California resulted in a design study to adapt the chassis as a 3 inch gun motor carriage. The design utilized the 3 inch gun mount M4 developed for the 3 inch gun motor carriage M5. The new vehicle was designated as the 3 inch gun motor carriage T55 and was popularly known as the "Cook Interceptor". As originally proposed, the vehicle had two engines, one in front and one in the rear, with each engine driving one four wheel bogie. In the final design, both engines were installed at the rear. Steering was with the aid of a hydraulic booster and was accomplished by turning the entire front bogie about a center pivot point. Two pilots were constructed with the second somewhat modified in design. The latter could be readily identified by the angular shape of the hull compared to the curved hull design of the original T55.

The second pilot of the "Cook Interceptor", the 3 inch gun motor carriage T55E1, is pictured here at Aberdeen on 10 September 1943. The .50 caliber machine gun has not been installed.

The second pilot was designated as the 3 inch gun motor carriage T55E1. Tests at Aberdeen Proving Ground revealed that the cross-country mobility of the Cook vehicle was inferior to that of a full track tank destroyer such as the T49 then under test. Both the T55 and the T55E1 were canceled without further production.

Earlier wheeled carriages for the 3 inch gun had been considered. The first was the previously mentioned T7 which was a modified version of the armored car T13. The second was the 3 inch gun motor carriage T15 which proposed to mount a 3 inch gun on a special Ford, four wheel drive, chassis. Later plans changed the special Ford chassis to a six wheel drive version. However, the project was dropped completely in October 1941 and the two T55 series vehicles were the only wheeled 3 inch gun motor carriages actually constructed.

The 3 inch gun motor carriage T55E1 is crossing rough terrain in the photograph above. Below, the interior of the fighting compartment can be seen at the left and the engine compartment is at the right. The various components and stowage items are identified in the drawing at the bottom of the page.

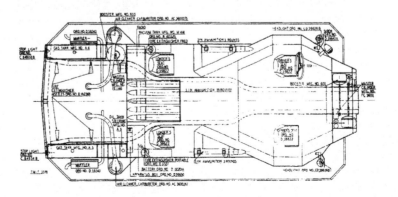

The 4.2 inch mortar carrier based upon the Jeep appears in the photographs above taken at Aberdeen Proving Ground on 9 March 1944. The mortar base plate is folded into the travel position.

WHEELED ARTILLERY MOTOR CARRIAGES

Two attempts were made to mount the 105 mm howitzer on wheeled self-propelled carriages. As already mentioned, the first was on the chassis of the armored car T13 where the combination was designated as the 105mm howitzer motor carriage T39. The second project proposed mounting the howitzer on a Mack wheeled chassis and designated the vehicle as the 105mm howitzer motor carriage T45. Both projects were dropped without any further development.

In early 1944, an extremely lightweight carrier for the 4.2 inch mortar was tested at Aberdeen Proving Ground. This carrier was based upon the $\frac{1}{4}$ ton truck. The vehicle was modified to carry the mortar in place of the rear seat. For travel, the base plate folded up and forward over the top of the mortar. For firing, the base plate was folded down onto the ground so that it lifted the vehicle off of the rear suspension. Because of the limited space available, a second vehicle was required to carry the ammunition and crew.

In August 1942, authorization was received to convert two 37mm gun motor carriages M6 as pilot models for a self-propelled rocket launcher. Two of these vehicles without the guns, but with their pedestal mounts, were shipped to Rock Island Arsenal. A single 4.5 inch rocket launcher was installed on the pedestal of each vehicle and they were designated as the 4.5 inch rocket motor carriage T62.

The driver's compartment was equipped with a shield to protect the crew from the rocket exhaust. The

launcher was aimed forward with 60 degree traverse range and a maximum elevation of 45 degrees. Ten 4.5 inch M8 series rockets were stowed on the vehicle and, with a crew of two, the combat loaded weight was slightly over 7,000 pounds. The two pilot vehicles were tested at Aberdeen Proving Ground. The firing tests were satisfactory and several modifications were suggested to improve the efficiency of the vehicle. However, by the time the tests were complete, Army policy had decided that the major development effort would be on launchers that could be fired from the ground or be mounted upon any suitable vehicle in the field. No further development work was done on the rocket motor carriage T62 and the project was officially terminated in June 1944

At the right, the 4.2 inch mortar base plate is emplaced in the firing position.

Above, the 4.5 inch rocket motor carriage T62 is at Aberdeen Proving Ground on 14 November 1942. A left rear view of the vehicle appears below at the left. Below at the right, a 24 inch extension tube has been installed on the launcher and it is at the maximum elevation of 45 degrees.

Below, the modified blast shield on the 4.5 inch rocket motor carriage T62 can be seen in the driving position (left) and the firing position (right).

167

The multiple rocket motor carriage T75 is shown in the photographs on this page. A dummy 10 inch rocket can be seen on the guide rails which were the launch tubes for the 4.5 inch rockets.

In April 1943, a project was initiated to develop a self-propelled rocket launcher for 10 inch rockets using the chassis of the Fargo $1\frac{1}{2}$ ton six wheel drive truck. Several configurations were studied. The first considered the use of two 10 inch rocket launchers. However, the final version installed two sets of launchers each capable of firing two 4.5 inch rockets and one 10 inch rocket. This vehicle was designated as the multiple rocket motor carriage T75.

The tubes for the 4.5 inch rockets served as guide rails for the 10 inch rocket. The cab was enclosed to protect the driver and assistant driver from the blast during firing. One pilot was completed and shipped to Aberdeen for evaluation. The 10 inch rocket ammunition proved to be faulty and the tests on the launcher were suspended. In October 1944, the multiple rocket motor carriage T75 was canceled without further development.

The installation of launchers for Navy 4.5 inch barrage rockets and 7.2 inch rockets on the DUKW amphibian truck was described in an earlier section. Two T45 launchers for the 4.5 inch barrage rocket also

168

The T45 launcher for the 4,5 inch barrage rockets is mounted on a Jeep above. At the top right is a 12 tube launcher for 4.5 inch rockets installed on a Jeep. This improvised launcher appears to consist of one lower section from the 4.5 inch multiple rocket launcher T34 intended for installation on a tank.

were mounted on the $\frac{1}{4}$ ton truck. The 7.2 inch multiple rocket launcher T32 was installed on the $2\frac{1}{2}$ ton truck. This launcher was loaded with 24 7.2 inch rockets and a rack was included with the launcher for 24 additional rounds. These rounds were either T21 7.2 inch chemical rockets or T24 7.2 inch high explosive rockets. The T37 7.2 inch high explosive rockets also could be used.

At the right and below is the T32 7.2 inch rocket launcher mounted on a $2\frac{1}{2}$ ton truck.

Above, the multiple gun motor carriage T1, based upon the Dodge 4x4 truck, is at Aberdeen Proving Ground on 25 June 1941. Note that it is armed with aircraft type, air cooled .50 caliber machine guns.

WHEELED MACHINE GUN MOTOR CARRIAGES AND VEHICULAR MOUNTS

The work in the 1930s had anticipated the need for motorized multiple machine gun mounts to protect mechanized columns from attack by aircraft. In October 1940, the Ordnance Committee recommended the development of a multiple machine gun motor carriage utilizing the latest type of power operated aircraft gun mount. To comply with this recommendation, a twin .50 caliber machine gun turret was procured from the Bendix Aviation Corporation and installed on a $^1/_2$ ton Dodge 4x4 truck. Designated as the multiple gun motor carriage T1, it was evaluated at Aberdeen Proving Ground during June and July 1941. The $^1/_2$ ton 4x4 truck

proved to be unstable and it was recommended that the turret be tested on a $1^1/_2$ ton truck and a half-track vehicle. However, an improved twin machine gun mount had now appeared. Developed by the W. L. Maxson Corporation, it was standardized as the twin .50 caliber machine gun mount M33. For test purposes, the M33 was installed on several truck chassis. These included the Fargo $^3/_4$ ton 4x4 weapons carrier and $1^1/_2$ ton 6x6 truck. Both chassis had the truck bed removed. The $^3/_4$ ton vehicle lacked stability, but the installation on the $1^1/_2$ ton 6x6 was considered to be satisfactory. When the M33 mount was installed on the $1^1/_2$ ton Fargo 6x6 with

Below, the twin .50 caliber M33 machine gun mount built by Maxson is installed on the Fargo 4x4 weapons carrier. Once again, the mount is armed with .50 caliber aircraft machine guns. These photographs from Aberdeen Proving Ground were dated 2 March 1942.

Above, the twin .50 caliber M33 machine gun mount is installed on a Fargo 6x6 truck from which the truck bed has been removed. The M33 mount retained the aircraft type machine guns in these Aberdeen photographs dated 6 June 1942.

the truck bed in place, it was designated as the twin .50 caliber gun motor carriage T74. However, the test program had concluded that the half-track was a superior vehicle for the antiaircraft gun motor carriages and further work on the truck carriers was canceled.

The twin .50 caliber M33 mount was installed experimentally on a trailer under the designation T45, but it was not adopted. With the appearance of the superior four gun .50 caliber M45 mount on the M16 and M17 multiple gun motor carriages, it also was

Below, the twin .50 caliber gun motor carriage T74 has the M33 mount installed on the Fargo 6x6 truck with the truck bed in place. Note that the mount is now armed with the .50 caliber M2HB ground type machine guns. At the bottom of the page is a drawing of a proposed armored body for the multiple gun motor carriage T74.

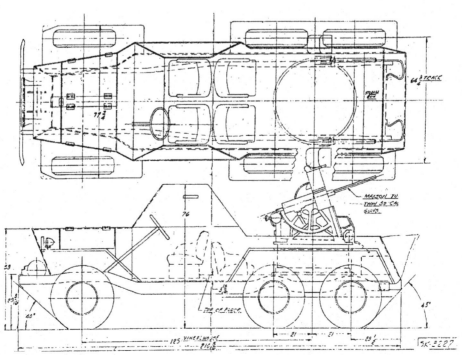

171

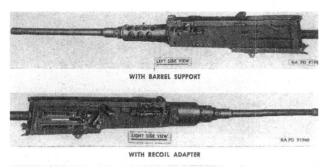

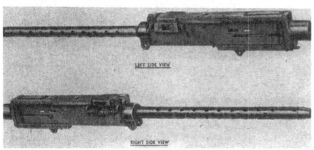

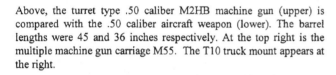

Above, the turret type .50 caliber M2HB machine gun (upper) is compared with the .50 caliber aircraft weapon (lower). The barrel lengths were 45 and 36 inches respectively. At the top right is the multiple machine gun carriage M55. The T10 truck mount appears at the right.

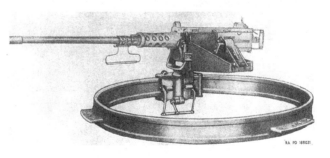

adapted for a trailer mount. When installed on the M7 generator trailer, it became the multiple machine gun carriage M51. The M45C mount on the two wheel trailer M20 became the .50 caliber multiple machine gun carriage M55. The latter was intended for airborne operations.

To provide truck convoys some protection against both air and ground attack, gun mounts were installed on a great variety of vehicles. These included both ring and pedestal mounts for .30 and .50 caliber machine guns.

The M49 ring mount armed with a flexible .50 caliber M2HB machine gun is at the right. Below are two views of the twin .50 caliber pedestal mount T54 installed on a Jeep.

172

PART III

THE COLD WAR, KOREA AND VIETNAM

Above, M8 light armored cars engage in target practice on a firing range near Taegu, Korea. Below at the right, an M20 armored utility car is operating in the Pusan Perimeter during the Summer of 1950.

THE POSTWAR PERIOD AND KOREA

After the end of World War II, there was little interest in the development of new wheeled combat vehicles. The limited budget for development projects was allocated to more critical programs. Although the Army Ground Forces Equipment Review Board had recommended the retention of an M38 type armored car for use in the postwar army, the later Stilwell Board completely eliminated the future requirement for an armored car.

The large number of M8 and M20 armored cars still available more than met the needs of the smaller postwar army. Many of the excess vehicles were supplied as foreign aid to friendly nations.

With the outbreak of war in Korea during the Summer of 1950, the World War II M8 and M20 armored cars soldiered on in another war.

Additional views of the World War II light armored cars operating in Korea appear below and at the right.

175

The armored chemical car T30 was never completed during World War II, but in Korea, the troops installed a flame thrower in the armored utility car M20. Unfortunately, its light armor and limited cross-country mobility precluded its use as an assault weapon. Below at the left, the M8 light armored car is being used by the Military Police guarding a prisoner of war compound.

The Military Police made considerable use of the M20 as well as the M8. Above, they are providing air field security. Below, they are protecting the prisoner exchange at the left and preventing any disruption of the proceedings by the civil population at the right.

After World War II, the light armored cars were evaluated as carriers for a variety of weapons. Above, the armored utility car M20 is armed with a 75mm recoilless rifle installed on the ring mount for the .50 caliber machine gun. Below, the drawing and the photograph show the NAPCO modified M8 with the TOW missile launcher and the .50 caliber machine gun replacing the 37mm gun.

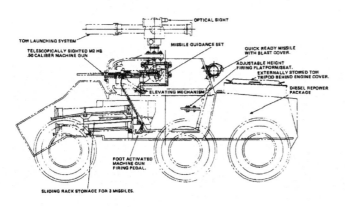

The continued use of the M8 and M20 provided a market for improvements. Napco Industries, Inc. developed a Repower/Modernization kit for the two vehicles. It replaced the original power train with a Detroit Diesel 4-53N engine and an Allison AT-545 automatic transmission. Columbia received 24 of these conversion kits to upgrade their armored cars.

Another Napco modification installed the TOW missile system on the M8. The missile launcher was mounted on top of the turret, but it also could be removed and fired from the tripod ground mount. The 37mm gun was removed from the turret mount and replaced with a .50 caliber M2HB machine gun using the same elevation mechanism. Five TOW missiles were carried including the one in the launcher. Three missiles were stowed in the right front hull and one was attached to the rear of the turret. This TOW installation was applied to the armored cars in Columbia.

177

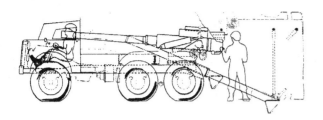 

Above are concept drawings for the WS-5 110 self-propelled howitzer (left) and the WS-6 156mm self-propelled howitzer (right)

NEW DESIGN CONCEPTS

During the second Questionmark conference in September 1952, two wheeled chassis had been proposed as the basis for 110mm and 156mm self-propelled howitzers. About the same time, studies of a new armored car were initiated at the Detroit Arsenal.

The new Army Equipment Development Guide, dated 3 May 1954, now included a requirement for the development of an armored car and an armored wheeled utility vehicle. When the Questionmark III conference was convened the following June, the proposals included four armored cars and two types of wheeled self-propelled artillery. The latter two were similar to those proposed during Questionmark II. Designated as WS-5 and WS-6, they were to be armed with the new experimental 110mm and 156mm howitzers respectively. The four proposed armored cars were designated as the 76mm gun WS-1, the 105mm rifle WS-8, the 90mm gun WS-26, and the 105mm gun WL-1. Other wheeled vehicles proposed were the twin 40mm gun motor carriage WS-4, the multiple gun motor carriage WS-7, and the armored infantry vehicle WS-3. An armored 5 ton 8x8 cargo truck also was proposed. Once again, wheeled combat vehicles were being considered in the army development program.

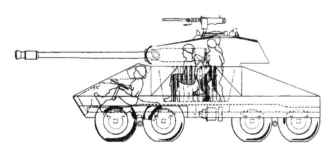 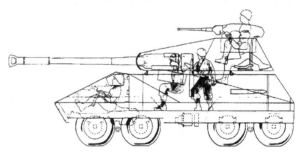

The four armored car concepts are shown in these four drawings. Above, the WS-1 armed with the 76mm gun is at the left and the WS-26 mounting the 90mm gun is at the right. Below, WS-8 fitted with the 105mm recoilless rifle is at the left and the WL-1 carrying the 105mm rocket boosted gun is at the right.

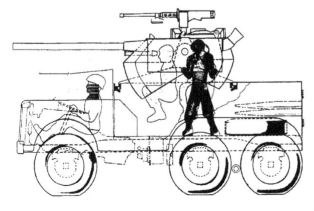 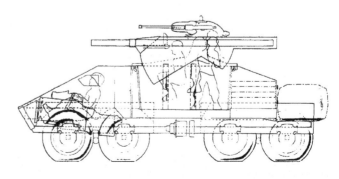

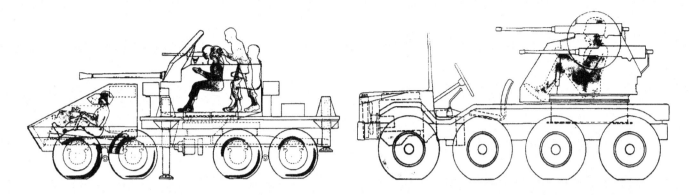

These three concepts from Questionmark III are the twin 40mm gun motor carriage WS-4 (top left), the multiple gun motor carriage WS-7 (top right) and the armored infantry vehicle WS-3. (below right). They were intended to replace the twin 40mm gun motor carriage M42, the multiple gun motor carriage M16 and the armored infantry vehicle M75 respectively.

The Questionmark IV conference during August 1955 proposed vehicles that would be required for an army that could be completely transported and supplied by air. Among the many lightweight vehicle concepts presented were two armored cars and numerous other wheeled vehicles. In fact, a complete wheeled vehicle family was under consideration. The two armored cars were designated W5 and W31. Both were 6x6 vehicles intended as replacements for the 76mm gun tank M41A1. The W5 and W31 were armed with a 105mm rocket boosted gun and a 90mm T132 gun respectively. Both vehicles had an estimated weight of 24,000 pounds and were to be powered by a Packard V8 engine developing 180 horsepower at 3,600 rpm. The front armor on both was only $\frac{1}{2}$ inch thick at 70 degrees from the vertical.

Despite the many wheeled proposals presented during the design concept studies, the Army continued to prefer tracked vehicles because of their superior cross-country mobility.

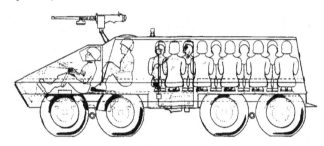

At the right is the concept mockup of a light infantry vehicle presented at the Questionmark IV conference. Below, the concept drawings show the W5 at the left with the 105mm rocket boosted gun and the W31 armed with a 90mm T132 gun at the right.

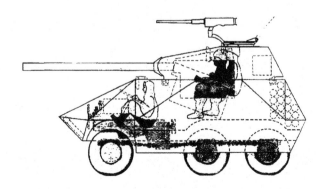

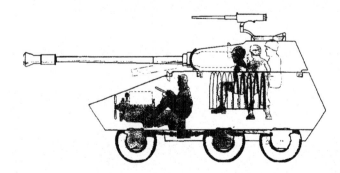

Above are models of the proposed 4 man (left) and 10 man (right) wheeled armored infantry vehicles. The 4 man vehicle is shown with the 106mm recoilless rifle.

The Army Field Forces issued military characteristics for two armored carriers in September 1954. The weights for the two vehicles were to be 8,000 and 16,000 pounds. Each was to be amphibious and provide the basis for a family of vehicles which could be either wheeled or tracked. The lighter carrier was to be manned by a crew of four and would serve as a command and reconnaissance vehicle or as the mount for the recoilless battalion antitank rifle. The heavier vehicle was intended as a ten man infantry carrier and the chassis was proposed as the mount for self-propelled weapons, a cargo carrier, or an ambulance. Feasibility studies of both the wheeled and tracked variants were presented by the Ordnance Tank Automotive Command on 28 June 1955. Once again the tracked versions won out. However, the wheeled four man vehicle was designated as the T115 armored, wheeled, personnel carrier and a mockup was assembled. The mockup was configured both as the command and reconnaissance vehicle and as the battalion antitank vehicle armed with the 106mm recoilless rifle. Unfortunately, the latter arrangement was considered to be unsatisfactory because the gunner had to expose himself when loading the rifle. The mockups of both the wheeled and tracked vehicles were demonstrated in June 1957. With the adoption of the tracked T114 command and reconnaissance vehicle, further work on the T115 was canceled.

The mockup of the T115 armored, wheeled, personnel carrier can be seen in the photographs above. The vehicle is armed with a .50 caliber machine gun in the left view and with the 106mm recoilless rifle at the right. The operation of the 106mm recoilless rifle and its ammunition stowage can be seen below.

Above, the French man leftovers from World War II in Vietnam. An M3A1 scout car is at the left and a M8 light armored car is at the right.

VIETNAM

When the French returned to reclaim their colonies in Indochina after World War II, their forces were still equipped with weapons and vehicles from that war. Most of this was American equipment furnished under the foreign aid program including numerous M8 and M20 armored cars as well as some M3A1 scout cars. After the French defeat by the Vietminh and the country was divided under the Geneva Accords of 1954, much of this equipment was turned over to the army of the new South Vietnam. After the departure of the last French soldier in 1956, support for the southern armed forces came from the United States.

In the early 1960s, the old M8 and M20 armored cars were still being employed, although they were now considered obsolete and badly in need of replacement.

However, the development of the armored car had essentially been dropped by the U.S. Army and a commercial source was sought to meet this requirement.

Formed in 1954, the Defense Operations Division of Chrysler Corporation designed three armored cars. Two of these, designated light and medium, were four wheel, four wheel drive (4x4) vehicles. None of these were acquired by the United States, but about 30 of the medium cars were exported to Mexico. The third type was an eight wheel vehicle referred to as a Special Warfare Armored Transporter (SWAT). Intended for use as an armored assault vehicle or as an armored personnel carrier, it was amphibious and driven in the water by its spinning wheels. However, the SWAT did not go into production.

Dimensions of the Chrysler light (left) and medium (right) armored cars are shown in the sketches below.

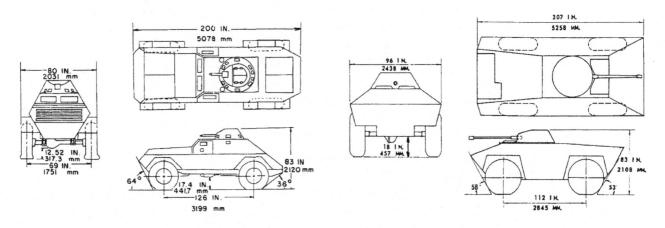

Above, a model of the Chrysler medium armored car is at the left and the SWAT vehicle appears at the right.

A vehicle that was to be much more successful was an armored car designed by the Cadillac Gage Company of Detroit, Michigan. This was a new four wheel (4x4) vehicle named the Commando and later designated as the V-100. The prototype was completed and began testing in June 1962. The results of the prototype tests were incorporated in the construction of a second Commando. The latter was designated as #1 and was the first of six pilot vehicles built prior to the start of production. Compared to the prototype, #1 had a wider hull that extended over the tires to prevent mud from being thrown up all over the car when traversing swamp-like terrain. The floor also was modified and was sloped down to cover the axles to prevent the vehicle

being hung up when crossing objects such as tree stumps. The new car also was equipped with power steering to permit easy handling at high speed on rough terrain. Tests of the prototype and pilot #1 continued through the Winter of 1962-63 and the results were applied to pilot #2 which was completed and became operational on 25 April 1963.

In early March 1963, pilot #1 was driven to Aberdeen Proving Ground for evaluation by the Army. The vehicle was delivered without a turret as a new turret was under development. A weight was bolted to the roof to simulate the weight of the new turret. The test results from Aberdeen were applied to pilot #2 and the new turret was installed. Pilot #2 then replaced #1 at

The early Cadillac Gage Commando armored car can be seen below with the original turret. Note the large number of periscopes in this vehicle.

182

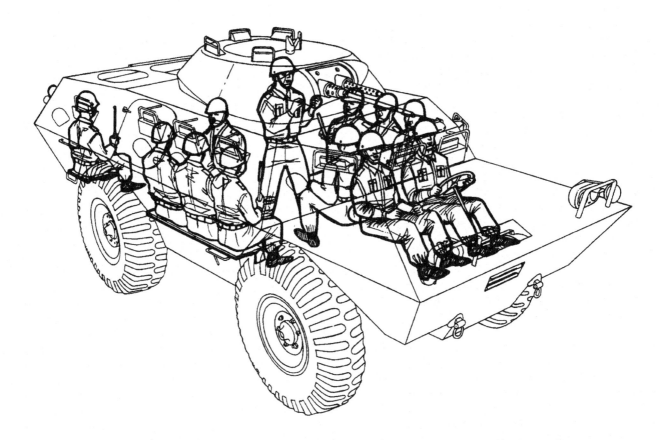

The location of the 12 man crew inside the early Cadillac Gage Commando armored car is illustrated in the drawing above.

Above is a front view of the early Cadillac Gage Commando armored car armed with one .30 caliber and one .50 caliber machine gun in the turret mount.

Aberdeen for the remainder of the test program including the turret tests. Pilot #1 was returned to Cadillac Gage and reworked to the latest specification.

All of the recommended changes were incorporated in a fourth Commando (pilot #3) which became operational on 11 June 1963. Construction of pilots #4 and #5 began during the Spring of 1963 and pilot #4 became operational in August. The tests at Aberdeen also were completed in August and pilot #2 was returned to Cadillac Gage. Capable of carrying up to 12 men, these vehicles could be armed with a variety of weapons. These included two .30 caliber M37 machine guns, two 7.62mm MG42 NATO machine guns or one .30 caliber M37 weapon and one .50 caliber M2 machine gun. A total of ten firing ports were installed in the hull of the early vehicles along with twelve periscopes. Six additional periscopes were mounted in the early turret. On the later pilots, the periscopes were replaced by vision blocks and an additional firing port was located between the two front vision blocks. The vehicle was protected against .30 caliber ball ammunition at zero obliquity by high hardness homogeneous steel armor $\frac{1}{4}$ inch thick. Plate $\frac{3}{8}$ inches thick could be provided in critical areas for protection against .30 caliber armor piercing rounds or .50 caliber ball ammunition. This resulted in a weight increase of about 500 pounds.

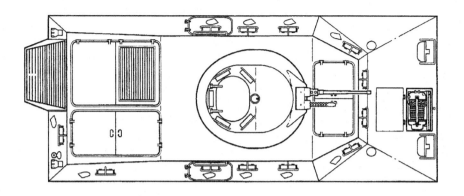

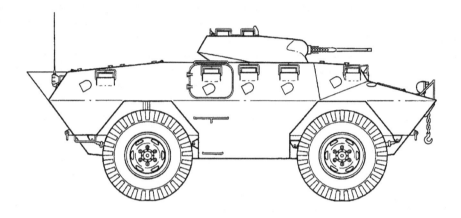

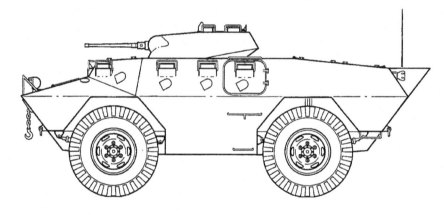

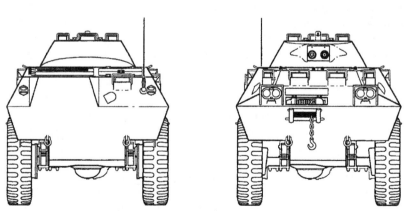

Scale 1:48

Armored Car V-100 Commando, early

© M. Duplessis

This pilot Cadillac Gage Commando armored car is being evaluated by the Armor and Engineer Board at Fort Knox on 20 May 1963.

This additional view of the pilot Cadillac Gage Commando at Fort Knox still shows the large number of periscopes in the hull. However. in the new turret, the periscopes have been replaced by vision blocks.

The Commando was powered by a Chrysler 361 gasoline engine developing 210 gross horsepower at 4,000 rpm. It drove the vehicle through a manual, five speed, transmission. The suspension consisted of leaf springs with full control shock absorbers at each of the four wheels. The "run flat" 14 x 20 combat tires could be operated at 35 miles per hour completely flat and at 60 miles per hour with the internal pressure reduced to 5 psi. The maximum speed on a level road was 60 miles per hour. The car was completely amphibious without any special preparation and could reach a maximum speed in water of $3^{1}/_{2}$ miles per hour driven by the rotating tires. Two 40 gallon fuel tanks provided a maximum cruising range on roads of about 550 miles. An hydraulically operated winch with a 10,000 pound line pull was installed in the front of the vehicle. The combat weight of the Commando was a little over seven tons.

Pilot #1 was purchased by the Army Tank Automotive Command in Detroit and pilots #2 and #3 were procured by the Advanced Research Projects Agency (ARPA) for testing in Vietnam. During the first week in September 1963, Pilots #2 and #3 were processed for shipment to Vietnam along with a supply of spare parts. In the third week of November, they departed by rail to Baltimore for shipment by sea to Vietnam.

In the meantime, pilot #5 became operational in September. It differed from the earlier vehicles in several features. The side armor was now formed by bending the hull panel from a single piece compared to the welded assembly of several pieces on the earlier cars. It also was fitted with larger two piece side doors and a new rear door. The new doors proved to be so satisfactory that pilot #4 also was reworked to the same configuration. Initially, the rear door consisted of a single piece, but this was later changed to a two piece design similar to the side doors. A new power operated turret was designed during the Fall of 1963 and installed on pilot #5. This turret was armed with a 20mm gun and a coaxial .223 caliber Stoner 63 machine gun. Another armament option was the installation of the 90mm low recoil MECAR cannon with two coaxial .30 caliber machine guns.

186

Above, the V-100 Commando is now fitted with the two piece side doors and a single piece rear door. The vehicle is swimming at the top right. At the right, the V-100 is armed with the turret mounted, low recoil, Energa 90mm gun and two .30 caliber machine guns.

The last pilot vehicle (#6) was completed in early 1964 and production of the V-100 Commando began in January. The production vehicles incorporated the various modifications recommended by the tests at Aberdeen and the results of the field evaluation of pilots #2 and #3 in Vietnam. The latter, during February through April 1964, had shown that the Commando could be effectively employed under the conditions prevailing in Vietnam. One recommendation from these tests was the installation of self-cleaning combat tires. Pilots #2 and #3 had been fitted with non-directional combat tires. In rice paddies and other deep mud the tread of these tires filled with mud and they completely lost traction. It also was recommended that a seat be provided for the turret gunner.

Below and at the right, the Commando turret is armed with a 20mm automatic gun and a coaxial Stoner .223 caliber machine gun. The hull periscopes have been replaced by vision blocks in all of these vehicles.

The XM706 was evaluated by the Armor and Engineer Board at Fort Knox. The vehicle above was photographed on 2 May 1966. The remaining views were dated 26 July 1965

The V-100 was procured for Vietnam under the designation XM706. The final T50 turret design could be armed with either the two .30 caliber machine guns or the combination of one .30 caliber and one .50 caliber weapon. The later vehicles were armed with the 7.62mm M73 machine guns in place of the earlier .30 caliber M37 guns. In either case, the weapons were offset to the right side of the turret front. The gun sight was mounted in the turret roof and a ring of seven vision blocks were installed around the bottom of the turret walls. The early XM706 vehicles retained the angular cutouts for the wheels, but these were soon replaced by semicircular cutouts on the later cars. The later vehicles also were fitted with an engine access hatch on the left side at the rear and an extension to the exhaust housing to prevent water intake when climbing out of water at a steep angle.

The late production Commando appears above. Note the circular wheel cutouts and the engine access hatch on the left side at the rear. There is only one side vision block forward of the side doors. The hatches over the driving compartment have raised center sections to increase the headroom.

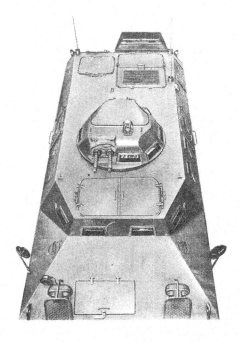

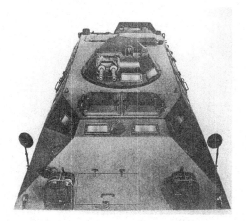

The early XM706 at the left can be compared with the later version above. Note the flat driving compartment hatches on the early vehicle compared with the later XM706 above.

The driver's controls in the Commando are identified in the two views below.

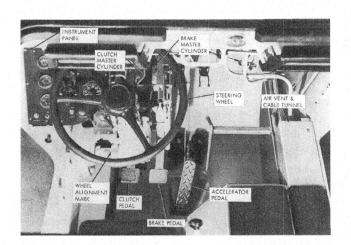 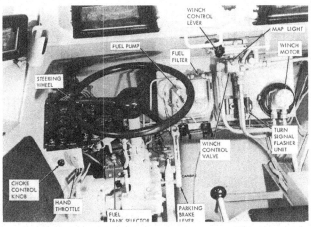

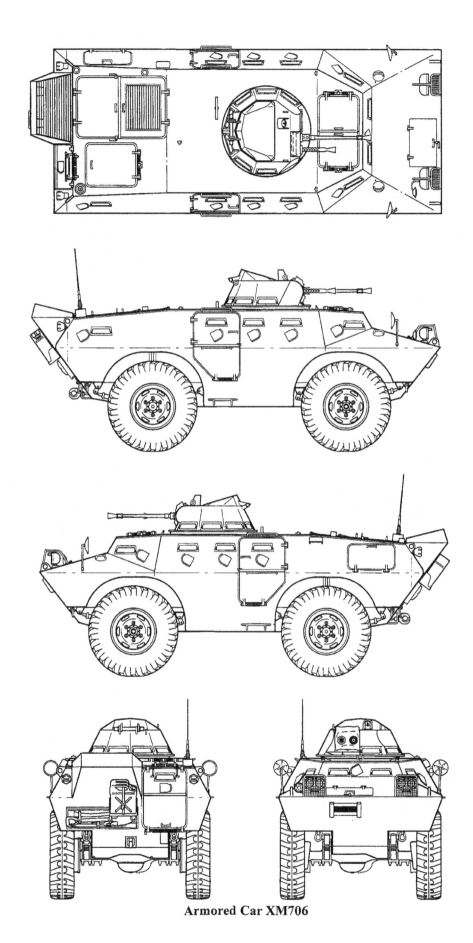

Scale 1:48

Armored Car XM706

© M. Duplessis

190

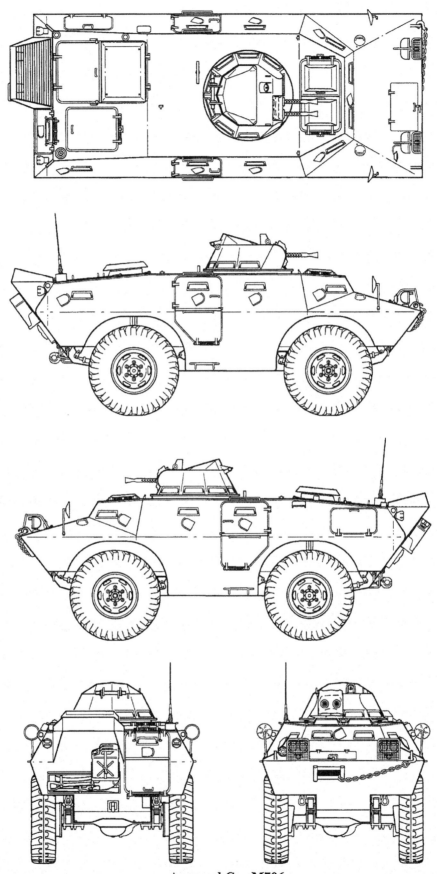

Scale 1:48

© M. Duplessis

Armored Car M706

191

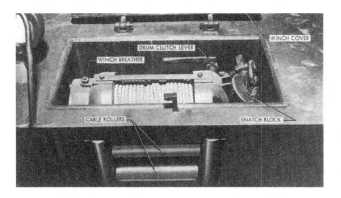 

Details of the 10,000 pound capacity winch can be seen above at the left. At the top right, the use of a snatch block with the winch is being demonstrated.

Further modifications were made before the V-100 was standardized by the U. S. Army. One vision block and one firing port were eliminated from each side of the vehicle forward of the doors and a cover was installed over the intake grill on the rear deck. New spring loaded roof hatches with raised center sections were provided to give more head room for the driver and assistant driver. With these changes the vehicle was designated as the XM706E1 and later standardized as the M706. Three of the XM706E1 vehicles were completed with a turret mounted XM182 40mm grenade launcher as the main armament. A turretless version of the Commando procured for the U. S. Air Force was designated as the XM706E2. The turret was replaced by an armored parapet with folding doors. Armament installed in the field frequently included the 7.62mm machine gun, the .50 caliber M2 machine gun, or the 7.62mm minigun. The XM706E2 was used mainly to provide air base security.

In addition to the M706, the basic V-100 was produced in a wide variety of armament configurations for foreign sales.

The XM706E2 armored car is shown in the two photographs above. This vehicle has the late production features such as the circular wheel cutouts and the raised center section in the driving compartment hatches. The top views below show the mounting points for the 7.62 machine gun and details of the bi-fold doors over the crew compartment open and closed.

  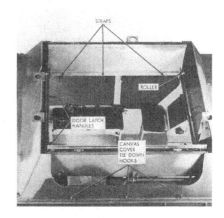

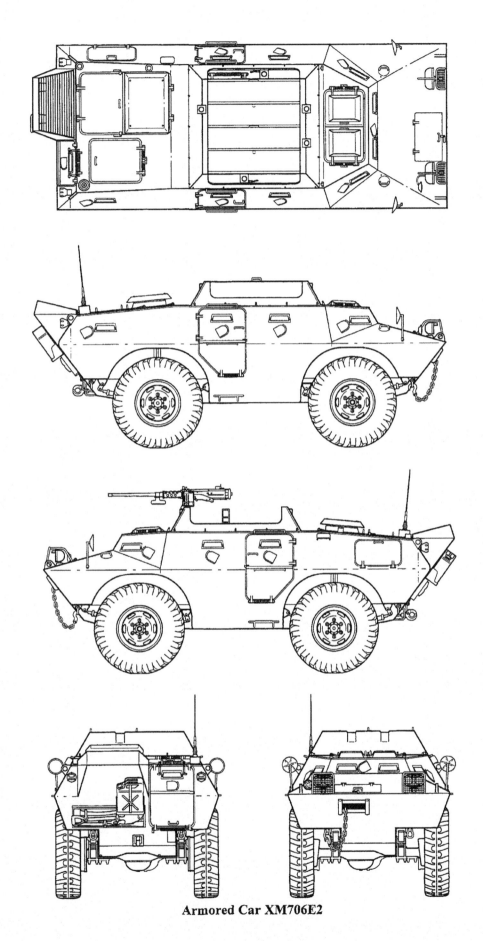

Scale 1:48

Armored Car XM706E2

© M. Duplessis

193

COMPONENT	XM706		M706	XM706E2
	Early Models (Before Serial number 10619)	Current Mofels (Beginning with Serial number 10619)		
Hull Vision Blocks	12	10	10	10
Gun Ports	11	9	9	9
Drivers Hatches	Flat	Raised Contour	Raised Contour	Raised Contour
Anti-Molotov Cocktail Shield	No	Yes	Yes	Yes
Turret for M73 Machinegun	No	No	Yes	Without Turret
Turn Signals	No	Yes	Yes	Yes
Turret Gearbox with two Handwheels	No	Yes	Yes	None
Turret accommodates various Machineguns (M37, M1919A4, MG42, M2 .50 Cal.)	Yes	Yes	No	None
Provision for mounting M60 Machinegun	No	No	No	Yes

The table above indicates when various features were introduced into the Commando series. Below, the gun handles and triggers are shown for both the early (left) and late (right) Commandos.

M37

Some of the machine guns installed on the Commando can be seen in these photographs. At the left is the .30 caliber M37 machine gun. Below, the 7.62mm M73 machine gun is at the left and the .50 caliber M2HB machine gun is at the right.

Above, these Commandos are performing one of their most important duties, that of escorting truck convoys in Vietnam. These Military Police Commandos are on the road to An Khe in the Vietnam central highlands. Below, the XM706 at the left is armed with the combination of one .30 caliber and one .50 caliber machine gun. The XM706 at the right has two .30 caliber weapons.

The XM706E2 armored cars below are operating with the U. S. Air Force in Vietnam and Thailand providing air base security.

The XM706 armored cars on this page were photographed by James Loop during his service in Vietnam. Note that the vehicles are armed with the combination of one .30 caliber and one .50 caliber machine gun.

196

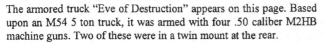

The armored truck "Eve of Destruction" appears on this page. Based upon an M54 5 ton truck, it was armed with four .50 caliber M2HB machine guns. Two of these were in a twin mount at the rear.

Although the M706 was an excellent vehicle for the escort of truck convoys in Vietnam, there were never sufficient numbers available. As frequently happened, the problem was solved by the troops themselves. The transportation truck battalions armored some of their trucks and fitted them with machine guns and other weapons to provide escorts for their convoys. Although several types of trucks were modified, a favorite was the 5 ton M54A2 cargo truck. With a payload of 10 tons on roads or 5 tons cross country, it was well suited to carry the weight of the armor and weapons installed. Powered by Continental LD 465-1A turbocharged diesel engine, the M54A2 was a 6x6 vehicle with dual tires on the rear four wheels. The trucks were frequently protected by a double wall of armor with stowage space in between. Armament usually included several .50 caliber machine guns or in some cases an XM134 7.62mm Minigun. The complete hull of an Armored Cavalry Assault Vehicle (ACAV) was occasionally installed on the chassis of the 5 ton truck, the cab of which had also been armored. The M35 series of 6x6 2$\frac{1}{2}$ ton trucks also were armored for escort duty. Some of these were armed with the quadruple .50 caliber machine gun mount giving the vehicle the firepower of the M16 multiple gun motor carriage. Light trucks and Jeeps also were armed for combat duty during operations in Vietnam. The U.S. Marine Corps even installed the 106mm recoilless rifle on the M274 Mule.

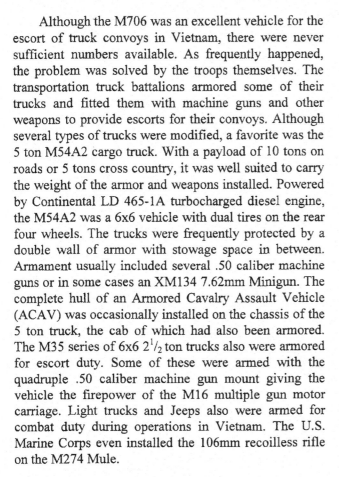

At the upper right, the double wall of armor with a spare tire in between is visible as well as the twin .50 caliber machine gun mount. At the lower right, "Eve of Destruction" is driving along Route 19 in Vietnam.

The gun truck above was converted from a $2\frac{1}{2}$ ton M35 truck by adding armor to the cab doors, sides and rear. Named "THE GAMBLERS", it retained the .50 caliber machine gun on the truck ring mount over the cab and added a 7.62mm machine gun to each side of the rear body. Below at the left, the 444th Transportation Company created the powerful gun truck "NANCY" by installing an M45 quad .50 caliber mount.

"UNTOUCHABLE", above at the right, carried an XM134 7.62mm minigun on each side with a single M2HB .50 caliber machine gun at the rear. In the two views below, the "BIG KAHUNA" of the 58th Transportation Company put the armored hull and complete armament of an M113 armored personnel carrier on the bed of their gun truck. This provided one .50 caliber and two 7.62mm machine guns with armor protection.

Above is an extreme example of heavy firepower on a small self-propelled mount. A 106mm recoilless rifle is installed on an M274 Mule. Below at the left is a small gun truck resulting from the application of armor to this ³/₄ ton truck. It is armed with a .50 caliber machine gun.

Above at the right even the M151 Jeep is pressed into service for convoy protection. Although armed with a 7.62mm machine gun, it had no armor protection. The gun truck below had the truck body protected by armor plate and sand bags are on the running boards and in front of the windshield. Although it did not carry any heavy armament, firing ports have been cut into the side armor.

The two photographs above show the Cadillac Gage V-200 Commando in service with the Singapore Army. An automatic 20mm gun provides the main armament on the vehicle at the left. The V-200 at the right is a mortar carrier armed with a 120mm mortar.

In 1960, Cadillac Gage produced a larger version of the Commando designated as the V-200. This longer vehicle had more interior room and could be used to mount heavier weapons. However, it was not a success although a number were sold to Singapore. The U.S. Army evaluated a product improved version of the M706 designated by Cadillac Gage as the V-150. Introduced in late 1971, it was the most successful and widely produced version of the Commando. The V-150 retained the same overall dimensions and configuration of the V-100. Lessons learned during the service of the V-100 in Vietnam were applied to the design of the new vehicle. For example, rough handling of the car, often by inexperienced drivers, frequently resulted in axle failures. To prevent this, heavier axles were installed on the V-150. Except for modifications to the leaf springs, the suspension remained the same as on the V-100. To permit the installation of heavier weapons, the payload was increased from 3,000 pounds to 5,000 pounds. The same Chrysler 361 gasoline engine was retained with the five speed manual transmission, but optional power train components were offered. These consisted of a V6 diesel engine developing 155 horsepower and a three speed automatic transmission. On later vehicles, the power train consisted of the Cummins V8 diesel engine producing 202 horsepower with an Allison four speed automatic transmission. Initially, the V-150 used the same 14 x 20 tires as on the V-100, but they were replaced on the later vehicles by 14.5 x 21 "run flat" tires.

One obvious identification point on the V-150 was the addition of a second front vision block for the driver. The two vision blocks also protruded out at a slight angle from the front armor. The firing port in the front plate was eliminated.

The Cadillac Gage V-150 Commando is shown in these three photographs. The two piece doors are open above at the right. A 7.62mm machine gun could be mounted at the troop hatch on the roof at the rear. Note the slight protrusion of the driver's two front vision blocks in the view below at the left.

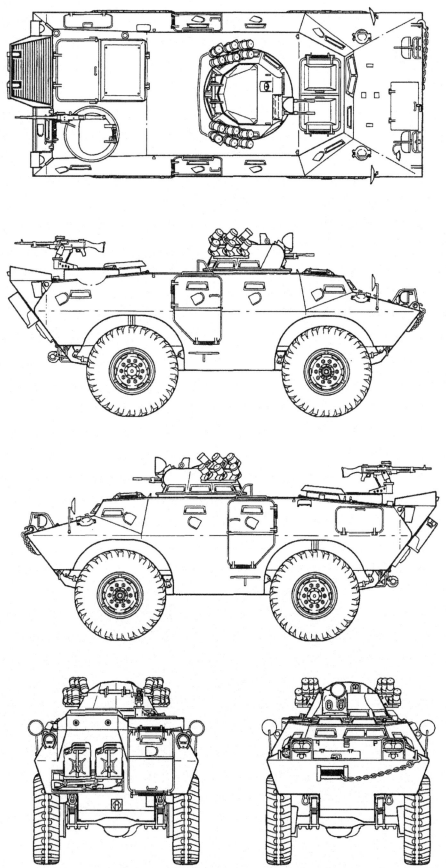

Scale 1:48

Armored Car M706 Product Improved

V-150 DUAL MACHINEGUN

V-150 20MM

V-150 81MM MORTAR

Three versions of the V-150 Commando are shown in the drawings above.

The Cadillac Gage V-150 Commando in these photographs is armed with the 20mm Oerlikon automatic gun with a 7.62mm coaxial machine gun. An additional 7.62mm machine gun is mounted on top of the turret. At the right above, the V-150 is swimming.

202

V-150 COMMAND

V-150 A.P.C.

V-150 90MM

Additional versions of the V-150 Commando are sketched above. At the right, the V-150 is fitted with the command pod and armed with a single 7.62mm machine gun.

The V-150 was produced in several variations. The product improved M706 retained the twin machine gun turret as on the earlier vehicles. It was manned by a crew of four consisting of the driver, commander, gunner, and radio operator, however, it could carry up to ten men.

More powerful armament provided on the V-150 included a 20mm Oerlikon automatic gun or a low recoil 90mm, manually operated, gun installed in a turret mount. These vehicles were manned by a crew of three, but had a capacity of eight. Turretless versions of the V-150 were used as a carrier for the 81mm mortar, a command car, and as a personnel carrier. The capacity of the latter was 12 men. Later the vehicle was adapted as a carrier for a number of other weapons including use as an antiaircraft vehicle. The latter was armed with the 20mm six barrel Gatling type gun of the M167A1 air defense system.

An 81mm mortar is installed in the V-150 at the right and the roof hatches are open in the firing position. The drawings below show the turret armed with two 7.62mm machine guns (left) or a 20mm Oerlikon automatic gun with a coaxial 7.62mm machine gun (right). The latter also has a 7.62mm machine gun on the turret roof.

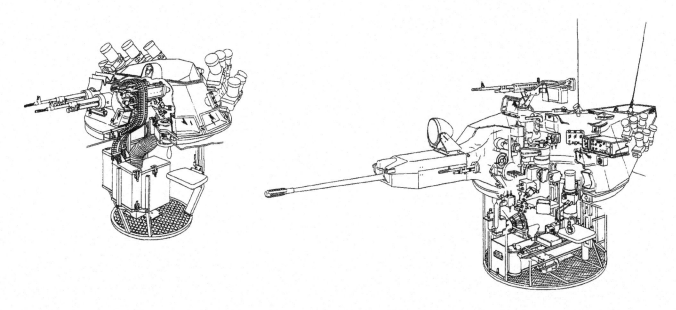

203

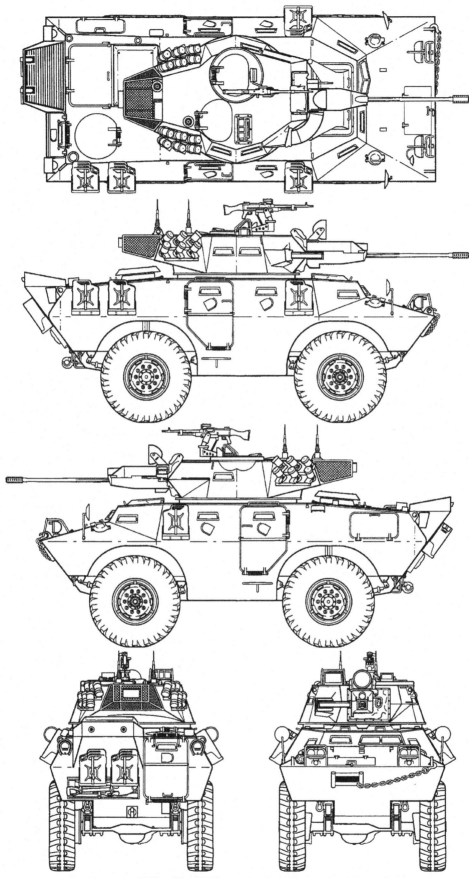

Scale 1:48

Armored Car V-150 Commando, 20mm Oerlikon Gun

© M. Duplessis

Below, the V-150 Commando is armed with the Mecar 90mm low recoil force gun. At the right, it has been fitted with Cockerill Mark III 90mm low recoil force gun. Both vehicles have 7.62mm coaxial machine guns and a 7.62mm machine gun on the turret roof. Note the smoke grenade launchers on the turret of each vehicle.

At the right are the Mecar (upper) and the Cockerill (lower) Mark III 90mm low recoil force guns. An additional view of the V-150 Commando can be seen below.

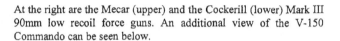

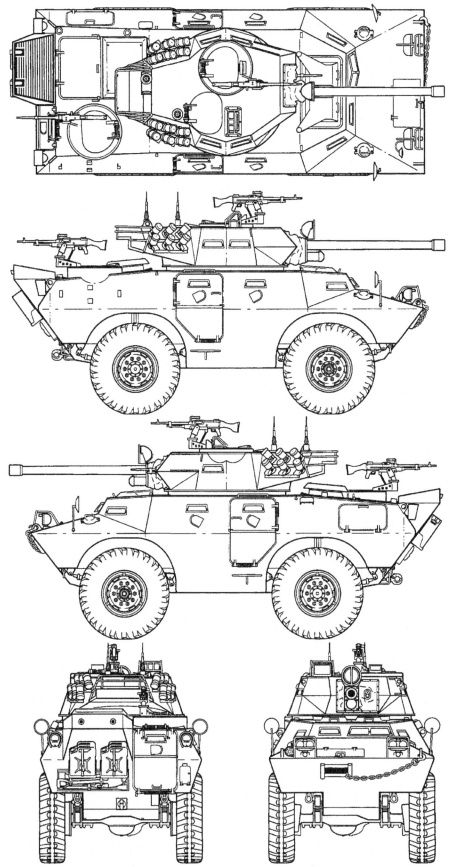

© M. Duplessis

Armored Car V-150 Commando, 90mm Mecar Gun

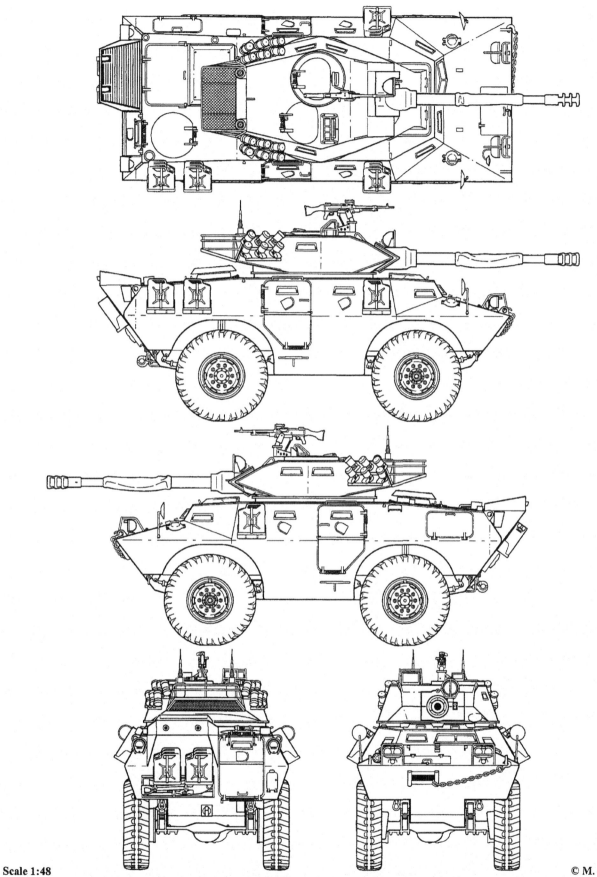

Scale 1:48

Armored Car V-150 Commando, 90mm Cockerill Gun

The Vulcan/Commando air defense system appears in the photographs and the drawing on this page. Based upon the V-150 armored car, it is armed with the M167A1 20mm turret as a "drop in" installation. The gross vehicle weight is 20,000 pounds. The 20mm ammunition supply consisted of 500 ready rounds plus 800 stowed rounds. The rate of fire was 1000/3000 rounds per minute.

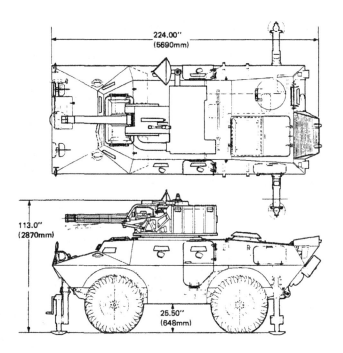

Above, the Cadillac Gage Commando Scout is armed with one 7.62mm and one .50 caliber machine gun in the turret. Below, the turret does not appear to have any weapons mounted. At the bottom of the page is the command version of the Scout without a turret, but armed with a single .50 caliber machine gun.

In late 1977, Cadillac Gage introduced a lightweight 4x4 armored vehicle dubbed the Commando Scout. With a combat weight of $7\frac{1}{2}$ tons, it was protected by the high hardness homogeneous steel armor referred to as Cadloy by Cadillac Gage. The Commando Scout was driven by a 155 horsepower V6 diesel engine with a four speed automatic transmission and a two speed transfer case. Coil springs were used on both the solid front axle and the split rear axle. Both axles were provided with locking differentials and the wheels were fitted with 15.5 x 21 "run flat" tires. The maximum speed was governed to 55 miles per hour and the operating range was about 500 miles. The vehicle was not amphibious and had a maximum fording depth of 46 inches. The Commando Scout was offered in several versions manned by two or three men. The armament selection included twin 7.62mm machine guns, combination 7.62mm and .50 caliber machine guns, a 7.62mm machine gun and a 40mm Mark 19 automatic grenade launcher, or a power turret with a 20mm or 30mm gun. A mount also could be installed for a 106mm recoilless rifle or a TOW missile launcher. As a command vehicle, it could be fitted with a ring or pintle machine gun mount.

The Commando Scout was not adopted by the United States, but it was sold to several foreign countries.

209

Above, the Cadillac Gage Commando Ranger is fitted with a turret armed with two 7.62mm machine guns. At the bottom of the page, the Ranger is shown with a roof mounted shield and spotlight (left) and without any roof mounted armament (right).

The United States Air Force requested proposals from industry in late 1978 for an armored security vehicle to provide air base protection. In October 1978, proposals from the Cadillac Gage Company, the Oshkosh Truck Corporation, and the Vehicle Systems Development Corporation were considered to meet the technical requirements for the new vehicle. In March 1979, the Air Force selected the Cadillac Gage Commando Ranger on the basis of lowest cost to meet the requirement for a security vehicle to patrol its air bases. Named Peacekeeper by the Air Force, the Commando Ranger was based upon a 4x4 Chrysler truck with a shortened wheelbase. The 180 horsepower gasoline engine was coupled to a four speed automatic transmission. The solid front and rear axles were suspended by leaf springs and the wheels were fitted with "run flat" tires. The loaded weight was between five and six tons and the Cadloy high hardness homogeneous steel armor offered protection against 7.62mm ball ammunition. The Commando Ranger was purchased by both the U.S. Air Force and the U.S. Navy. It was offered in a variety of configurations for foreign sales. These included a command vehicle, an armored personnel carrier, a medical transport vehicle, and various weapon carriers. Depending upon the type, it carried from two to eight men.

PART IV

NEW WHEELED COMBAT VEHICLES

Above are two concept models of the Twister designed to carry light and heavy armament.

TWISTER

In the late 1960s, The Lockheed Missiles and Space Company developed a new eight wheel (8x8) vehicle with superior cross-country mobility. The testbed, dubbed the Twister, consisted of two bodies joined by a pivotal yoke which allowed movement about the pitch, roll, and yaw axes. Each half of the vehicle was powered by a 110 horsepower Corvair, air-cooled, engine. The four wheels on the front section used an independent "A" frame suspension with double acting shock absorbers. The four wheels on the rear body operated in pairs on walking beams sprung by coil springs. The articulation of the two bodies allowed all eight wheels to remain in ground contact while crossing rough terrain. This also greatly reduced the shock transmitted to the crew. The Lockheed testbed weighed 12,070 pounds and measured 200 inches long, 103 inches wide, and 77 inches high. It was capable of a top speed of 55 mile per hour on roads. The driver guided the vehicle by a combination of conventional steering of the front wheels and yaw steering of the front body.

Below, the Lockheed Twister test bed is shown during its development and test program.

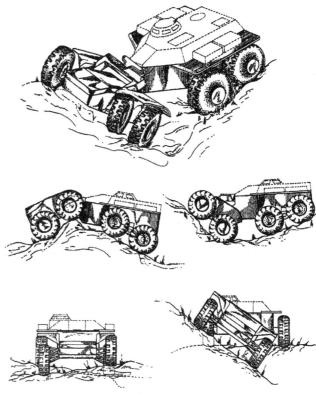

The Army Twister test bed can be seen above and the XM808 itself is at the bottom of the page during September 1969. The drawing at the right illustrates the articulation of the two Twister bodies when moving across rough terrain.

After extensive testing of the original testbed, Lockheed received a contract from the U. S. Army Tank Automotive Command to provide three second generation prototypes for evaluation. Two of these vehicles were delivered to the Army in January 1970. One was a new testbed for army evaluation and the other was an armored vehicle armed with a 20mm turret mounted gun. The latter vehicle was designated as the XM808. Both vehicles were larger and heavier than the original prototype. The gross vehicle weight was 16,570 pounds for the new testbed and 20,450 pounds for the XM808. However, the power to weight ratio was increased for both vehicles by the installation of two militarized Chrysler 440 V8 engines. It was now 69 horsepower per

The XM808 Twister is shown above and at the bottom of the page during the tests by the Armor and Engineer Board on 10 July 1970. At the right is a photograph of the amphibious Twister prototype emerging from the water.

ton for the new testbed and 56 horsepower per ton for the XM808. The testbed and the XM808 were 220 inches long and 105 ·inches wide. The height was 82 inches for the testbed and 97 inches for the XM808. The third vehicle on the Army contract was delivered during the Summer of 1970. Like the testbed it was not armed or armored, but it was modified for amphibious operation. Propulsion in the water was provided by two water jets driven by the rear engine. The maximum speed in the water was six miles per hour.

Details of the 20mm gun mount on the XM808 Twister can be seen in the views on this page.

Above are front and rear views of the XM808 Twister. Below at the right is the prototype Twister logistics vehicle often referred to as the Dragon Wagon. Note that this vehicle is not armored.

The Army also considered the Twister configuration for use as a logistic vehicle. In early 1972 an unarmored version was completed for test. Known as the Dragon Wagon, it was powered by a single diesel engine in the front body. A cab for a three man crew was installed on the front body. All eight wheels were driven. Power was transmitted to the four wheels on the rear body through the flexible yoke joining the two halves of the vehicle.

Although the Twister did not go into production, lessons learned from its development were applied to future programs.

Below, the XM808 Twister is crossing rough terrain during the Armor and Engineer Board tests on 7 December 1970

Above, a concept model of the wheeled Armored Reconnaissance Scout Vehicle appears at the left and the prototype vehicle is at the right.

SCOUT

On 23 May 1972, Lockheed Missiles and Space Company received a contract to develop a wheeled vehicle to meet the requirement for an Armored Reconnaissance Scout Vehicle (ARSV). This was in competition with the Food Machinery Corporation which was developing a tracked vehicle to meet the same requirement. The wheeled and tracked ARSVs were designated as the XM800W and the XM800T respectively.

The XM800W made considerable use of the experience gained from the Twister program. The Lockheed ARSV was a six wheel (6x6), two body, vehicle with roll articulation between the two sections. The front body carried the two wheel front suspension, steering, and drive line as well as the fuel tank. The rear body was fitted with a two man turret armed with an M139 20mm gun. The driver was seated in the left front of the rear body and the General Motors 6V53T diesel engine with the Allison MT650M transmission were located in the rear. This engine developed 300 gross horsepower at 2,800 rpm. The four rear wheels operated in pairs on coil sprung walking beams. The maximum road speed was 65 miles per hour and water jet propulsion drove the amphibious vehicle at a maximum water speed of six miles per hour.

After evaluation, the Army preferred the full track XM800T and there was no further development of the wheeled Scout.

The ARSV XM800W is shown below during its test program. Note the rotation of the front body when crossing uneven ground.

Above are side views of the ARSV XM800W at Fort Knox during its evaluation by the Armor and Engineer Board. The rotation of the front body when crossing a ditch can be seen in the view below at the left.

Details of the turret and engine deck are visible on the XM800W at the right. Below, the tracked XM800T (left) can be compared with the wheeled XM800W.

Above are the Alvis Scorpion (left) with the 90mm Cockerill Mark III gun and the Alvis Stormer (right) armed with the 25mm gun. These vehicles were evaluated during the light armored vehicle program.

THE LAV PROGRAM

The formation of the Rapid Deployment Task Force in response to developments in the Persian Gulf region during 1978-1980 established a requirement for a light armored vehicle (LAV) to equip the units which might be needed in the region. Because of both cost and time constraints, it was intended to procure an off-the-shelf vehicle to meet the new requirement.

On 15 April 1981, twenty firms, both American and foreign, were invited to submit proposals for the new LAV. By September of the same year, the number of competitors had been reduced to three and four test and evaluation contracts were awarded. The remaining contenders were the British company Alvis Limited which was teamed with Martin Marietta Aerospace, General Motors of Canada, and the Cadillac Gage Company. The latter received two contracts. Each entrant was to submit three vehicles. Two of these were to be armored personnel carriers armed with the 25mm Bushmaster gun. The third was to carry the 90mm Cockerill cannon for test purposes, although final selection of the weapon was still to be made. A Marine Corps requirement limited the weight of the LAV to 16 tons to permit the vehicles to be moved by helicopter. Except for the tracked Alvis vehicles, all of the candidates were wheeled.

Alvis submitted one Scorpion 90 armed with the 90mm Cockerill cannon and three Stormer armored personnel carriers. The Scorpion 90, manned by a crew

One of the Cadillac Gage candidates, the V150S, is at the right. This version is armed with the 90mm Cockerill gun. Note the greater distance between the side door and the front wheel compared to the V-150.

of three, had a combat weight of almost ten tons and was powered by a Perkins diesel engine providing 200 horsepower at 2,700 rpm. The maximum road speed was 45 miles per hour with a cruising range of over 500 miles.

The Stormer personnel carrier had space for eight men in addition to its three man crew. Its maximum combat weight was about 14 tons. It also was driven by a Perkins diesel giving it a maximum road speed of almost 50 miles per hour and a cruising range of about 400 miles. As an amphibious vehicle it could reach a maximum water speed of four miles per hour driven by the tracks or about six miles per hour when driven by propellers. A complete family of vehicles was proposed based on the Stormer chassis.

Cadillac Gage had two entries. The first was a stretched version of our old friend the four wheel V-150 now designated as the V-150S. The overall length and wheelbase were both extended by 18 inches increasing the space available inside the vehicle. It retained the 202 horsepower diesel engine and the automatic four speed

Above are two of the Cadillac Gage contenders. At the left is the four wheel V-150S armed with the 25mm Bushmaster gun and at the right is the six wheel V-300 mounting the 90mm low recoil force Cockerill cannon.

transmission. The combat weight of the V-150S was 12 tons and the suspension was strengthened to improve the ride characteristics. Other changes included a new transfer case for improved performance on steep grades, an improved cooling system, and a new hydraulic boost brake system with an electrohydraulic backup. A later version of this vehicle was powered by a turbocharged engine and the designation became the V-150ST.

The second Cadillac Gage entry was a new six wheel (6x6) vehicle designated as the V-300. The V-300 had a combat weight of about $14^{1}/_{2}$ tons. It was powered by a Cummins VT-504 turbocharged V8 diesel engine that produced 235 horsepower at 3,000 rpm driving the vehicle through an automatic four speed transmission. The front wheels were mounted on a beam type axle with coil springs, but the intermediate and rear wheels were independently sprung, also with coil springs. The wheels were fitted with 14.5 x 21 "run flat" combat

tires. The maximum road speed was 57 miles per hour and the amphibious vehicle could reach three miles per hour in water by the action of the tires.

General Motors of Canada submitted a version of the eight wheel Piranha. This was one of a family of 4x4, 6x6, and 8x8 vehicles which had been developed by Motorwagenfabrik AG (MOWAG) of Switzerland. All of these vehicles were designed with the driver in the left front hull alongside the engine on the right. This arrangement provided maximum space in the rear hull. The 8x8 Piranha had much in common with the six wheel Armored Vehicle General Purpose (AVGP) also manufactured under license by General Motors for Canada since 1977. The latter was produced in three types. These were the Grizzly armored personnel carrier, the Cougar fire support vehicle, and the Husky maintenance and recovery vehicle. All were part of the 6x6 Piranha family.

The General Motors of Canada eight wheel Piranha light armored vehicle can be seen below armed with 25mm gun.

Above, another view of the General Motors of Canada Piranha light armored vehicle (LAV-25) is at the left and at the right, the same type vehicle mounts the Cockerill 90mm low recoil force cannon.

The eight wheel Piranha had a combat weight of about 14 tons and was powered by a General Motors 6V53T diesel engine developing 275 horsepower at 2,800 rpm. The Allison automatic transmission had five speeds forward and one reverse. The vehicle could be operated with only the rear four or all eight wheels powered. All eight wheels were independently sprung with coil springs on the front four and torsion bars on the rear four. The wheels were fitted with 11.00 x 16 steel belted, radial, tubeless tires using Hutchinson "run-flat" inserts. Power steering was applied to the front four wheels. An aluminum trim vane stowed on the lower front hull was extended for operation in water. A 15,000 pound capacity self-recovery winch was installed in the left front hull. The maximum road speed was 60 miles per hour and it could swim at six miles per hour driven by two propellers. The cruising range on roads was about 485 miles.

After evaluation by the U. S. Marine Corps, the eight wheel Piranha was selected as the new LAV in September 1982. The initial production contract in 1982 was for 969 LAVs, most of which were intended for the Army. At that time, the Army saw the eventual need for

2,350 vehicles of the light squad carrier version armed with the .50 caliber machine gun. However, a subsequent decision substituted the high mobility multipurpose wheeled vehicle (HMMWV) for the LAV. At that time, the Army planned to use a version of the LAV armed with the 25mm M242 gun (LAV-25) as an interim mobile protected gun to provide fire support for light infantry riding in the HMMWVs. This vehicle was designated by the Army as the M1047. It was manned by a crew of three with the rear hull used for the stowage of ammunition or cargo. However, Congress canceled the funds for the LAV-25 and the Army withdrew from the program. Although the entire program was jeopardized for a time by the Army withdrawal, the Marine Corps managed to obtained funds for the procurement of 758 LAVs during Fiscal Years 1982 through 1985. This covered six types including 422 LAV-25s. The other five versions of the LAV were the command and control vehicle (LAV-C2), the mortar carrier (LAV-M), the TOW antitank vehicle (LAV-AT), the recovery vehicle (LAV-R), and the logistics vehicle (LAV-L). Work also continued on the development of an air defense vehicle (LAV-AD) and an assault gun (LAV-AG) based upon the LAV chassis.

The Army M1047 version of the LAV-25 is shown below. Note the lack of vision blocks or gun ports on the side of the hull at the rear. The power train and suspension system on the eight wheel Piranha can be seen in the drawing at the right.

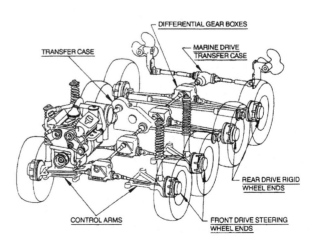

 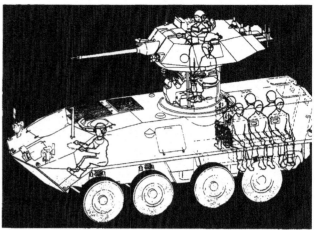

The drawings above compare the internal arrangement of the Army M1047 (left) with Marine Corps LAV-25 (right).

At the right and below are views of the early Marine Corps LAV-25. Note the vision blocks in the sides of the rear hull. The bottom photograph was taken by Michael Green.

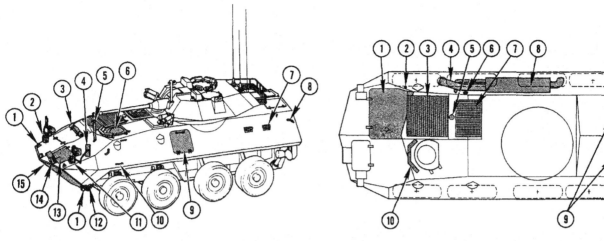

1. TOWING LUG, 2. RIGHT HEADLIGHT CLUSTER, 3. WEATHER PROTECTION GRILL COVER, 4. REAR VIEW MIRROR, 5. ATGM WIRE CUTTER, 6. DRIVER'S HATCH, 7. VISION BLOCKS, 8. LIFTING LUG, 9. EMERGENCY HATCH, 10. MOUNTING HANDLE, 11. LEFT HEADLIGHT CLUSTER, 12. TIE-DOWN LUG, 13. SELF-RECOVERY WINCH, 14. SELF-RECOVERY WINCH FAIR LEAD, 15. TRIM VANE.

1. ENGINE COVER, 2. INCENDIARY PROTECTION DRAIN, 3. AIR INLET GRILL, 4. EXHAUST PIPE AND COVER, 5. RADIATOR CAP, 6. BILGE PUMP OUTLET, 7. AIR EXHAUST GRILL, 8. MUFFLER, 9. TROOP COMPARTMENT HATCHES, 10. DRIVER'S PERISCOPES.

The external components and stowage on the Marine Corps LAV-25 are identified by the numbers above.

As its designation indicated, the LAV-25 was armed with the 25mm M242 Bushmaster and a coaxial 7.62mm M240 machine gun in a fully stabilized turret mount. Another 7.62mm machine gun was installed on a pintle mount adjacent to the vehicle commander's hatch. An M257 smoke grenade launcher was mounted on each side of the turret front. The vehicle commander and the gunner rode in the turret. The commander had seven M27 periscopes around the sides and rear of his hatch. With his sight in front, this provided 360 degree vision. The gunner had a single M27 periscope on the left side of the turret. The head of the gunner's day/night sight (thermal sight) was installed in front of his hatch. A remote display of the thermal channel was provided to the commander's video display. As in all of the Piranha vehicles, the driver was located in the left front hull alongside the engine. Three M17 periscopes provided him a field of view of about 180 degrees. For night vision, an AN/VVS-2(V)4 passive image intensifier with a 135 degree field of view could be substituted for the center M17 periscope. The space in the rear hull could accommodate six infantrymen although the Marine Corps usually reduced the number to four and referred to them as scouts. Two doors were provided in the rear of the hull as well as two hatches in the roof. For safety reasons, sensors on these hatches detected when they were open and the 25mm gun and the coaxial machine gun were prevented from firing toward the rear. However, during Operation Desert Storm, the Marines found it necessary for the scouts to be able to observe from the roof hatches to the sides and rear. As a result, they disconnected the sensors and the scouts ducked out of the way when fire was required to the rear.

An emergency hatch was located in the left side of the upper hull and two vision blocks were mounted in each side of the troop compartment. A single vision block was installed in each rear door. The hull and turret were welded assemblies of armor steel providing protection against 7.62mm ball ammunition or equivalent fragments. Applique armor could be added to increase the protection for critical areas. The vision blocks provided protection equal to the basic armor.

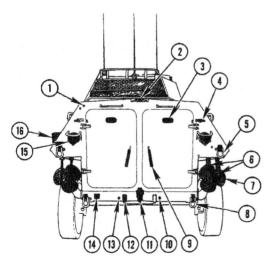

Components on the rear of the Marine Corps LAV-25 can be seen in the sketch at the left and are identified by the numbers below.

1. EXTERNAL TELEPHONE BINDING POSTS, 2. FUEL FILLER CAP, 3. VISION BLOCK, 4. REAR DOOR LATCH, 5. REAR TOWING LUG, 6. TWIN RUDDERS, 7. PROPELLER, 8. TIE-DOWN LUG, 9. REAR DOOR HANDLES, 10. EMERGENCY AIR HOSE COUPLING, 11. SWIVEL PINTLE HOOK, 12. SAFETY CHAIN LUG, 13. SERVICE AIR HOSE COUPLING, 14. INTERVEHICLE RECEPTACLE, 15. REAR LIGHT, 16. HULL ANTENNA MOUNT

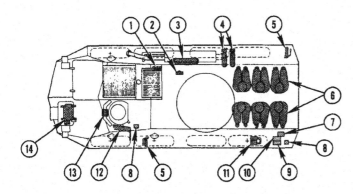

1. ELECTRIC BILGE PUMP, 2. MANUAL BILGE PUMP, 3. CREW HEATER, 4. FIXED FIRE EXTINGUISHERS, 5. PORTABLE FIRE EXTINGUISHERS, 6. SEATING, 7. AN/PRC-68 RADIO, 8. INTERCOM CONTROL BOX, 9. AN/PRC-104 RADIO, 10. TSEC/KY-65 SECURE VOICE SET, 11. PRECLEANER AND PARTICULATE FILTER ASSEMBLY, 12. INSTRUMENT PANEL, 13. DRIVER'S NIGHT PERISCOPE, 14. HYDRAULIC WINCH.

Components inside the LAV-25 are identified in the drawing above.

The controls in the driver's station in the LAV-25 are illustrated in the drawing at the right.

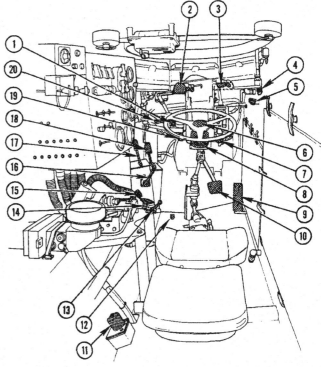

1. TURN SIGNAL, 2. MARINE DRIVE CONTROL, 3. TRIM VANE CONTROL, 4. WINCH CONTROLLER PLUG SOCKET, 5. ENGINE SHUT OFF, 6. HORN, 7. PARKING BRAKE, 8. WHEEL POSITION INDICATOR, 9. ACCELERATOR, 10. SERVICE BRAKE, 11. SLAVE RECPTACLE, 12. HEADLIGHT DIMMER, 13. EIGHT WHEEL DRIVE, 14. MASTER SWITCH, 15. HAND THROTTLE, 16. DRIVER'S SEAT CONTROL, 17. GEAR RANGE SELECTOR. 18. TRANSFER CASE GEAR LOCK, 19. TRAILER CONTROL VALVE, 20. TURN SIGNAL.

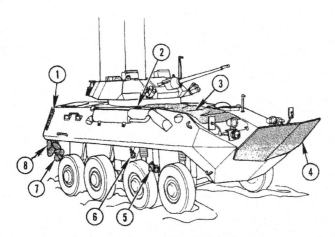

1. EMERGENCY STEERING LEVER, 2. ELECTRIC BILGE PUMP OUTLET, 3. WEATHER PROTECTION GRILL COVER, 4. TRIM VANE, 5. ELECTRIC BILGE PUMP, 6. HAND OPERATED BILGE PUMP, 7. PROPELLER, 8. RUDDERS.

The LAV-25 in the drawing at the left is configured for swimming with the weather protection grill cover in place and the trim vane extended. All of these components are identified below the sketch.

Below, the power train of the LAV-25 appears at the left and the fuel system is depicted at the right. The various components are identified in each drawing.

1. ENGINE, 2. TRANSMISSION, 3. DRIVE SHAFTS, 4. MARINE DRIVE TRANSFER CASE, 5. PROPELLER DRIVES, 6. TRANSFER CASE, 7. WHEEL DRIVE ASSEMBLIES, 8. DIFFERENTIALS

1. MECHANICAL FUEL PUMP, 2. FUEL FILTER, 3. SHUT-OFF VALVE, 4. FUEL SUPPLY LINE, 5. CHECK VALVE, 6. ELECTRIC FUEL PUMP, 7. FUEL FILLER PIPE, 8. FUEL TANK, 9. ELECTRIC FUEL PUMP, 10. FUEL RETURN LINE, 11. FUEL FILTER.

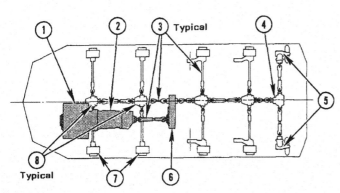

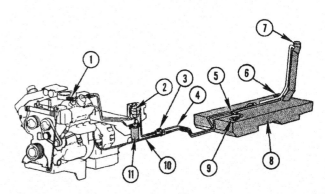

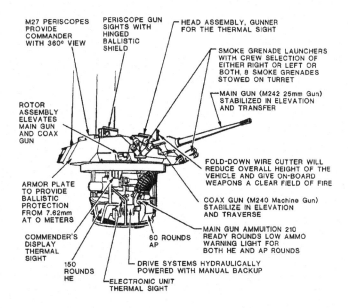

M27 PERISCOPES PROVIDE COMMANDER WITH 360° VIEW

PERISCOPE GUN SIGHTS WITH HINGED BALLISTIC SHIELD

HEAD ASSEMBLY, GUNNER FOR THE THERMAL SIGHT

SMOKE GRENADE LAUNCHERS WITH CREW SELECTION OF EITHER RIGHT OR LEFT OR BOTH, 8 SMOKE GRENADES STOWED ON TURRET

MAIN GUN (M242 25MM Gun) STABILIZED IN ELEVATION AND TRANSFER

ROTOR ASSEMBLY ELEVATES MAIN GUN AND COAX GUN

FOLD-DOWN WIRE CUTTER WILL REDUCE OVERALL HEIGHT OF THE VEHICLE AND GIVE ON-BOARD WEAPONS A CLEAR FIELD OF FIRE

ARMOR PLATE TO PROVIDE BALLISTIC PROTECTION FROM 7.62MM AT 0 METERS

COAX GUN (M240 Machine Gun) STABILIZE IN ELEVATION AND TRAVERSE

COMMENDER'S DISPLAY THERMAL SIGHT

MAIN GUN AMMUITION 210 READY ROUNDS LOW AMMO WARNING LIGHT FOR BOTH HE AND AP ROUNDS

60 ROUNDS AP

150 ROUNDS HE

DRIVE SYSTEMS HYDRAULICALLY POWERED WITH MANUAL BACKUP

ELECTRONIC UNIT THERMAL SIGHT

Turret components on the LAV-25 can be identified in the drawings above and at the top right.

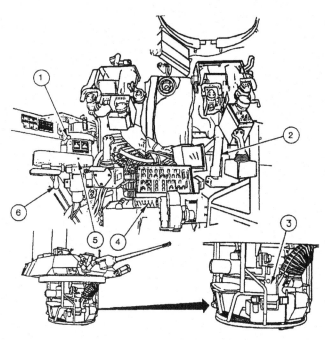

1. DRIVE SELECT LEVER, 2. ELEVATION DRIVE, 3. HYDRAULIC POWER SUPPLY, 4. ELEVATION HAND CRANK, 5. TRAVERSE DRIVE, 6. TRAVERSE HAND WHEEL.

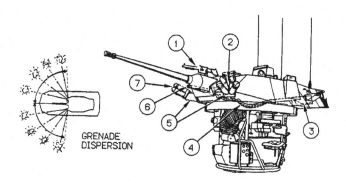

GRENADE DISPERSION

Armament details on the LAV-25 turret are shown in the drawings at the left including the dispersion pattern for the M257 smoke grenade launcher. These components are identified below.

1. M60 MACHINE GUN, 2. LEFT GRENADE LAUNCHER, 3. COAX GUN AMMO READY BOX AND FEED CHUTE, 4. COAX GUN FEED CHUTE, 5. GRENADE LAUNCHER MOUNTS, 6. M240 COAX GUN, 7. RIGHT GRENADE LAUNCHER, 8. M242 25MM CANNON, 9. 25MM AMMO READY BOX AND FEED CHUTE, 10. AP LINK EJECTION CHUTE, 11. HE LINK EJECTION CHUTE, 12. HE FEED CHUTE, 13. AP FEED CHUTE, 14. 25MM HE AMMO READY BOX AND FEED CHUTE.

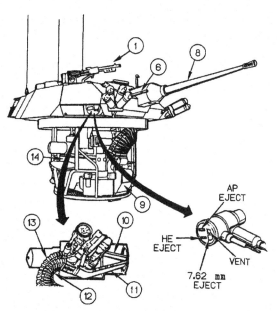

AP EJECT

HE EJECT

VENT

7.62 mm EJECT

Below are further turret details on the LVA-25.

1. DOME LIGHTS, 2. GUNNER'S M27 PERISCOPE, 3. TURRET HATCHES, 4. GRENADE STOWAGE SHELF, 5. UTILITY LIGHT, 6. COMMANDER'S M27 PERISCOPES, 7. ARMOR SHELL, 8. BUSTLE RACK, 9. M-30 LIGHTS, 10. HEAD ASSEMBLY, 11. THERMAL SIGHT

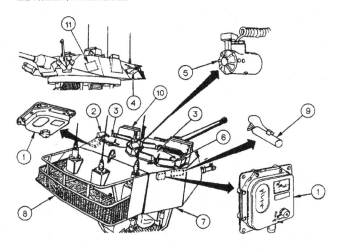

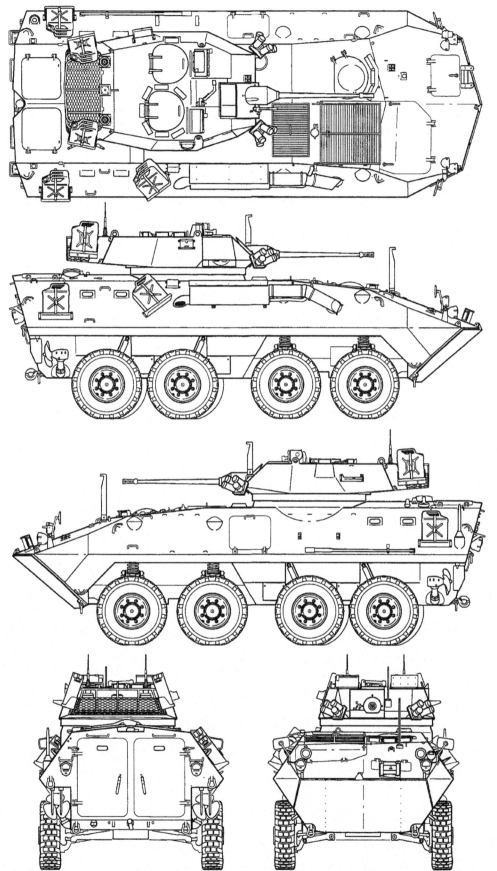

Scale 1:48

Light Armored Vehicle, 25mm Gun (LAV-25)

Above, this Marine Corps LAV-25 is parked alongside its transport aircraft. The LAV-25 below belongs to the Marine 4th Light Armored Reconnaissance Battalion at Camp Pendleton, California. This photograph and those on the three following pages were taken by Wade Barttels.

These Marine Corps LAV-25s from the 4th Light Armored Reconnaissance Battalion were photographed at Quantico, Virginia.

The LAV-25 above from the 4th Light Armored Reconnaissance Battalion is at the Marine Corps gunnery range, Quantico, Virginia. Below, this LAV-25 from the Marine 2nd Light Armored Reconnaissance Battalion appears to be stuck in the mud at Camp LeJeune.

The LAV-25 from the 4th Light Armored Reconnaissance Battalion is operating above at Camp Pendleton, California, Below, a commander's LAV-25 from the 3rd Light Armored Reconnaissance Battalion is at Fort Irwin.

The photographs above and at the bottom of the page show the Marine Corps LAV-C2 battalion command and control vehicle.

The LAV-C2 battalion command and control vehicle gave the battalion commander an armored, mobile, command post. As mentioned later, a single LAV-C2 also was assigned to each LAI company during Operation Desert Storm. The power train, suspension, and running gear were identical to those on the LAV-25. The hull was modified with a raised roof over the staff compartment to provide additional headroom. The driver remained in the left front hull with the vehicle commander just to his rear under a raised cupola. Five M17 periscopes around the front of the

cupola gave the vehicle commander a viewing range of at least 180 degrees. A mount was installed on top of the cupola for a 7.62mm machine gun for use by the vehicle commander. The battalion commander's hatch was located in the roof at the left front of the staff compartment surrounded by eight M17 periscopes providing a 360 degree view. AN/VVS-2(V)4 night vision periscopes were provided for the driver, the vehicle commander, and the battalion commander. A seat for a staff officer was at the front of the staff compartment and a vision block was installed at the

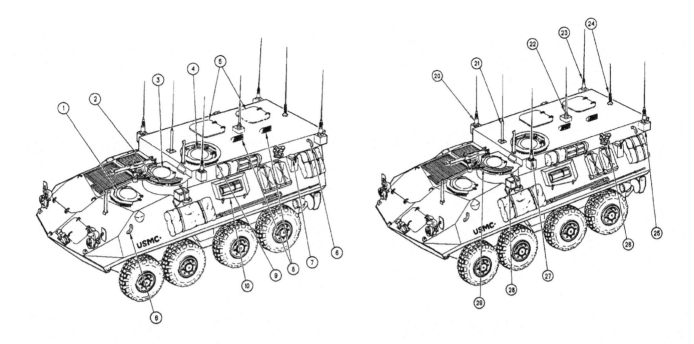

The components on the outside of the LAV-C2 are identified in the four drawings above and below.

1. DRIVER'S HATCH, 2. COMMANDER'S PERISCOPES, 3. COMMANDER'S HATCH, 4. BATTALION COMMANDER'S HATCH, 5. CREW COMPARTMENT HATCHES, 6. LIFTING LUGS, 7. FUEL FILLER CAP, 8. OPERATORS'S PERISCOPES, 9. BATTALION CAOMMANDER'S PERISCOPES. 10. DRIVER'S WINDSHIELD, 11. DOORS, LEFT AND RIGHT, 12. DOOR CATCH, 13. DOOR LATCH, 14. GAS SPRING ASSEMBLY, 15. DOOR HANDLE, EXTERIOR, 16. DOOR HANDLE, INTERIOR, 17. GAS SPRING ASSEMBLY ARM, 18. DOOR LOCK HOOK, 19. VISION BLOCK, 20. AS-3900, VHF ANTENNA, 21. AS-3588, UHF ANTENNA, 22. MP-65B, HF ANTENNA, 23. AS-3900, VHF ANTENNA, 24. AS-3449, UHF ANTENNA, 25. AS-3900, VHF ANTENNA, 26. SMOKE GRENADE LAUNCHERS, 27. AS-3900, VHF ANTENNA, 28. SMOKE GRENADE STOWAGE SHELF, 29. MACHINE GUN MOUNT.

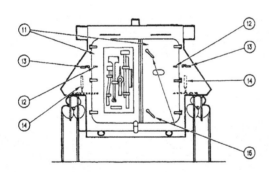

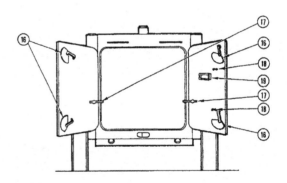

Below is a sketch of the M257 smoke grenade launcher.

front of the right side wall. Seats for three radio operators were located under two hatches in the roof. Two periscopes were in the roof for use when the hatches were closed. As many as seven radio antennas were mounted on the turret roof. Two overlapping rear doors could be opened to provide unobstructed access to the rear of the vehicle. A vision block was installed in the right door. An M257 smoke grenade launcher was mounted on each side of the hull. A total of 50 LAV-C2s were authorized during Fiscal Year 1985. Production began in January 1987 and was completed in May of the same year.

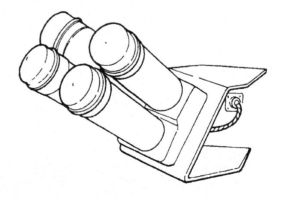

233

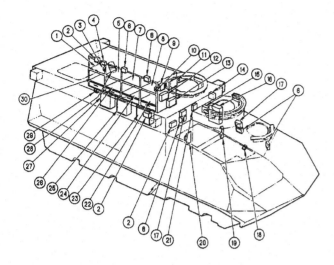

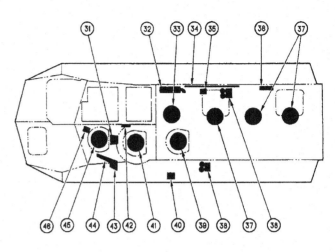

1. KY-65 SPEECH SECURITY SET, 2. C-11133/VIC-2(V) CONTROL, 3. M800R CLOCK (SLAVE CHRONOMETER), 4. SLAVE CLOCK JUNCTION BOX, 5. PLRS RADIO, RT-2343/TSQ-129 RECEIVER-TRANSMITTER, 6. C-11135/VIC-2(V) CONTROL, 7. AN/VRC-92A VHF #2 RADIO, 8. AN/VRC-83(V)2 RADIO/KY-57 SPEECH SECURITY SET, 9, MASTER CLOCK JUNCTION BOX, 10. M877 CLOCK, 11. JV-3179 DISTRIBUTION BOX, 12. AM-7162/VIC-2(V) AUDIO FREQUENCY AMPLIFER, 13. JV-2805 POWER DISTRIBUTION UNIT, 14. SLAVE RECEPTACLE (EXTERIOR), 15. BATTLE SHORT PANEL, 16. VOLTMETER AND SWITCH PANEL, 17. C-1129/VRC CONTROL MONITOR, 18. SLAVE RECEPTACLE (INTERIOR), 19. USER READOUT OF PLRS, 20. AN/PRC-68 RADIO, 21. SELECTOR SWITCH BOX, 22. AN/VRC-92A VHF #4 RADIO, 23. 28 Vdc POWER DISTRIBUTION PANEL, 24.

AN/VRC-92A VHF #3 RADIO, 25. 120 Vac SHORE POWER PANEL, 26. AN/VRC-92A VHF #1 RADIO, 27 PP-7333 AC/DC CONVERTER, 28. NBC DECONTAMINATION APPARATUS, 29, CONVENIENCE RECEPTACLE, 30 AN/GRC-213 RADIO, 31. COMMANDER'S TOE GUARD, 32. CREW HEATER, 33. STAFF OFFICER'S SEAT (STATION #4), 34. MAP BOARD, 35. RATION WARMER RECEPTACLE, 36. NBC ALARM UNIT, 37. RADIO OPERATOR'S SEATS (STATIONS #1, 2, 3), 38. NBC PRECLEANER AND PARTICULATE FILTER, 39. BATTALION COMMANDER'S SEAT (STATION #5), 40. AMMUNITION RACK, 41. COMMANDER'S SEAT (STATION #6), 42. SMOKE GRENADE LAUNCHER CONTROL BOX, 43. CIRCUIT BREAKER PANEL, 44. INSTRUMENT PANEL, 45. DRIVER'S SEAT (STATION #7), 46. NBC CONTROL BOX, 47. VISION BLOCK, 48. DOME LIGHTS.

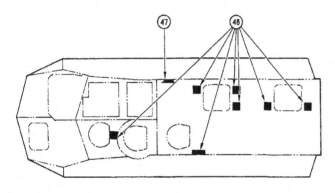

The general arrangement and location of major components inside the LAV-C2 can be seen in the drawings above and at the left.

Below, components of the electrical system are identified at the left and the various parts of the fuel system are shown at the right.

1. ALTERNATOR, 2. STARTER MOTOR, 3. SHORE POWER BOX. 4. CONVENIENCE RECEPTACLE, 5. PP-7333 AC/DC CONVERTER, 6. 120Vac SHOREPOWER PANEL, 7. 28Vdc POWER DISTRIBUTION PANEL, 8. VEHICLE BATTERY, 9. BATTLESHORT PANEL, 10. VOLTMETER AND SWITCHING PANEL, 11. SLAVE RECEPTACLE (EXTERIOR), 12. SLAVE RECEPTACLE (INTERIOR), 13, CIRCUIT BREAKER PANEL, 14. INSTRUMENT PANEL, 15. MASTER SWITCH.

1. MECHANICAL FUEL PUMP, 2 FUEL FILTER, 3. SHUT-OFF VALVE, 4. FUEL SUPPLY LINE, 5. CHECK VALVE, 6. ELECTRIC FUEL PUMP, 7. FUEL FILLER PIPE, 8. ELECTRIC FUEL PUMP, 9. FUEL TANK, 10. FUEL FILTER, 11. FUEL RETURN LINE.

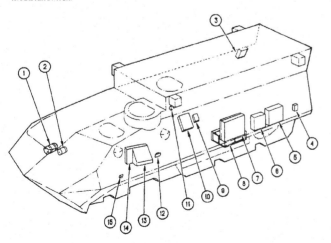

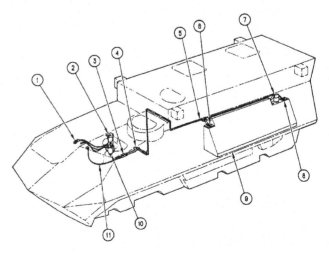

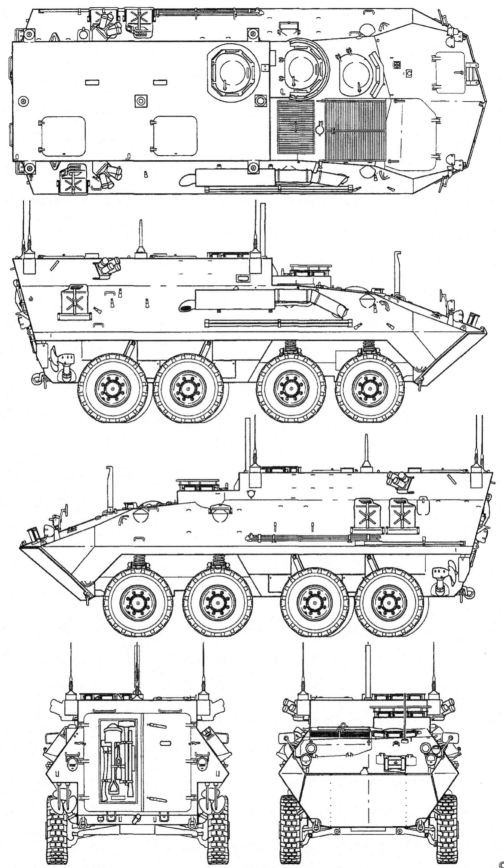

Scale 1:48

Light Armored Vehicle, Command and Control (LAV-C2)

The Marine Corps LAV-M 81mm mortar carrier appears above with the roof hatch closed (left) and open (right). An additional view with the hatch open appears below at the right.

The LAV-M was armed with an 81mm M252 mortar installed in the center of the vehicle. A three section hatch in the hull roof opened to allow the mortar to fire. The center section of the hatch folded over the right hand section and then both folded back to the right. The left section folded to the left. The LAV-M was manned by a crew of five including the driver and the vehicle commander. The driver occupied his usual position in the left front hull with the vehicle commander to his immediate rear under a raised cupola. The commander's cupola was fitted with eight M17 periscopes providing a 360 degree view. A 7.62mm machine gun was mounted on the commander's cupola. The three man mortar crew had a folding troop seat on the right side of the rear compartment. Mortar ammunition was stowed on the left side opposite the troop seat. Space was available for 90 81mm rounds

with a normal mix of 13 illuminating, 9 smoke, and 68 high explosive. A side mounted fuel tank was installed on the left side of the hull. Two doors opened out from the hull rear and the right door was fitted with a vision block. An M257 smoke grenade launcher was installed on each side of the vehicle.

The interior of the LAV-M can be seen in the drawing below.

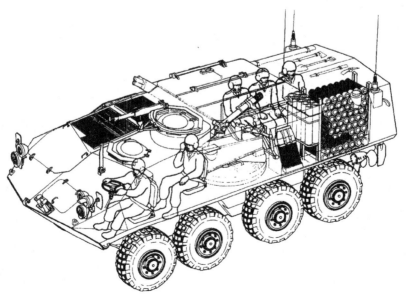

236

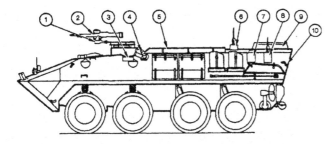

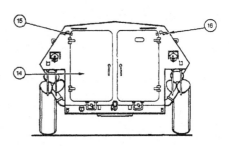

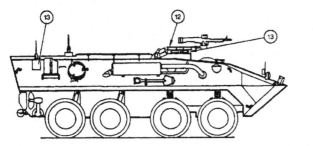

1. M60E3 MACHINE GUN MOUNT, 2. M60E3 MACHINE GUN, 3. SMOKE GRENADE STOWAGE SHELF, 4. SMOKE GRENADE LAUNCHERS, 5. ROOF HATCH, 6. ANTENNA, 7. FUEL FILLER CAP, 8. ANTENNA, 9. DRIVER'S WINDSHIELD, 10. LIFTING LUGS, 11. COMMANDER'S PERISCOPES, 12. COMMANDER'S HATCH, 13. ANTENNA, 14. REAR DOORS, 15. REAR DOOR CATCH, 16. REAR DOOR LATCH.

The exterior components on the LAV-M are identified in the sketches at the left and above.

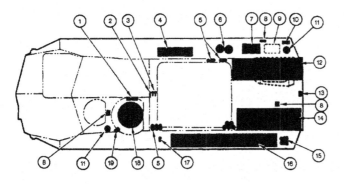

The interior components of the LAV-M are identified in the drawing at the left.

1. SMOKE GRENADE LAUNCHER CONTROL BOX, 2. PORTABLE RADIO BRACKET, 3. NIGHT VISION PERISCOPES, 4. HEATER, 5. RIFLE STORAGE, 6. FIXED FIRE EXTINGUISHER, 7. TOOLKIT BOX, 8. DOME LIGHT, 9. STOWAGE AREA, 10. NBC DECONTAMINATION APPARATUS ALARM, 11. PORTABLE FIRE EXTINGUISHER, 12. TROOP SEAT, 13. LOUDSPEAKER, 14. AMMUNITION RACK, 15. NBC DECONTAMINATION APPARATUS ABC M11, 16. FUEL TANK, 17. RECEPTACLE, RATION WARMER, 18. COMMANDER'S STATION, 19. PLRS USER READ OUT.

Originally, the LAV-M was intended to be armed with either the 81mm mortar or a 107mm (4.2 inch M30) mortar. Mounts were designed for both types. The 81mm mount could be traversed 360 degrees, but the mount for the 107mm mortar was limited by stops. Later, successful firing tests were performed using a 120mm mortar.

A total of 50 LAV-Ms were purchased during Fiscal Year 1985. Production began in September 1985 and was completed in December 1986.

Various parts of the 81mm mortar are identified in the drawing below and components of the turntable and mount for the 107mm mortar and the 81mm mortar can be seen at the bottom left..

1. MORTAR TURNTABLE, 2. MORTAR CANNON, 3. TIE DOWN STRAP, 4. TURNTABLE LOCK HANDLE, 5. TRAVERSING STRAPS, 6. BIPOD ASSEMBLY, 7. MORTAR TUBE SOCKET, 8. GROUND BASEPLATE, 9. GROUND BIPOD ASSEMBLY

MORTAR MOUNT SOCKET
TURNTABLE BRIDGE
TURNTABLE ASSEMBLY
81-MM MORTAR BIPOD ASSEMBLY
RECOIL BUFFER ASSEMBLY
TRAVERSING HANDWHEEL ASSEMBLY
BIPOD YOKE
LEVELING MECHANISM
MORTAR ELEVATION ASSEMBLY
BIPOD ASSEMBLY
STOWAGE BRACKET
SOCKET GROUP
ANGLE BRACKET
MORTAR SUPPORT AND LATCH GROUP
TURNTABLE
MORTAR MOUNT

107-MM MORTAR TURNTABLE AND MOUNT

81-MM MORTAR TURNTABLE AND MOUNT

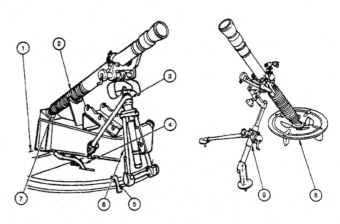

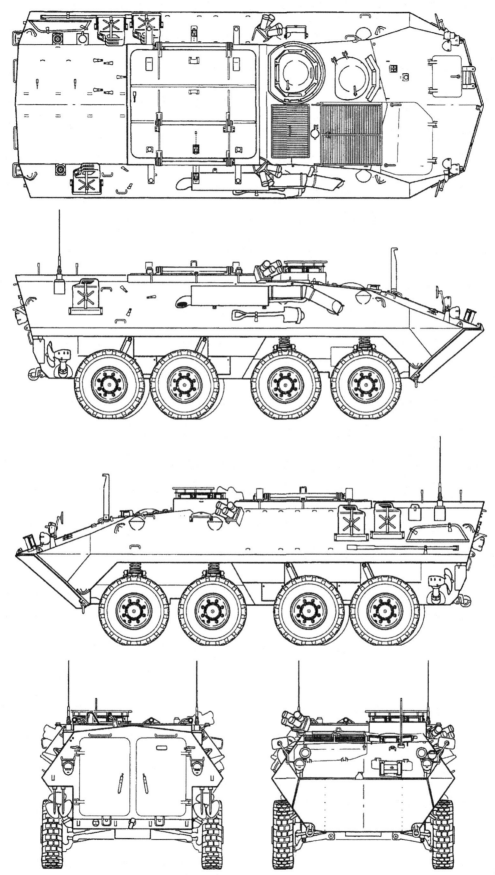

© M. Duplessis

Light Armored Vehicle, Mortar (LAV-M)

The Marine Corps LAV-AT TOW missile carrier is shown in the two photographs above with the missile launcher stowed in the travel position.

The LAV-AT mounted the two tube Emerson TOW missile launcher turret as used on the improved TOW vehicle. It carried a four man crew consisting of the driver, the commander, the gunner and the loader. The gunner rode in the turret and the loader in the rear hull. A hatch in the rear deck allowed the loader to reload the missile launcher with partial protection. Three M17 periscopes were provided for the driver and eight for the commander. Each also had an AN/VVS-2(V)4 night vision periscope. In addition to the sighting equipment,

seven vision blocks in the turret provided the gunner a 280 degree field of view. Two TOW missiles could be carried in the launcher and 14 additional missiles could be stowed in the hull. A 7.62mm machine gun was mounted on the commander's cupola. An M257 smoke grenade launcher was installed on each side of the hull roof just in front of the turret.

Procurement of the LAV-AT totaled 96 vehicles, all during Fiscal Year 1985. These vehicles were built between January and June 1987

The installation of the LAV-AT turret onto the automotive hull is illustrated in the drawing below. At the right is a rear view of the LAV-AT with the doors open.

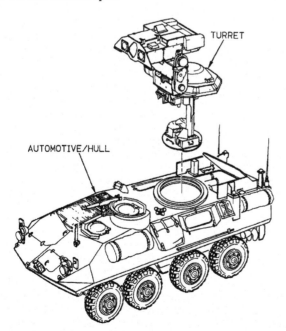

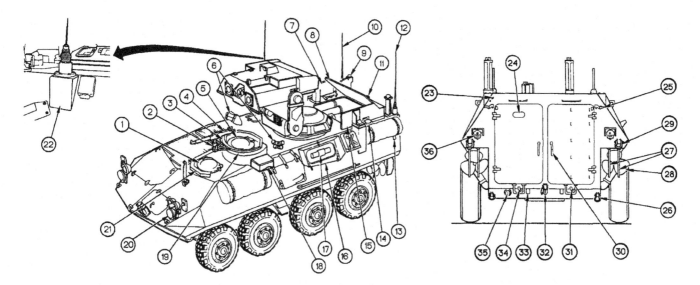

HEADLIGHT ASSEMBLY, 21. DRIVER'S PERISCOPES, 22. HULL ANTENNA MOUNT, 23. EXTERNAL TELEPHONE BINDING POSTS, 24. VISION BLOCK, 25. REAR DOOR EXTERIOR LATCH, 26. TIE DOWN LUG, 27. TWIN RUDDERS, 28. PROPELLER, 29. REAR TOWING LUG, 30. REAR DOOR HANDLES, 31. EMERGENCY AIR HOSE COUPLING, 32. TOWING PINTLE HOOK, 33. SAFETY CHAIN LUG, 34. SERVICE AIR HOSE COUPLING, 35. INTERVEHICLE RECEPTACLE, 36. REAR LIGHT.

1. DRIVER'S HATCH, 2. M60E3 MACHINE GUN PINTLE MOUNT, 3. M60E3 MACHINE GUN MOUNT, 4. M60E3 MACHINE GUN, 5. COMMANDER'S HATCH, 6. SMOKE GRENADE LAUNCHERS, 7. BALLISTIC SHIELD, 8. CARGO HATCH, 9. LAUNCHER SUPPORT, 10. ANTENNA, 11. CARGO HATCH EXTERIOR LATCH, 12. ANTENNA, 13. LIFTING LUG, 14. FUEL FILLER CAP, 15. BALLISTIC SHIELD, 16. DRIVER'S WINDSHIELD, 17. ENGINE GRILL COVER, 18. SMOKE GRENADE STOWAGE SHELF, 19. COMMANDER'S PERISCOPES, 20.

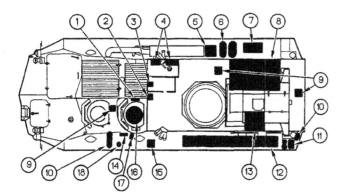

Components and stowage on the LAV-AT are identified in these three drawings.

1. SMOKE GRENADE LAUNCHER CONTROL BOX, 2. PORTABLE RADIO BRACKET, 3. DECONTAMINATION APPARATUS ALARM, NBC, 4. NIGHT VISION PERISCOPES, 5. TOOL KIT BOX, 6. FIXED FIRE EXTINGUISHERS, 7. STORAGE AREA, 8. MISSILE STOWAGE RACKS, 9 DOME LIGHT, 10. PORTABLE FIRE EXTINGUISHERS, 11. NBC DECONTAMINATION APPARATUS, ABE M11, 12. FUEL TANK, 13. LOADER'S STATION, 14. RADIO MOUNT MT 6352/VRC, 15. RECEPTACLE, 16. COMMANDER'S STATION, 17. PLRS USER READ OUT, 18. MOUNT FOR AM-7162 AMPLIFIER.

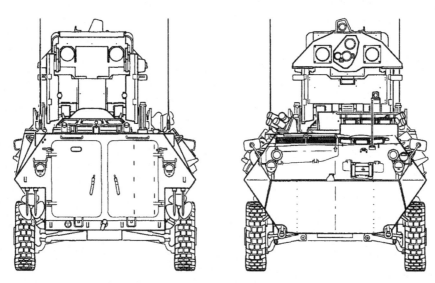

Scale 1:48

© M. Duplessis

Light Armored Vehicle, Antitank (LAV-AT)

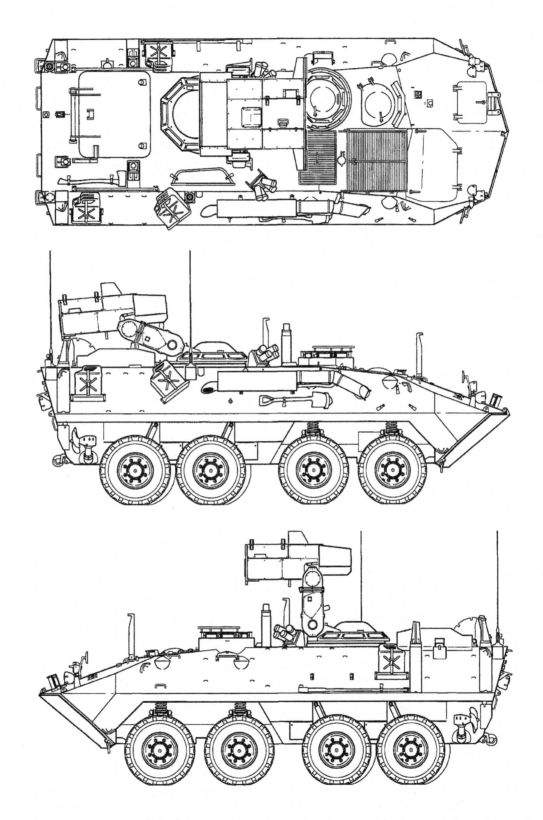

© M. Duplessis

Light Armored Vehicle, Antitank (LAV-AT)

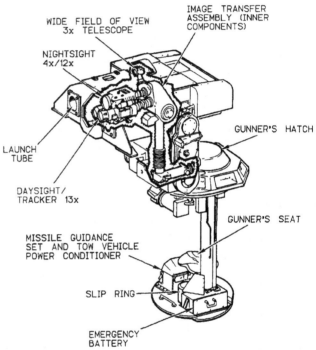

WIDE FIELD OF VIEW
3x TELESCOPE

IMAGE TRANSFER
ASSEMBLY (INNER
COMPONENTS)

NIGHTSIGHT
4x/12x

GUNNER'S HATCH

LAUNCH
TUBE

DAYSIGHT/
TRACKER 13x

GUNNER'S SEAT

MISSILE GUIDANCE
SET AND TOW VEHICLE
POWER CONDITIONER

SLIP RING

EMERGENCY
BATTERY

The photographs above from Michael Green show the LAV-AT in service with the Marines. A little maintenance is being performed. The drawing at the right identifies the various components on the turret and the TOW missile launcher. Below, the TOW missile can be seen in flight after being fired from the LAV-AT.

The LAV-AT has the missile launcher raised in the firing position in the views above and at the left below. The vehicle commander and the driver can be seen at the bottom right. These photographs were from Greg Stewart.

The LAV-R appears in the two photographs above with the crane stowed in the travel position. The spades can be seen stowed on the rear of the vehicle.

The LAV-R was fitted with a rotating hydraulic crane capable of lifting a 6,600 pound maximum load and a rear mounted winch with a maximum pull capacity of 30,000 pounds. It was manned by a crew of three consisting of the driver, the commander, and a rigger. Space was available for two additional men to be carried. A workbench and interior lights permitted on site repairs. A welding generator and equipment were carried inside the LAV-R. The vehicle was fitted with spades for winching operations. Outriggers and stabilizers were provided to stabilize the LAV-R when using the crane. Two offset overlapping doors allowed unobstructed access to the rear of the vehicle. Armament consisted of a single 7.62mm machine gun on the commander's cupola and the M257 smoke grenade launchers mounted on each side of the roof.

A total of 46 LAV-Rs were authorized during Fiscal Years 1984 and 1985. Production began in May 1986 and was completed in June 1987.

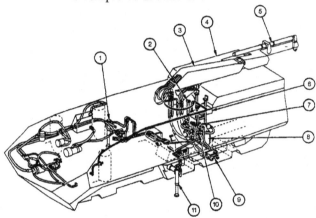

1. RIGHT OUTRIGGER, 2. FAST IDLE CONTROL, 3. INNER BOOM, 4. OUTER BOOM, 5. EXTENSION, 6. RIGGER'S PANEL, 7.CRANE CONTROL VALVE, 8. MAIN ELECTRIC BOX, 9. REAR HYDRAULIC MANIFOLD, 10. EMERGENCY LOWERING VALVES, 11. LEFT OUTRIGGER.

The 6600 pound capacity crane and its hydraulic system are sketched above at the right and the various components are identified. Below, the location and identification of major components are shown on the exterior (left) and interior (right) of the hull.

1. M60E3 MACHINE GUN MOUNT, 2. COMMANDER'S HATCH, 3. CRANE, 4. SMOKE GRENADE LAUNCHERS, 5. DRIVER'S WINDSHIELD, 6. FUEL FILLER CAP, 7. SPADES, 8. LOUDSPEAKERS, 9. STABILIZERS, 10. LIFTING LUG, 11. REAR DOORS, 12. ANTENNA, 13. FLOODLIGHTS, 14. OUTRIGGERS, 15. SMOKE GRENADE STOWAGE SHELF, 16. COMMANDER'S PERISCOPES.

1. FIXED FIRE EXTINGUISHER, 2. DOME LIGHTS, 3. RIGGER'S STATION, 4. BRACKET FOR PLRS MOUNT, 5. FUEL TANK, 6. DECONTAMINATION APPARATUS ALARM, 7. PLRS USER READOUT, 8. SMOKE GRENADE LAUNCHER CONTROL BOX, 9. COMMANDER'S STATION, 10. AN/PRC-68 RADIO BRACKET, 11. PORTABLE FIRE EXTINGUISHERS, 12. STOWAGE AREA, 13. RADIO BRACKET, MT-6353 VRC/MT-632 VRC MOUNT, 14. NIGHT VISION PERISCOPES, 15. TOOL BOX, 16. RECEPTACLE FOR RATION WARMER, 17. STOWAGE AREA, 18. DECONTAMINATION APPARATUS, ABC-M 11.

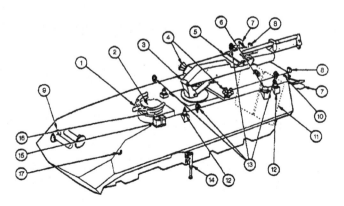 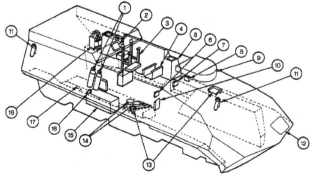

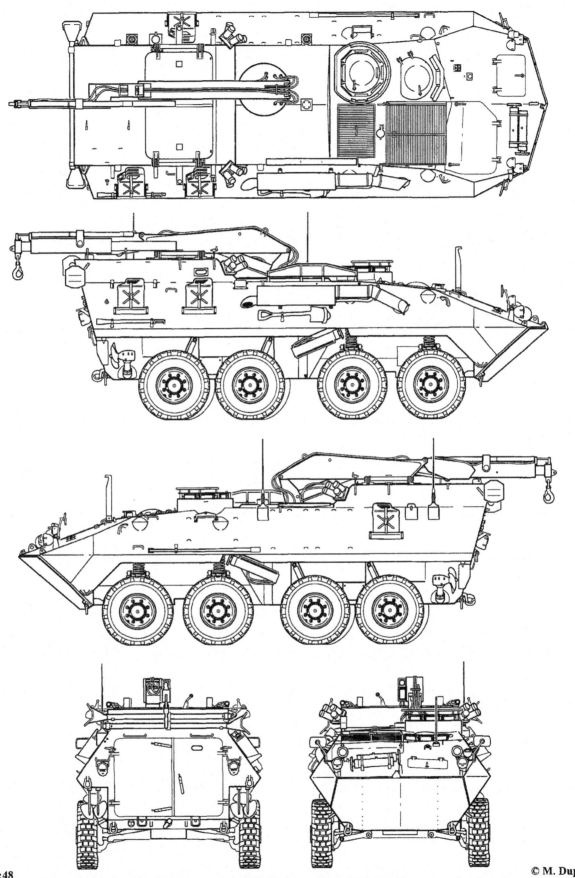

Scale 1:48

Light Armored Vehicle, Recovery (LAV-R)

The late production LAV-L above can be compared with the early vehicle at the right. Note the sloped front on the raised section on the early vehicle.

The roof of the LAV-L was raised to increase the stowage space inside the hull and a single roof hatch was provided measuring 54.3 x 64.9 inches. Access to the rear hull was through two overlapping doors through which pallets could be moved. The three man crew consisted of the driver, the commander, and an additional crew member to handle the cargo. The driver and commander were in their usual positions in the left front hull. The third crew member had a stowable seat in the left front of the cargo compartment. A 1 ton capacity hand chain hoist was stowed in a box on the hull roof. For use it was mounted at the left rear corner of the roof. A folding platform for the hoist operator was stowed on the side at the left rear. The maximum payload for the LAV-L was 4,000 pounds of cargo plus 1,440 pounds for arms and ammunition. Armament consisted of a single 7.62mm machine gun on the commander's cupola and the M257 smoke grenade launchers on each side at the front of the raised roof section.

A total of 94 LAV-Ls were procured during Fiscal Years 1984 and 1985. Production began in November 1985 and was completed in August 1986.

At the right is another view from Greg Stewart of the late production LAV-L

Above, the late production LAV-L is at the left and the early version is at the right. The driver's windshield is raised in the latter view.

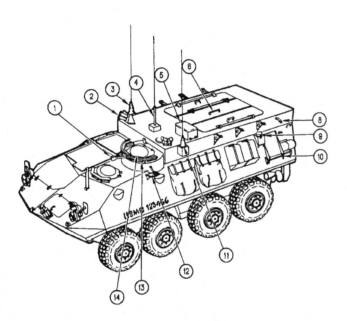

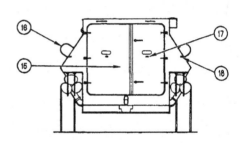

1. M240E1 MACHINE GUN, MOUNT, 2. SMOKE GRENADE LAUNCHERS, 3. VHF ANTENNA, 4. PLRS ANTENNA, 5. HAND CHAIN HOIST STOWAGE BOX, 6. CARGO COMPARTMENT ROOF HATCH, 8. LIFTING LUG, 9. FUEL FILLER CAP, 10. HOIST OPERATOR'S PLATFORM, 11. VHF ANTENNA, 12. SMOKE GRENADE STOWAGE SHELF, 13. COMMANDER'' PERISCOPES, 14. COMMANDER'S HATCH, 15. REAR DOORS, 16. REAR LIGHT, 17. REAR DOOR CATCH, 18. REAR DOOR LATCH.

Components and exterior stowage on the LAV-L can be seen in the two upper drawings. The machine gun is not shown mounted at the commander's hatch. The location of items inside the vehicle is illustrated in the sketch at the lower right.

1. SMOKE GRENADE LAUNCHER CONTROL BOX, 2. PORTABLE RADIO BRACKET, 3. DECONTAMINATION APPARATUS ALARM, 4. DRIVER'S WINDSHIELD, 5. NIGHT VISION PERISCOPES, 6. FIXED FIRE EXTINGUISHER, 7. TOOL KIT BOX, 8. STWOAGE AREA FOR RATION WARMER, 9. PORTABLE FIRE EXTINGUISHER, 10. DOME LIGHT, 11. DECONTAMINATION APPARATUS, ABC M11, 12. FUEL TANK, 13. PROTECTIVE BARRIER, LOCATION FOR 3 M16 RIFLES, 14. RATION WARMER RECEPTACLE, 15. CREW'S STATION, 16. COMMANDER'S STATION, 17. PLRS USER READ OUT.

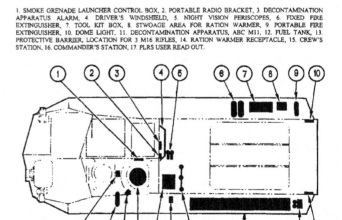

247

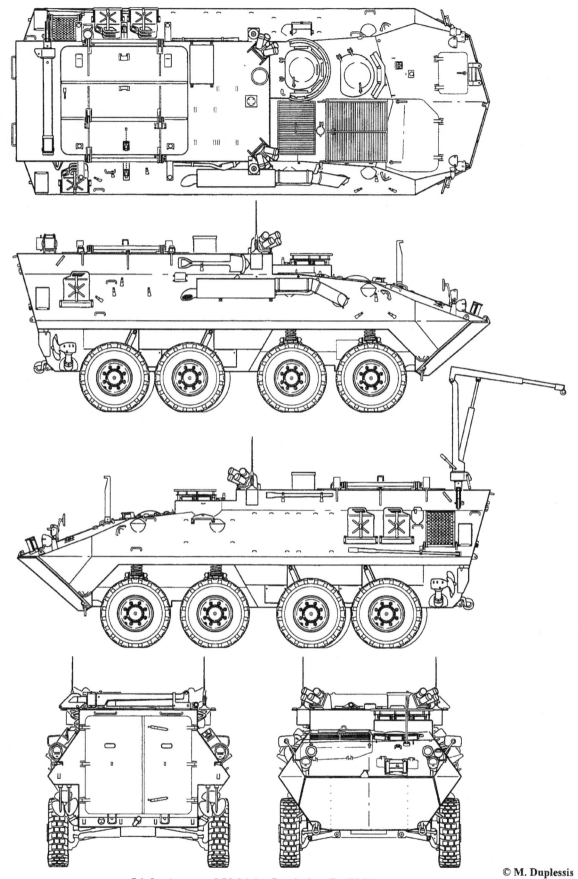

© M. Duplessis

Light Armored Vehicle, Logistics (LAV-L)

248

The three photographs on this page show the MEWSS with slightly different antenna configurations. Below at the right, one of the prototype vehicles has its antenna mast fully extended.

Two prototypes of the mobile electronic warfare support system (MEWSS) were delivered by General Motors of Canada to the Marine Corps in 1986. After tests, a production order for 12 vehicles was placed during 1987 and delivery was complete in early 1989. The configuration of this LAV was similar to that of the LAV-C2 with two hatches in a raised roof. Manned by a crew of four, the MEWSS was type classified as the AN/MLQ-36. It was equipped with the Racal AN/VLQ-19 communications jammer and radios, the AN/PRD-10 radio direction finders and the WJ-8618B radio receiver.

249

These LAV-25s from the Marine Corps 2nd LAI battalion are in Panama prior to Operation Just Cause. The top photograph was dated 14 May 1989. The bottom view shows a column from D Company, 2nd LAI Battalion being blocked in La Chorrera by supporters of Manuel Noriega during Operation Chisum on 31 October 1989.

The initial concept of the Marine LAV battalion envisioned that its equipment would include assault gun and air defense versions of the LAV in addition to the six variants previously described. However, delays in the development of the LAV-AG and the LAV-AD required that the battalion organization be modified. Also, the name was changed in the late 1980s to the light armored infantry (LAI) battalion. Among the changes reflected by the new name was the permanent assignment to the battalion of the infantry scout teams.

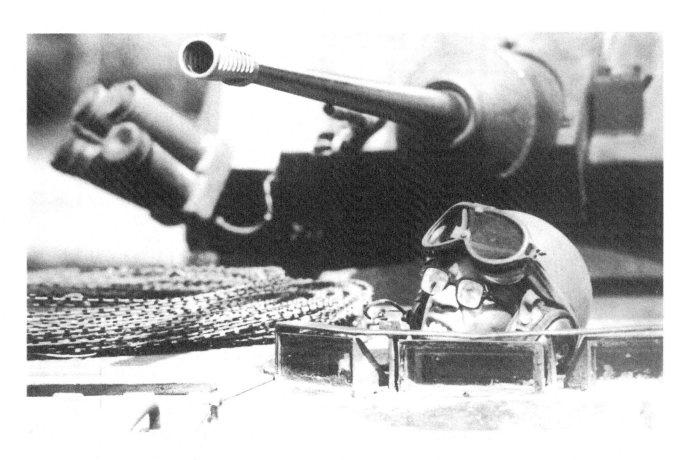

These LAV-25s from D Company, 2nd LAI Battalion in Panama. The upper view, taken during Operation Chisum, was dated 31 October 1989. The lower photograph shows the vehicles on a route reconnaissance patrol during Operation Rough Rider on 22 November 1989.

Both photographs above show the Marine Corps LAV-25s in Panama during Operation Just Cause.

Prior to this time, the infantry component was borrowed from other units. It was this new organization that the Marine Corps took into action in Panama during December 1989 and in the Persian Gulf during 1990-91.

The LAI battalion consisted of a headquarters, four LAV companies, and a weapons company. The LAV company had two or three LAV platoons and a company headquarters. The LAV platoon contained two or three sections each equipped with two LAV-25s. The company headquarters had one additional LAV-25 for use by the commanding officer. Usually, this brought the company total to 13 LAV-25s. An LAV-C2 was provided for the company executive officer. One LAV-R and two LAV-Ls were included in the company headquarters. During operations, LAV-ATs and LAV-Ms were attached from the battalion weapons company.

Below, a Marine Corps LAV-25 and a HMMWV armed with a TOW missile launcher approach the beach in a landing craft at Vieques, Puerto Rico on 30 January 1990.

Above at the left, this Marine Corps LAV-25 from the 2nd LAI Battalion is coming ashore at Vieques, Puerto Rico on 30 January 1990. At the top right, these LAVs are ready to debark from an LCAC. The latter photograph was dated May 1990. The Lav-25 below at the right is operating in desert terrain.

The role of the Marine Corps LAI battalions during Operation Desert Storm was to provide reconnaissance and a screen for the heavy forces. Subsequently, this mission was recognized by another name change. They now became light armored reconnaissance (LAR) battalions.

In addition to the Marine Corps LAVs, the Army employed one LAV platoon during Desert Storm. This was the scout platoon of the 3/73rd Armor in the 82nd Airborne Division. Equipped with 14 LAV-25s and one LAV-R borrowed from the Marine Corps, they were extremely effective while operating with the Sheridan light tanks of the 3/73rd.

Below are the LAV-25s assigned to the Scout Platoon of the 3/73rd Armor in the 82nd Airborne Division. These vehicles, obtained from the Marine Corps, are operating in Saudi Arabia during Operation Desert Shield.

253

These Marine Corps LAV-25s are training in Saudi Arabia during Operation Desert Shield.

Above, the Marine Corps LAV-25s are becoming familiar with desert conditions in Saudi Arabia in preparation for Operation Desert Storm. Below, this LAV-25 demonstrates its agility in moving at high speed over rough terrain.

Marine Corps LAV-25s are shown in these views during training operations.

These Marines are training in wooded terrain with their LAV-25s.

The reason for the weight limitation on the lAV-25 is illustrated in these photographs. In the view below, the helicopters are being refueled while carrying the LAV-25s.

Above, this LAV-25 is back training in the desert. Below, one of the vehicles is entering the water. The extended trim vane is clearly visible in this photograph.

Above, the prototype LAV-AD produced by FMC (left) can be compared with the candidate built by General Electric (right). Note the two seven tube Hydra 70 rocket launchers on the FMC vehicle.

In December 1987, contracts were awarded to FMC Corporation and the General Electric Company to build prototypes for an air defense vehicle based upon the LAV. Each company was to build two vehicles. The contracts required that the new LAV-AD be armed with a 25mm gun, a quadruple launcher for the Stinger missile, and a seven tube launcher for 70mm Hydra 70 unguided rockets. Each company delivered one prototype for testing in May 1990 with the remaining vehicle to follow in August. The FMC prototype, named Guardian, was armed with a high rate of fire (500 rounds/minute) version of the 25mm Bushmaster gun. The four missile Stinger launcher was installed on the left side of the turret and two seven tube Hydra 70 rocket launchers were mounted on top. The air defense turret on the General Electric vehicle was a modified version of their Blazer turret and it retained that name. It

was armed with a 25mm GAU12, five barrel, Gatling type gun installed between the two halves of the cleft turret. The quadruple Stinger missile launcher was mounted at the top center above the gun and a single seven tube Hydra 70 rocket launcher was attached to the right side of the turret. The test program indicated that the Hydra 70 rockets were ineffective in this application and they were replaced on both prototypes with a second quadruple Stinger missile launcher. After further evaluation, the General Electric Blazer was selected as the winner. General Dynamics received the contract to assemble the LAV-ADs. Although a production run of 125 vehicles was originally planned, it was subsequently reduced to 17 with the last LAV-AD delivered in late 1998. Later versions of the basic Piranha vehicle had been developed by this time and the LAV-AD was the last of the 8x8 Piranha I vehicles to be produced.

Below, the FMC LAV-AD prototype at the left has just fired a Stinger missile. The General Electric LAV-AD prototype at the bottom right is moving at speed.

The production version of the LAV-AD appears above armed with the two quadruple Stinger launchers and the 25mm GAU-12 five barrel gun. Details of the Blazer turret can be seen in the drawing below.

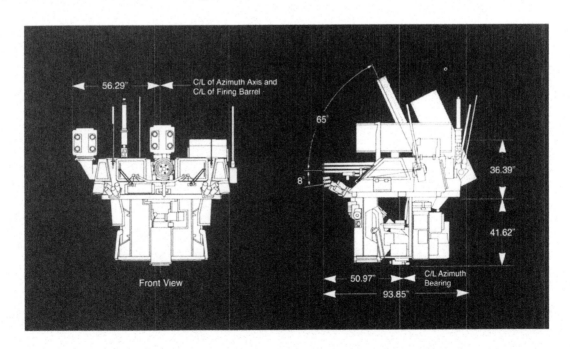

These photographs show details of a new fully stowed LAV-AD

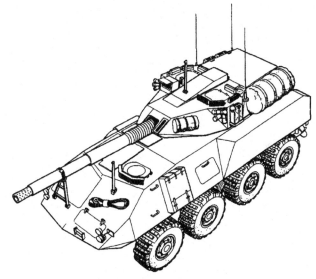

Above are views of the LAV-105 and a drawing of the vehicle appears at the right. The 105mm ammunition in the Fairey automatic loader can be seen through the open door in the turret bustle at the top left.

As described earlier, the original LAV requirement included an assault gun and each of the original competitors submitted a vehicle armed with the low recoil force Cockerill 90mm gun. At that time, no decision had been made on what weapon would be selected. Other armament candidates included the Israeli Military Industries 60mm hypervelocity gun, the Ares XM274 75mm gun, the Mecar low recoil force 90mm gun, and a low recoil force version of the 105mm gun M68. These weapons were evaluated at Aberdeen Proving Ground during 1983 and early 1984. All were rejected for various reasons. The ballistic performance of the 105mm gun M68 was satisfactory, but the recoil force limited it to firing within a 60 degree frontal arc. During emergency battle conditions, it could be fired within a 90 degree frontal arc.

In 1987, General Motors installed the new low recoil force 105mm gun EX35 on an LAV chassis. After promising test results, Cadillac Gage Textron received a contract in June 1990 to provide three LAV-105s to the Marine Corps for testing. The LAV-105 was fitted with a new two man turret mounting the 105mm EX35 gun with a Fairey automatic loader. Unfortunately, lack of funds canceled the project in 1991. However, it was revived in 1993 and exceeded the Marine Corps requirements during firing tests both while stationary and moving, but there was no production contract.

Dimensions of the 105mm turret with the automatic loader are shown on the drawing at the right.

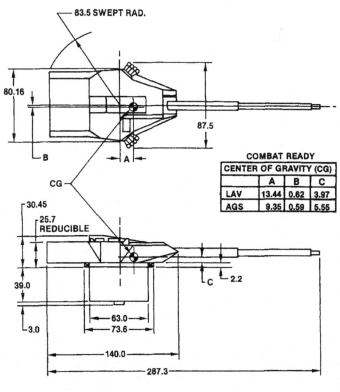

COMBAT READY			
CENTER OF GRAVITY (CG)			
	A	B	C
LAV	13.44	0.62	3.97
AGS	9.35	0.59	5.55

263

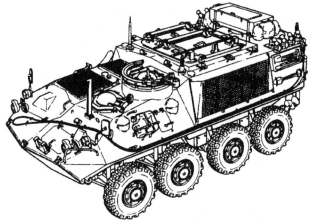

A photograph and a drawing of the Bison armored personnel carrier are shown above. Below at the right is the Bison command post vehicle and at the bottom of the page, the Bison 81mm mortar carrier appears at the left and the Bison mobile team repair vehicle is at the right.

A modified version of the 8x8 LAV, designed and built by General Motors of Canada, was submitted for evaluation by the Canadian Armed Forces in 1988. After tests of the prototype and minor modifications, a production order for 199 of the new vehicles, now named the Bison, was received in July 1989. This order consisted of 149 infantry section carriers, 18 command post vehicles, 16 81mm mortar fire support vehicles, and 16 mobile repair team vehicles. In 1999, 12 of the Bison vehicles were procured for the U. S. Army National Guard.

In the Bison, the driver remained in his usual location in the left front hull just forward of the vehicle commander. There was no turret, but a 7.62mm machine gun could be mounted on the commander's cupola. The roof of the troop compartment was raised and fitted with one large hatch and two small rear roof hatches. A power operated ramp that opened the complete rear of the vehicle replaced the two doors on the earlier LAV-25. A single door with a vision block was installed in the ramp. Like the earlier LAVs, the Bison was fully amphibious driven by two propellers at the rear. The mobile repair team vehicle was fitted with same crane installed on the earlier Husky 6x6 recovery vehicle.

The Canadian LAV-25 Coyote reconnaissance vehicle is above. At the top right, the various sensors have been removed and mounted on two tripods. Further details and the interior arrangement of the Coyote can be seen in the drawing at the bottom of the page.

Another version of the LAV adopted by Canada was the reconnaissance vehicle designated as the LAV-25 Coyote. In 1993 a contract was awarded to General Motors of Canada for the production of 203 vehicles and the first four were delivered in January 1996. The configuration of the Coyote was similar to the U. S. Marine Corps LAV-25, but the vehicle was not amphibious. The driver was in the left front hull and it carried a turret armed with the M242 25mm gun and a 7.62mm coaxial machine gun. The commander and gunner rode in the turret on the right and left respectively. The turret was powered by an all electric drive compared to the electric-hydraulic drive in the original LAV-25. The surveillance operator was seated on the left side of the rear compartment with the display equipment on the right. Two rear roof hatches opened to the left and right and two doors with vision blocks were in the rear. The LAV-25 reconnaissance vehicle was equipped with either the fixed brigade kit which included an extendible sensor mast in the rear compartment or the battle group kit equipped with man portable dismounted sensors.

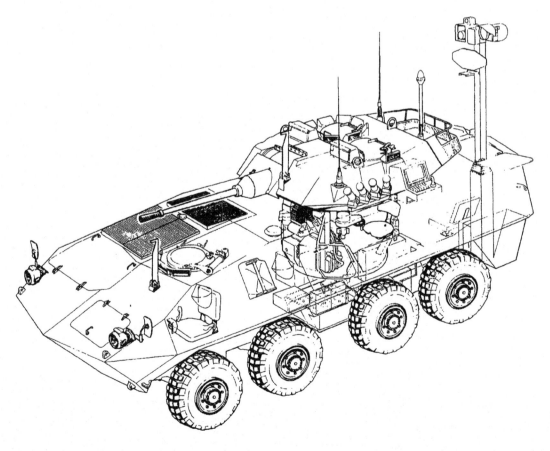

At the right is a rear view of the production Bison armored personnel carrier with the rear ramp open. Note the improved access to the vehicle. In this view, the roof hatches are also open.

In the early 1990s, MOWAG introduced a series of improvements to the Piranha including some of those such as the rear ramp previously described on the Bison. This improved version of the Piranha was referred to as the Piranha II. The Piranha II chassis retained the same spring arrangement as the Piranha I with coil springs on the steering wheels and torsion bars on the rear four. Later, the spacing between the wheels was increased to permit the installation of larger 325/85 R 16 or 335/80 R 20 tires. This reduced the ground pressure thus improving cross-country performance. The General Motors 6V53T engine and the Allison MT653 transmission were the same as on the Piranha I, but the single speed transfer case on the earlier vehicles was replaced by a two speed unit. The redesigned hull provided more usable space without significant increases in the external dimensions. The ramp which opened the entire rear of the vehicle allowed easy movement in and out of the troop compartment.

A popular weapon station for the Piranha was the Delco turret armed with the 25mm M242 gun as on the Marine Corps LAV-25. Further development of this turret incorporated a TOW missile launcher to provide a powerful antitank capability. An early concept mounted a two tube launcher on the right side of the turret. As on the Bradley fighting vehicle, it was stowed against the side of the turret and raised to a vertical position for firing. A later type of the antitank turret was fitted with two single tube TOW launchers with one on each side of the turret.

Applique armor also was designed to protect the turret against 14.5mm armor piercing ammunition at zero range through the 30 degree frontal arc. It could defeat the 14.5mm round at a range of 400 meters on the sides and rear. Air burst protection was provided for 155mm rounds at 10 meters overhead. The armor panels had multi-hit capability and were replaceable in the field.

Below, the early concept for the installation of a TOW launcher on the Delco turret armed with the 25mm M242 gun appears in the two drawings.

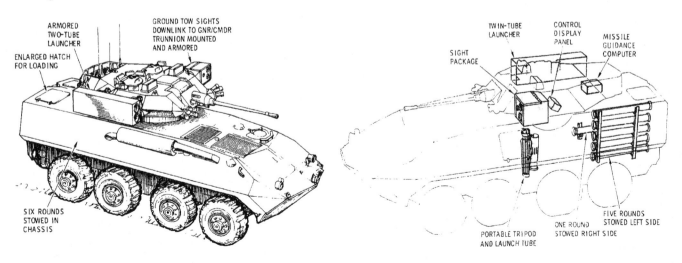

Above and at the right, the two single tube TOW launchers are installed on the Delco turret armed with the 25mm gun. The various instruments and controls inside the turret appear at the bottom right. The drawing below illustrates the installation of applique armor on the Delco turret.

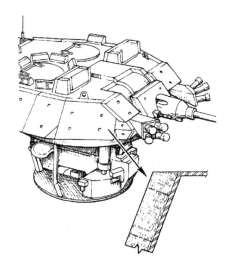

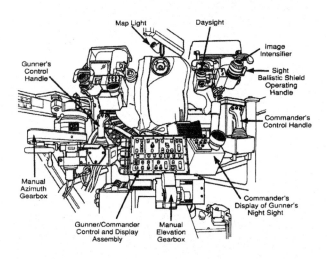

Map Light

Daysight

Gunner's Control Handle

Image Intensifier

Sight Ballistic Shield Operating Handle

Commander's Control Handle

Manual Azimuth Gearbox

Commander's Display of Gunner's Night Sight

Gunner/Commander Control and Display Assembly

Manual Elevation Gearbox

The photographs on this page show the Canadian LAV III Kodiak armored personnel carrier armed with the 25mm M242 gun.

In 1996, MOWAG introduced further improvements with the Piranha III. Subsequently, a version of this design was manufactured by General Motors of Canada for the Canadian armed forces as the LAV III. A contract was awarded in January 1997 for 240 armored personnel carriers named the Kodiak. This contract also included options for 411 additional LAV IIIs. The redesigned hull was longer and slightly wider than the earlier vehicles providing greater interior space. The two man Delco turret was armed, as before, with the 25mm M242 gun and a coaxial 7.62mm M240 machine gun in addition to a pintle mounted 5.56mm or 7.62mm machine gun. With the larger hull and improved armor protection, the combat weight of the LAV III had now risen to about 19 tons. It was powered by a 350

horsepower Caterpillar 3126B diesel engine with an Allison MD 3066 P, six speed, automatic transmission. Another change in the LAV III was the replacement of the coil springs and torsion bars by a hydropneumatic suspension system with optional height control.

In July 1999, General Motors purchased MOWAG, however, the Swiss organization remained responsible for the basic Piranha design, research, and development. In September 1999, MOWAG announced the development of the eight wheel Piranha IV. With a maximum vehicle weight of about 27 tons, it offered a 11 ton payload. The new vehicle could be fitted with the Delco two man turret armed with a 25mm or 30mm gun. The new design also was intended to reduce the radar signature of the vehicle.

268

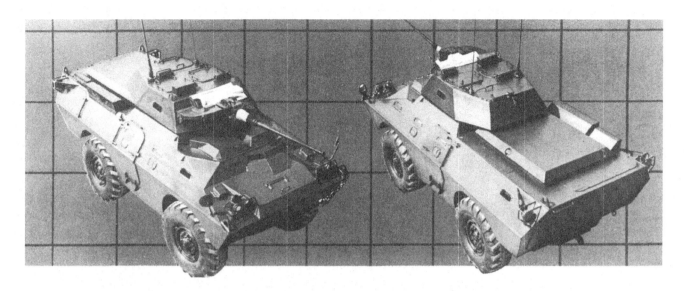

The general arrangement of the Dragoon 300 armored car can be seen in the two views above. This version is armed with a turret mounted 20mm gun.

OTHER WHEELED COMBAT VEHICLES

Although the General Motors MOWAG Piranha had been selected for the LAV, work continued on other wheeled armored vehicles.

Another vehicle originally proposed for the LAV program was the 4x4 armored car Dragoon 300 series. It had been developed by the Verne Corporation and marketed by the Arrowpointe Corporation. These subsequently merged forming the AV Technology Corporation. At a later date, this became part of General Dynamics Land Systems. The Dragoon 300 weighed about 13 tons and was powered by a 300 horsepower version of the General Motors 6V53T V6 diesel engine. The Allison MT653 automatic transmission had five

speeds forward and one reverse. The vehicle was amphibious and had a maximum speed of 65 miles per hour on roads and 3.4 miles per hour by action of the wheels in water. The Dragoon 300 was offered in several versions including an armored personnel carrier, a command vehicle, a mortar carrier, and a reconnaissance vehicle.

The drawing below shows the arrangement of the power train and other internal components of the Dragoon 300 armored car. The dimensions of the vehicle armed with a turret mounted 20mm gun and a coaxial machine gun can be seen at the right.

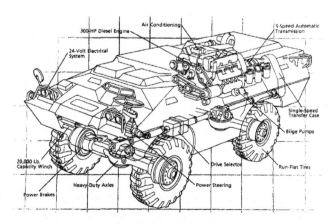

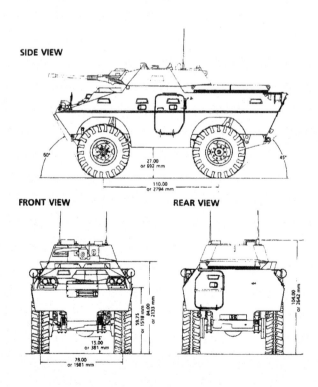

269

Later versions of the Dragoon were lengthened with the wheelbase increased from 110 inches to 121 inches. The original doors in the 300 series were replaced by double width doors in each side. The gross vehicle weight now increased to about 14 tons and it was offered, like the earlier armored car, in a variety of configurations.

The later version of the Dragoon with the longer wheelbase and the larger doors appears above. Dimensions for several versions of the new vehicle are given in the drawing below.

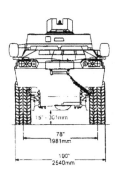

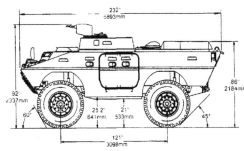

Mortar Carrier

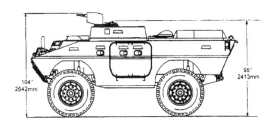

Command Vehicle

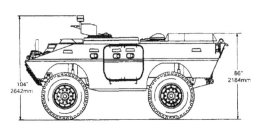

Armored Personnel Carrier

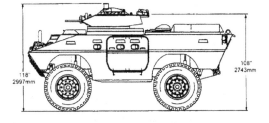

Reconnaissance Vehicle

270

The photographs above and below show the Cadillac Gage V-600 (later LAV-600) armored car armed with the Royal Ordnance low recoil force 105mm gun. Note the muzzle brake on this weapon. Dimensions of this vehicle are provided in the drawing at the bottom of the page.

Further development of the Cadillac Gage V-300 resulted in the V-300A1 armed with the Royal Ordnance low recoil force 105mm gun. The designation of this vehicle was subsequently changed to V-600. To accommodate the turret mounted cannon, the hull roof of the original V-300 was lowered. The rear suspension also was modified to use torsion bars in place of the coil springs which were retained on the front axle. The combat weight of the V-600 was about 19 tons. Later, both the V-300 and the V-600 were designated as the LAV-300 and the LAV-600.

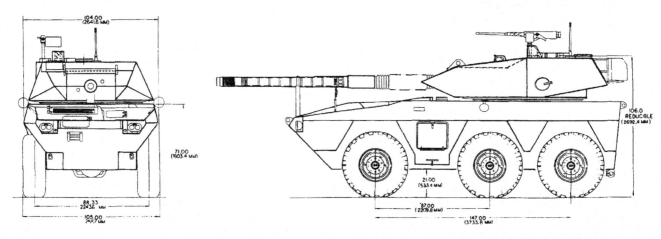

271

The M93 Fox NBC reconnaissance vehicle can be seen in the two photographs on this page. The Fox is operating in desert terrain with the driver's front armor open. The bottom view was taken by Greg Stewart at the National Training Center.

In March 1990, the U.S. Army awarded a contract to General Dynamics Land Systems with Thyssen Henschel GmbH as a major subcontractor to manufacture 48 of the German Fuchs (Fox) NBC (nuclear, biological, chemical) reconnaissance vehicles. Designated as the XM93, the Fox was a 6x6 armored car powered by a 320 horsepower V8 diesel engine with a six speed automatic transmission. The three solid axles were suspended by coil springs and the vehicle was steered by the front four wheels. Combat loaded, the Fox weighed about 19 tons and had a maximum road speed of 65 miles per hour. It was amphibious with a maximum water speed of 6 miles per hour driven by two propellers.

When the United States forces were deployed to the Persian Gulf during Operation Desert Shield in the Summer of 1990, none of the new NBC reconnaissance vehicles were yet available. To meet the emergency the German government transferred 60 of their Fox vehicles to the U.S. Army. Before the transfer, the vehicles were modified by the installation of American equipment such as radios and machine guns.

Standardized as the M93 NBC reconnaissance vehicle, the Fox was equipped to detect NBC hazards in its immediate vicinity. The crew was protected by an over pressure system that maintained the air pressure inside at a higher level than the outside air preventing airborne contaminants from entering the vehicle. It also was air conditioned. The Fox carried a radiation monitor and small sampling wheels picked up material from the ground at the rear of the vehicle. Trace materials picked up by the sensors were immediately analyzed by the on-board mass spectrometer. The Fox could mark a contaminated area and transmit warnings to nearby units.

Details on the front and rear of the M93 Fox NBC reconnaissance vehicle are visible in these two photographs by Greg Stewart.

These additional photographs from Greg Stewart show the M93 Fox NBC reconnaissance vehicle at the National Training Center. The view at the right shows the sampler deployed to pick up samples for analysis.

The M93A1 Fox NBC reconnaissance vehicle appears above. The detector has been raised out of the roof hatch.

Further development incorporated the M21 remote sensing chemical agent alarm system that could detect clouds of mustard or nerve gas at a distance of up to three miles (five kilometers). Initially designated as the XM93E1, with the new equipment, the Fox was standardized as the M93A1. The crew in the new vehicle was reduced to three compared to four in the M93.

Additional equipment added in the M93A1E2 included enhanced chemical and biological sensors that allowed detection of chemical agents at a distance while the vehicle was moving. A new chemical/biological mass spectrometer improved identification of chemical and provided first time detection of biological agents.

The NBC detection and analysis equipment on the M93A1 Fox is identified in the drawing at the right.

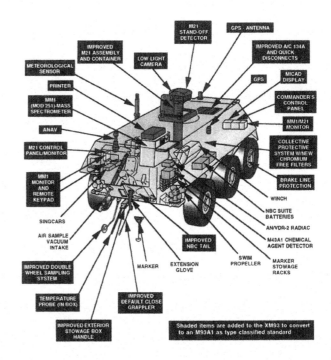

The M998 HMMWV appears above without (left) and with (right) the soft cover installed on the rear. At the right, the M1037 shelter carrier was photographed by Greg Stewart during operations at the National Training Center.

In March 1983, AM General Corporation was selected to produce the new high mobility multipurpose wheeled vehicle (HMMWV) that was to replace the Jeep and some other vehicles in use by the Army. Even more than its predecessor the Jeep, the HMMWV, because of its greater load carrying capacity, was adapted to a variety of roles as a weapon carrier. Since it was difficult to make a word out of HMMWV, the troops immediately dubbed the new vehicle as the Humvee, although the manufacturer named it the Hummer (a registered trademark of AM General Corporation). The basic vehicle was a $1^{1}/_{4}$ ton 4x4 truck powered by a General Motors, liquid cooled, V8 diesel engine which developed 150 gross horsepower at 3600 rpm. All four wheels were independently sprung by coil springs with hydraulic shock absorbers.

The HMMWV was assigned a large number of designations reflecting the modifications required for its many different roles. The basic cargo-troop carrier version was the M998 and when it was equipped with a front mounted winch, it became the M1038. These vehicles could be configured in a variety of ways with canvas tops and with two or four, metal framed, fabric covered doors. A two litter ambulance with a canvas top was designated as the M1035. The M1037 shelter carrier was used to transport a command, communications or electronic equipment shelter. The vehicle was fitted with a heavy duty airlift bumper and suspension system. Special brackets as well as cables with turnbuckles secured the removable shelter to the carrier. When the winch was installed, the designation became the M1042. Another version of the HMMWV was intended for use as the prime mover for the 105mm M119 lightweight howitzer. Designated as the M1069, it was not considered to be satisfactory after test because of the rough ride when towing the howitzer.

The M1035 soft top ambulance is shown above. Below, the M1069 HMMWV serves as a prime mover for light artillery. The latter photograph is from Greg Stewart.

276

The M1025 HMMWV armament carrier can be seen above. Note that these vehicles do not have the front mounted winch. At the right below, this armament carrier has its roof mounted machine gun installed.

An aluminum fiber glass body was installed on the HMMWV armament carrier versions and two types of ambulances. This body was considered to be the basic armor package. Along with the polycarbonate windows, it could protect against light fragments. The armament carrier M1025 did not have the winch. When the winch was installed, it became the M1026. Modified to carry the TOW missile launcher, the vehicle was designated as the M966 without a winch. With the winch, it was the M1036. The two litter ambulance was the M996 and the four litter version was the M997. All of the vehicles with the basic armor package could be identified by the X shaped stiffener configuration on the side doors.

The machine gun mount on the roof of the HMMWV armament carrier appears above. At the upper right are the M997 (left) and M996 (right) ambulance versions of the HMMWV. At the lower right is the M996 TOW missile carrier.

Above, the Marine Corps M1044 HMMWV armament carrier appears at the left and the M1043 is at the right. Note the winch on the M1044. Both of these vehicles are armed with the .50 caliber M2HB machine gun. All photographs on this page were from Greg Stewart.

The HMMWV armament carriers provided to the U.S. Marine Corps were fitted with supplemental armor for improved fragment protection. This included flat panels attached to the side door providing an easy point of identification. The air intake and exhaust extensions of the deep water fording kit also served to identify the Marine Corps vehicles. The basic armament carrier now became the M1043 without the winch and the M1044 with the winch. The Marine Corps TOW missile carrier with the supplemental armor was the M1045 without the winch and the M1046 with the winch.

The Marine Corps HMMWV armament carrier above at the right can be compared with Army M966 TOW missile carrier below. Note the flat supplemental armor on the doors and the deep water fording equipment on the Marine Corps vehicle.

278

The Army M966 HMMWV TOW missile carrier can be seen here in these photographs by Greg Stweart. Note the late type brush guard on the vehicle in the bottom view.

This Army M966 HMMWV TOW missile carrier also has its 7.62mm machine gun ready for action. The photograph below by Greg Stewart shows the M1069 HMMWV in its role as a prime mover for the M119 105mm howitzer.

The M998 HMMWV above without a roof or doors is armed with a 30mm automatic gun. The flat supplemental door armor and the winch on the Marine Corps M1044 at the right are clearly visible. The M998 below is armed with a Mark 19 40mm automatic grenade launcher.

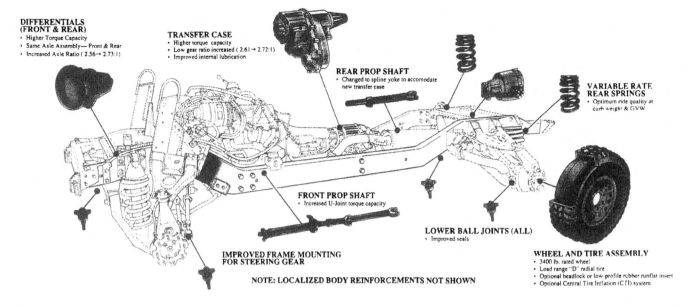

DIFFERENTIALS (FRONT & REAR)
• Higher Torque Capacity
• Same Axle Assembly— Front & Rear
• Increased Axle Ratio (2.56→ 2.73:1)

TRANSFER CASE
• Higher torque capacity
• Low gear ratio increased (2.61→ 2.72:1)
• Improved internal lubrication

REAR PROP SHAFT
• Changed to spline yoke to accomodate new transfer case

VARIABLE RATE REAR SPRINGS
• Optimum ride quality at curb weight & GVW

FRONT PROP SHAFT
• Increased U-Joint torque capacity

LOWER BALL JOINTS (ALL)
• Improved seals

IMPROVED FRAME MOUNTING FOR STEERING GEAR

WHEEL AND TIRE ASSEMBLY
• 3400 lb. rated wheel
• Load range "D" radial tire
• Optional beadlock or low-profile rubber runflat insert
• Optional Central Tire Inflation (CTI) system

NOTE: LOCALIZED BODY REINFORCEMENTS NOT SHOWN

Modifications introduced on the heavy version of the HMMWV are shown in the drawing above.

Because of ever greater payload requirements, a heavy version of the HMMWV was under development by AM General Corporation increasing the gross vehicle weight to 10,000 pounds. Designated as the M1097, it assumed the mission of transporting heavy payloads or towed loads that exceeded the capacity of the M1037. Changes incorporated in the M1097 included a reinforced frame, cross members, and lifting shackles as well as new heavy duty rear springs, shock absorbers, control arms, tires and rims. The gear ratio was increased from 2.61:1 to 2.72:1 in the transfer case and from 2.56:1 to 2.75:1 in the axle differentials. It retained the same 150 horsepower engine as the lighter HMMWV. A central tire inflation system also was developed as an option for the HMMWV.

AM General utilized the greater load carrying capacity of the M1097 to develop an armored version of the vehicle. Armor panels were installed to provide protection against 7.62mm M80 and 5.56mm M855 ball ammunition at 0 obliquity and a range of 15 feet. A roof ring mount with shield could be armed with a 7.62mm M60 machine gun, a .50 caliber M2HB machine gun, a 40mm Mark 19 grenade launcher, or a 30mm ASP-30 cannon.

Components of the central tire inflation system are illustrated below. The drawing at the bottom right shows details of the installation on the wheel.

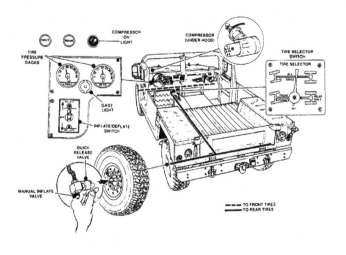

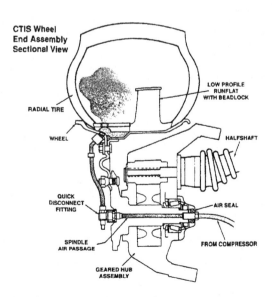

282

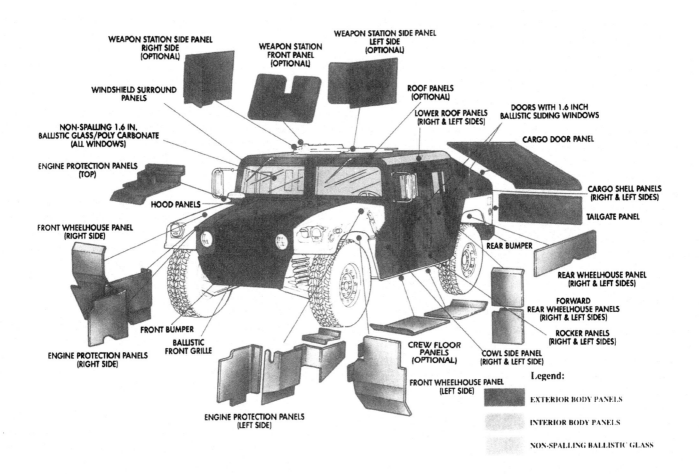

WEAPON STATION SIDE PANEL RIGHT SIDE (OPTIONAL)

WEAPON STATION FRONT PANEL (OPTIONAL)

WEAPON STATION SIDE PANEL LEFT SIDE (OPTIONAL)

WINDSHIELD SURROUND PANELS

ROOF PANELS (OPTIONAL)

LOWER ROOF PANELS (RIGHT & LEFT SIDES)

DOORS WITH 1.6 INCH BALLISTIC SLIDING WINDOWS

NON-SPALLING 1.6 IN. BALLISTIC GLASS/POLY CARBONATE (ALL WINDOWS)

CARGO DOOR PANEL

ENGINE PROTECTION PANELS (TOP)

CARGO SHELL PANELS (RIGHT & LEFT SIDES)

HOOD PANELS

TAILGATE PANEL

FRONT WHEELHOUSE PANEL (RIGHT SIDE)

REAR BUMPER

REAR WHEELHOUSE PANEL (RIGHT & LEFT SIDES)

FRONT BUMPER

FORWARD REAR WHEELHOUSE PANELS (RIGHT & LEFT SIDES)

BALLISTIC FRONT GRILLE

ROCKER PANELS (RIGHT & LEFT SIDES)

ENGINE PROTECTION PANELS (RIGHT SIDE)

CREW FLOOR PANELS (OPTIONAL)

COWL SIDE PANEL (RIGHT & LEFT SIDE)

FRONT WHEELHOUSE PANEL (LEFT SIDE)

ENGINE PROTECTION PANELS (LEFT SIDE)

Legend:

EXTERIOR BODY PANELS

INTERIOR BODY PANELS

NON-SPALLING BALLISTIC GLASS

The armor applied to the heavy HMMWV for protection against 7.62mm ball ammunition is illustrated above. Below, the unarmored heavy HMMWV is carrying a shelter in this photograph by Michael Green and in the two views at the right, the armored version is fitted with roof mounted armament.

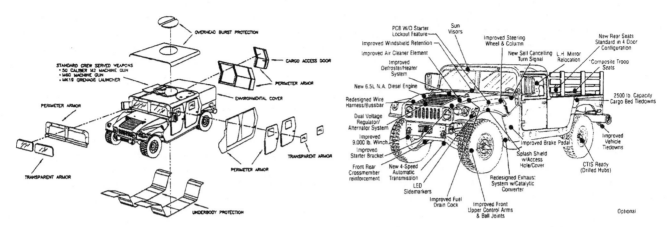

Above, the drawing at the left shows the armor added to the HMMWV on the M1109 by O'Gara-Hess & Eisenhardt. The drawing at the right indicates the improvements incorporated into the HMMWV M998A2 series. At the bottom of the page is a photograph of the M1025A2 armament carrier.

During the Summer of 1993, the improvements of the heavy HMMWV were incorporated into the M998A1 series. These changes included the heavy duty frame as well as the increase in the transfer case and axle differential gear ratios.

In 1994, the U. S. Army had an urgent requirement for a heavy HMMWV with a higher level of armor protection for operations in Somalia. Designated as the XM1109 (later it was the M1109), these vehicles were armored by O'Gara-Hess & Eisenhardt, a Division of the Kroll-O'Gara Company. The armor on these vehicles provided protection against 7.62mm armor piercing ammunition, 155mm artillery air bursts and the blast of a 12 pound mine under the body. The weight of this extra armor reduced the payload of the M1109 to only 1,300 pounds.

Further development of the HMMWV resulted in additional modifications. By the Spring of 1994, the latest version of the vehicle was designated as the M998A2 series. They were powered by a naturally aspirated V8 diesel engine developing 160 horsepower at 3400 rpm. This engine had a displacement of 400 cubic inches (6.5 liters) compared to the 379.4 cubic inches (6.2 liters) of the original 150 horsepower engine. In the A2 series, a four speed automatic transmission replaced the three speed type in the earlier vehicles.

Dimensions of the M998A2 series HMMWV are shown in the drawing at the right.

The M1097A2 was produced as a cargo-troop carrier, a cargo-troop carrier-prime mover, and a shelter carrier. Like the earlier vehicle, the M1025A2 armament-TOW missile carrier was protected against light fragments and the M1043A2 and the M1045A2 were fitted with supplemental armor for increased fragment protection. The M1035A2 ambulance remained without armor and the M997A2 ambulance retained the lighter fragment protection.

The HMMWV continued to evolve with the introduction of the expanded capacity version. Designated as the M1113, this vehicle was unarmored and was powered by a turbocharged version of the 400 cubic inch (6.5 liter) diesel engine. This engine produced 190 horsepower at 3400 rpm. The axle hypoid gear ratio also was increased to 3.08:1.

Another version of the expanded capacity vehicle was armored by O'Gara-Hess & Eisenhardt and designated as the M1114. The armor provided protection against 7.62mm armor piercing ammunition at a range of 100 meters. The crew compartment was protected against the blast of a 12 pound antitank mine at the front and a 4 pound contact detonated mine at the rear. A ring mount in the roof could accommodate a 7.62mm M60 machine gun, a .50 caliber M2HB machine gun or a 40mm Mark 19 grenade launcher.

An armored HMMWV similar to the M1114 was ordered by the U. S. Air Force in late 1997. Also based upon the expanded capacity vehicle, it was designated as the M1116 and was intended to replace the Peacekeeper (Ranger) in its security duties. A total of 71 M1116 vehicles were delivered between February and May 1998. The vehicle could be armed with a variety of weapons including the 7.62mm and .50 caliber machine guns and the Mark 19 40mm automatic grenade launcher.

The A3 designation was reserved for a planned program to refurbish the original A0 series of vehicles. In August 2001, a contract was awarded to AM General to study further modifications to the HMMWV. Results of this program would be applied to a future A4 variant.

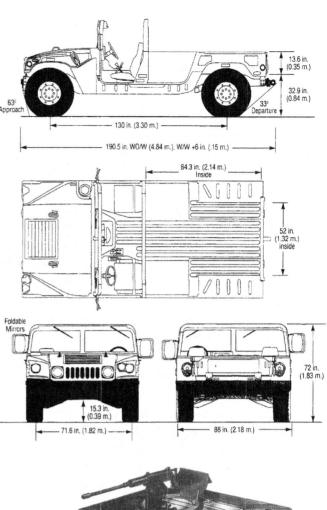

1. BIFOLD DOOR, 2. BLAST PROTECTION, 3. ARMORED DOORS, 4. ARMOR GLASS, 5. ARMORED ROOF.

The armored M1114 HMMWV appears above and below. At the bottom left is the unarmored expanded capacity M1113.

The Avenger antiaircraft system installed on the HMMWV can be seen in the photographs on this page taken by Greg Stewart. Above, the Avenger is at the National Training Center.

Several versions of the HMMWV were adapted as special weapon carriers. In addition to the TOW antitank vehicle mentioned previously, several pedestal mounts armed with the Stinger missile were installed to provide a highly mobile antiaircraft weapon. The most successful of these was the Avenger produced by the Boeing Aerospace Company. The first production Avengers were delivered in November 1988. They were armed with two launchers each carrying four Stinger missiles. One launcher was mounted on each side of the gunner's electrically driven turret. The missiles also could be fired by the driver of the HMMWV or from a remote location. For close in protection, the Avenger was armed with a .50 caliber M3P machine gun mounted under the right missile launcher. Other weapons were installed experimentally in the same location including two 7.62mm M240 machine guns.

At the right is another view of the Avenger at the National Training Center.

Other Stinger missile installations on the HMMWV included the Crossbow system from LTV Aerospace and the Defender I and II from General Electric. These systems frequently combined other weapons with the missile armament. The AMRAAM, the AIM-9X and the Hellfire missiles also were considered as antiaircraft weapons for installation on the HMMWV.

Above, the Avenger is in firing position. The .50 caliber machine gun mounted under the quadruple Stinger launcher is clearly visible. At the top right, the Avenger has just launched a Stinger missile. At the lower right, a production model of the pedestal mounted Avenger antiaircraft system is installed on its HMMWV.

Above, the Crossbow system launches a Hellfire missile. Another view of the pedestal mounted Crossbow on a HMMWV is at the right. The variety of weapons that could be launched from the Crossbow is obvious. In the photographs below, the system is armed with Stinger missiles and Hydra 70 rockets.

The early version of the XR-311 dune buggy appears above and its later versions are at the top right and below. It was evaluated by the Armor and Engineer Board during 1970-71. Originally built by FMC Corporation, the design was acquired later by AM General Corporation and contributed to the development of the HMMWV.

During 1982, the Ninth Infantry Division at Fort Lewis, Washington evaluated a number of vehicles to determine their suitability for use with the new light divisions. Among these were modified dune buggies capable of high speed over fairly rough terrain. Such vehicles also had been considered much earlier during the Force Development Test and Evaluation (FDTE) for the Armored Reconnaissance Scout Vehicle (ARSV) in the Summer of 1974. At that time, the XR-311 dune buggy had shown excellent performance, but the tracked XM800T was considered preferable for the ARSV.

At Fort Lewis, the most successful of the dune buggies were the vehicles built by Chenowth Racing Products. For a time, these vehicles were marketed by the Emerson Electric Company and later by a team composed of Lockheed-Martin Defense Systems and the Chenowth Corporation. Sometimes referred to as fast attack vehicles (FAV), they were employed by the Marine Corps and Special Forces. Several other manufacturers including NORDAC and Teledyne Continental

Note the armor added to the XR-311 above

Motors also produced candidates for evaluation as an FAV. However, none of these went into production. These vehicles were armed with variety of weapons including 7.62mm and .50 caliber machine guns as well as the TOW missile and its launcher.

The late version of the XR-311 below has been armed with a TOW missile launcher.

The original Chenowth dune buggy at the left above has been armed for test by the 9th Infantry Division at Fort Lewis, Washington. At the top right is a later version of the fast attack vehicle still armed with a .50 caliber machine gun. Other versions of the Chenowth fast attack vehicle or light strike vehicle appear below.

The Chenowth fast attack vehicle at the right is completely off the ground during its test run. Below, an FAV candidate produced by Teledyne Continental Motors is armed with a TOW missile launcher.

At the bottom right an FAV built by NORDAC is armed with 7.62 machine guns in front and in the rear.

At the top left is a Marine Corps FAV based upon the modified M151 jeep. One of the M151s fitted with HMMWV machine gun ring mount by Sergeant Ferry is shown above. At the left, the ring mount is being installed.

The U.S Marines also improvised an FAV of their own. These were modifications of the M151 $\frac{1}{4}$ ton truck. At least four of these were fitted with the .50 caliber M2HB machine gun on the ring mount from the HMMWV weapons carrier by Sgt. David Ferry, USMC.

Another interesting vehicle evaluated by the Ninth Infantry Division was built by the Standard Manu-facturing Company, Inc. and armed with the 20mm Vulcan air defense system. This was a slightly modified version of the towed Vulcan system and it was installed on the eight wheel carrier produced by Standard featuring an all wheel hydrostatic trailing arm drive. Weighing six tons, it had speed of 45 miles per hour on level roads and excellent cross-country mobility.

The eight wheel carrier built by the Standard Manufacturing Company, Inc. and armed with 20mm Vulcan air defense system can be seen in the photograph and drawing below.

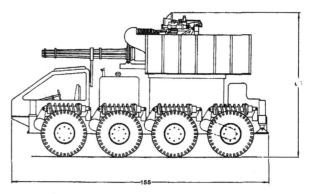

The XM1117 armored security vehicle appears in the photographs above. Note the location of the headlights.

In December 1995, Cadillac Gage, now a part of Textron Marine & Land Systems (TMLS) received a contract to build four prototypes of a new (4x4) armored security vehicle (ASV). Designated as the XM1117, it was the first new military police vehicle to appear since the employment of the M706 in that role during the Vietnam War. Although similar in appearance to the Cadillac Gage M706 and the later V-150, it was a new design featuring an independent coil spring suspension on all four wheels. With a combat weight of about 15 tons, the ASV was manned by a crew of three consisting of the commander, the gunner and the driver. An additional seat was provided for one passenger although the vehicle could be modified to carry more. The XM1117 was fitted with a turret armed with a .50 caliber M2HB machine gun and a 40mm Mark 19 grenade launcher. In addition to its basic steel armor,

ceramic composite applique armor and spall liners protected the crew area against .50 caliber armor piercing rounds at a range of 250 meters. The vehicle could withstand the overhead blast from a 155mm shell at a height of 15 meters and it could tolerate a mine explosion of 12 pounds of TNT at any wheel or four pounds of TNT at any point. Powered by a 260 horsepower Cummins diesel engine, the ASV had a maximum road speed of about 60 miles per hour and a cruising range of 440 miles at 40 miles per hour on level roads. The 14.00 R 20 tires were fitted with run flat inserts. All four prototype ASVs were delivered by February 1997. The accelerated test program was completed the following October and the prototypes were returned to the manufacturer for several modifications. In March 1999, TMLS was awarded a production contract for 94 ASVs.

Below is the production M1117 armored security vehicle. Note the relocation of the headlights.

The production M1117 armored security vehicle is shown in the photographs above. Note the ceramic composite armor on the vehicle.

Standardized as the M1117 and named Guardian, the ASV was produced at a rate of one vehicle every 21 working days. The U. S. Army deployed the M1117 to Kosovo as part of the United Nations peacekeeping operation.

Details on the top and rear of the M1117 ASV are visible in the views above and at the left. Note the armament of one .50 caliber machine gun and one 40mm automatic grenade launcher. The drawings below show other proposed vehicles based upon the ASV.

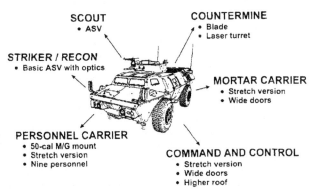

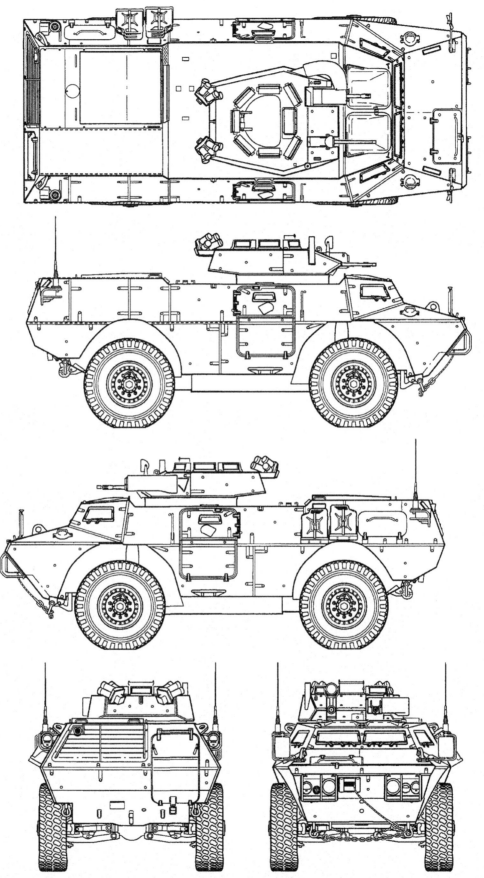

Scale 1:48

Armored Security Vehicle M1117

© M. Duplessis

293

During the Spring of 1999, the U. S. Army Tank-Automotive and Armaments Command (TACOM) awarded a contract to AV Technology, now a subsidiary of General Dynamics Land Systems, for four vehicles designated as the Armored Ground Mobility System (AGMS). The AGMS was based upon the Austrian Pandur armored vehicle developed by Steyr-Daimler-Puch Spezialfahrzeuge AG. At that time, AV Technology was producing the Pandur in the United States for several foreign countries. The AGMS was intended for use by the U. S. Special Operations Command. In addition to the four vehicles, the contract contained options for up to 50 additional units.

The Armored Ground Mobility System based upon the Pandur armored car is shown above as it appeared during the Platform Performance Demonstration at Fort Knox. The drawings below depict various versions of the Pandur armored car.

The basic Pandur on which the AGMS was based was a six wheel (6x6) vehicle powered by a six cylinder Steyr WD 612, turbocharged, diesel engine coupled to an Allison MT653DR transmission having five speeds forward and one reverse. The front four wheels were steered. The vehicle was amphibious with maximum speeds of 65 miles per hour on roads and about 7 miles per hour in water. The original Pandur was produced in several types including an infantry carrier, a mortar carrier, a command vehicle, an armored reconnaissance vehicle, and armored ambulance, and a mobile gun system.

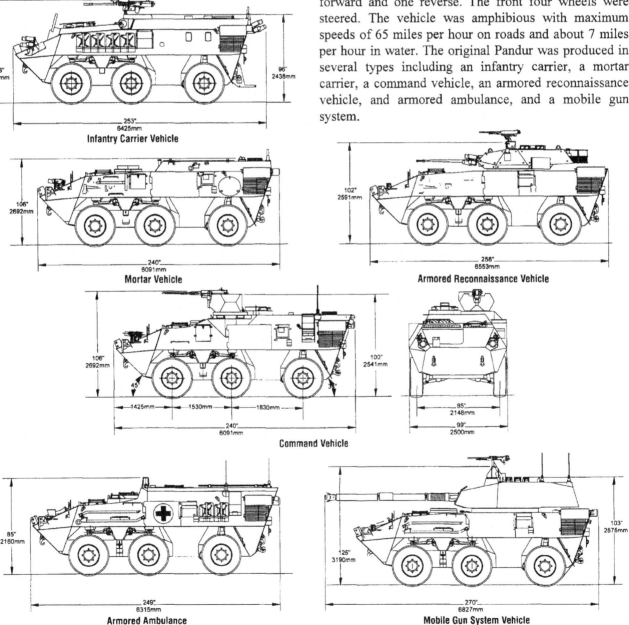

294

Two of the vehicles submitted by United Defense LP for the Platform Performance Demonstration can be seen above. At the left, the M8 armored gun system is emerging from its transport aircraft. At the right, the MTVL infantry fighting vehicle is being transported on a trailer.

THE FUTURE

In October 1999, General Eric K. Shinseki, the Army Chief of Staff, outlined a plan for the transformation of the Army into a future Objective Force. This transformation was to proceed along three paths that would eventually merge into the Objective Force. The first path was the existing heavy Legacy Force which would be maintained and upgraded to provide a powerful striking force during the transformation process.

The second path, referred to as the Objective Force itself, was the research and development program to produce the Future Combat System (FCS) which was to be its main armament. As proposed, the FCS was not to exceed 20 tons in weight and be transportable in C130 aircraft. However, its lethality and survivability were to be equal or better than Abrams main battle tank. Needless to say, this would require considerable research and development. It was hoped that appropriate technology and design concepts could be selected by 2003 to permit the construction of prototype demonstrators during the period 2004-2005. The goal was to equip the first Objective Force unit by 2010.

The third path of the Army transformation was the Interim Force. It was to consist of brigade size units equipped with presently available vehicles that could be carried in C130 aircraft. These brigades could deploy more rapidly than the heavy Legacy Force and support the light airborne units with greater firepower, mobility, and survivability. The ultimate objective of the new force was to be able to deploy a medium weight brigade combat team anywhere in the world within 96 hours and a division in 120 hours. Such an effort would not only

need lighter vehicles, but it also would require drastic reduction of the lift required for logistical support. To evaluate the new organization, six interim brigades were selected for conversion with the first being the 3rd Brigade, 2nd Infantry Division located at Fort Lewis, Washington. These interim brigade combat teams also would be used to develop training techniques and doctrine for the Objective Force.

In an effort to evaluate what might be available as an off the shelf armored vehicle, manufacturers were invited to submit both wheeled or tracked vehicles for evaluation during a platform performance demonstration (PPD) at Fort Knox starting in December 1999. Eleven manufacturers submitted a total of 35 vehicles for evaluation during the PPD which continued into January 2000. Among the 35 platforms submitted, 16 were infantry carriers, two were command vehicles, six were reconnaissance vehicles, two were mortar carriers, two were antitank vehicles, five were mobile gun systems, one was an engineer vehicle, and one was an armored ambulance. Nine of the platforms were only for display purposes and only 25 of the vehicles participated in the live fire tests. The swimming capacity was demonstrated on only four vehicles.

Among the manufacturers, United Defense LP submitted all tracked vehicles consisting of the M113A3 armored personnel carrier (APC), the medium tactical vehicle light (MTVL)APC, the MTVL infantry fighting vehicle with one and two man turrets, the XM1108 universal carrier, the M1068A3 command and control vehicle, the M1064A3 120mm mortar carrier, and the M8 armored gun system with level I and level II armor.

Above are two of the Cadillac Gage Textron candidates for the Platform Performance Demonstration. The LAV-300 Mark II is at the left and the M1117 armored security vehicle is at the right.

Singapore Technologies Automotive Ltd. also submitted variations of their tracked Bionix infantry fighting vehicle.

Wheeled entries in the PPD included versions of the Dragoon and Pandur vehicles presented by General Dynamics Land Systems.

Cadillac Gage Textron entered the M1117 armored security vehicle and versions of the V-300 and V-600 now designated as the LAV-300 and LAV-600.

General Motors of Canada submitted the LAV III and MOWAG provided the Swiss version of the same vehicle.

The German Fuchs (FOX) APC was presented by Henschel.

The objective of the PPD was not to select a particular vehicle at that time, but to review the technology available for future selection.

Below, the Bionix 25 infantry fighting vehicle from Singapore Technologies Automotive Ltd. is at the left. Above at the right, the Dragoon armored car is about to show off its swimming ability. At the bottom right, a turreted version of the Dragoon is firing its 25mm automatic gun during the PPD live fire demonstration.

296

The LAV III armed with the 105mm gun in the low profile turret is shown above. At the top left, it is firing during the Platform Performance Demonstration. Below at the left is the French VAB armored car during the evaluation at Fort Knox.

The German Fuchs armored car is above at the right during the Platform Performance Demonstration at Fort Knox. Below are two views of the LAV III fitted with a turret mounted 120mm mortar.

The Canadian LAV III armed with the turret mounted 25mm M242 automatic gun is shown in these photographs.

The LAV III armed with the 105mm gun in the low profile turret appears above. Details and dimensions of the low profile turret can be seen in the drawing below.

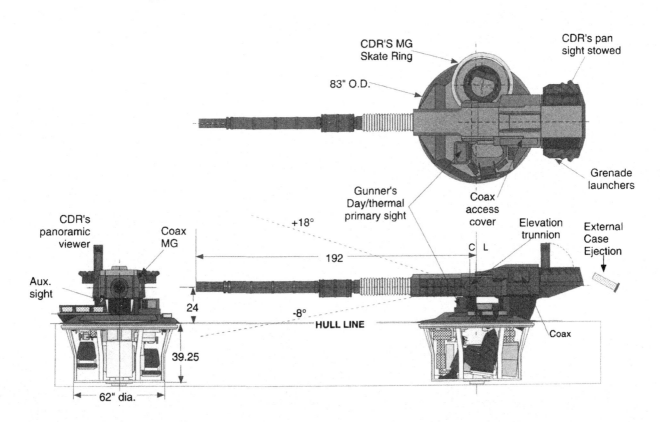

299

Above, the LAV III infantry carrier is emerging from the cargo compartment of a C130 transport aircraft. Note the lack of extra room on the top and sides of the vehicle.

On 16 November 2000, the U.S. Army awarded a contract to General Motors and General Dynamics Land Systems to build the interim armored vehicle. This was a joint venture of the two companies. Ten versions of the basic vehicle based upon the LAV III were planned. These included an infantry carrier, a reconnaissance vehicle, a nuclear-biological-chemical (NBC) reconnaissance vehicle, an antitank vehicle, a command vehicle, a mortar carrier, a fire support vehicle, a mobile gun system, an engineer vehicle, and an armored ambulance. The mobile gun system, the fire support vehicle and the NBC reconnaissance vehicle required further development, but the other vehicles could be scheduled for early production. In the case of the mobile gun system, considerable modification and weight reduction was required to meet the limits imposed by the C130 aircraft extending the date of its fielding to 2005.

At the right, the LAV III infantry carrier is moving at speed over rough terrain.

The LAV III infantry carrier appears in these photographs. The vehicle is fully stowed and armed with a .50 caliber machine gun.

An important factor in the selection of the wheeled LAV III was the maximum road speed of about 60 miles per hour. The normal speed of a convoy including tracked vehicles is usually limited to about 25 miles per hour with the various vehicles having an extra 5 to 15 miles per hour available for catch up. By using all wheeled vehicles based upon the LAV III, the convoy speed could be raised to 40 miles per hour with 20 miles per hour available for catch up. This ability to move rapidly on roads was considered to outweigh the reduced off road mobility of the LAV compared to a tracked vehicle.

The mobile gun system based upon the LAV III is shown above at Fort Knox during May 1999. At this point, it still required considerable modification and weight reduction.

Another consideration that favored basing all of the vehicles on the LAV III chassis was the reduction of the logistic requirements for spare parts and the simplification of maintenance and the training of personnel.

At the Winter meeting of the Association of the U. S. Army during 28 February-1 March 2002, the new wheeled carrier was named the Stryker Interim Armored Vehicle after two Medal of Honor recipients. These were Private First Class Stuart S. Stryker and Specialist Fourth Class Robert F. Stryker. They were both infantry soldiers and they served in World War II and Vietnam respectively.

To permit an immediate start to the training of the interim brigade combat teams, they were equipped with LAV IIIs on loan from the Canadian Army for use as infantry assault vehicles. Italian Centauro armored cars armed with the 105mm gun were provided to train the interim brigade combat teams pending the development of the new mobile gun system. The HMMWV equipped with the M707 Striker system (target designation for laser guided missiles) was issued for use until the fire support vehicle was available. The M93A1 Fox was used for training until development of the NBC reconnaissance vehicle was complete.

Thus the U. S. Army prepared to field a major force of wheeled armored fighting vehicles for the first time in its history, over a century after Colonel Davidson's first experiments.

Below are two views of the Italian Centauro armored car armed with the 105mm gun. These photographs were taken at Fort Lewis, Washington during December 1999. It was serving as the mobile gun system during training operations.

PART V

REFERENCE DATA

The Stryker interim armored vehicle appears above. This is the infantry carrier.

Details of the smoke grenade launchers and the .50 caliber machine gun mount can be seen in these photographs of the infantry carrier version of the Stryker interim armored vehicle.

The LAV-25s above and below are from the 3rd LAR Battalion. They were photographed by Wade Barttels during training exercises at Fort Irwin in August 1998. Note the different color schemes in the view below. The vehicles are fitted with the laser training device referred to as the Precision Gunnery System. It can be seen above the 25mm gun and on the side of the turret.

The LAV-25 above belongs to the 1st LAR Battalion at Camp Pendleton. It was photographed by Wade Barttels. Below, four LAV-ADs are lined up with their Stinger missile launchers elevated in the firing position.

Above, an LAV-25 from the 24th Marine Expeditionary Unit is crossing a temporary bridge in Kosovo during a training exercise between 19 March and 10 April 2000.

The M1117 armored security vehicle above can be compared with its ancestor, the Commando, below. The latter appears to be a late production XM706.

Above, a Marine Corps FAV, improvised from the M151 Jeep, is fitted with the machine gun ring mount from the HMMWV. The gunner is Corporal Wilkinson and the driver is Corporal Starr. This photograph came from Jeff McKaughan. The missile launchers on the Avenger below at the National Training Center are in the firing position. It was photographed by Greg Stewart.

Above, this line of M8 light armored cars, led by "Brenda Jean", is participating in a training operation during World War II.

Preparation of data sheets proved to be somewhat more difficult than those in previous volumes. One factor was the wide span of time that is covered. Detailed technical data on many of the early vehicles is very difficult to obtain and is frequently inaccurate. Thus the data sheets begin by covering vehicles of the World War II period. With some of the later vehicles, security restrictions limit the information that can be presented.

If possible, dimensions were taken from the official drawings. When these were not available, other sources were used such as characteristics sheets and test reports from Aberdeen Proving Ground and Fort Knox. Since some dimensions such as height and ground clearance vary with vehicle load, design values were used when available to permit comparison between the vehicles.

The meaning of most of the terms used in these sheets is obvious. However, some may require a little explanation. For example, the tread is the distance between the centerlines of the same pair of wheels. The wheelbase is the distance between the center of the front and rear wheels. If the vehicle has more than four wheels, the distance is given from the center of the front wheel to the center of each of the following wheels. The fire height is defined as the distance from the ground to the centerline of the main weapon bore at zero elevation. The meaning of the approach angle and the departure angle is illustrated in the sketch.

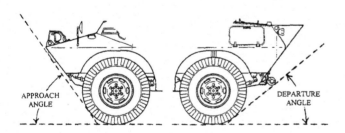

The combat weight of a vehicle includes its full combat load and crew. For experimental vehicles, the exact weight is given if it is available. For production vehicles, the average weight is often rounded off to the nearest 1000 pounds. The power to weight ratios were calculated using the combat weight.

Security restrictions limit the information available on some of the later vehicles. This is particularly true for composite or applique armor. On the early vehicles the armor is specified by type, thickness and angle with the vertical. This angle is measured between a vertical plane and the armor as indicated by the angle alpha in the simplified sketch. In this two dimensional drawing, the angle beta is the angle of obliquity defined as the angle between a line perpendicular to the armor plate and the path of a projectile impacting that plate.

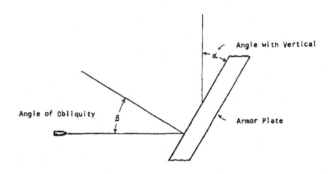

The terms left and right are used from the perspective of someone seated in the driver's seat. If available, the maximum values are quoted for the engine gross and net horsepower and torque. The gross horsepower and torque refers to values obtained with only the accessories necessary for the engine operation without the effect of such items as air cleaners or generators. The net values are those obtained with the engine installed in the vehicle including the effect of all of its accessories.

Frequently there were changes in the weight of a vehicle during its operational life. This resulted from modifications to the vehicle as well as stowage changes. If possible, the values quoted are for when the vehicle was new or during its period of greatest operational use.

SCOUT CAR M3A1
(4 Wheels, 4 wheels Driven)

GENERAL DATA

Crew:	6 to 8 men
Length: Overall	221.5 inches
Width: Overall	80 inches
Height: Overall	78.5 inches
Tread: Front	63.25 inches
Rear	65.25 inches
Wheelbase:	131 inches
Ground Clearance:	15.75 inches
Approach Angle:	37 degrees
Departure Angle:	35 degrees
Weight, Combat Loaded:	12,400 pounds
Weight, Unstowed:	9,100 pounds
Power to Weight Ratio: Net	14.0 hp/ton

ARMOR

Type: Rolled face hardened steel; Bolted assembly

Thickness:	Actual	Angle w/Vertical
Front, Radiator louvers	0.25 inches (6.4mm)	30 degrees
Windshield cover	0.50 inches (12.7mm)	30 degrees
Sides	0.25 inches (6.4mm)	0 degrees
Rear	0.25 inches (6.4mm)	0 degrees
Top, Hood only	0.25 inches (6.4mm)	85 degrees

ARMAMENT

(1) .50 caliber MG HB M2 flexible on skate mount
(1) .30 caliber MG M1919A4 flexible on skate mount
Provision for (1) .45 caliber SMG M1928A1

AMMUNITION

750 rounds .50 caliber
8000 rounds .30 caliber
540 rounds .45 caliber

VISION EQUIPMENT

Vision slots in windshield armor and front door armor
Open top vehicle

ENGINE

Make and Model: Hercules JXD
Type: 6 cylinder, 4 cycle, in-line

Cooling System: Liquid	Ignition: Battery
Displacement:	320 cubic inches
Bore and Stroke:	4.0 x 4.25 inches
Compression Ratio:	6.5:1
Net Horsepower: (max)	87 hp at 2400 rpm
Net Torque: (max)	220 ft-lbs at 1150 rpm
Weight:	750 pounds, dry
Fuel: 72 octane gasoline	54 gallons
Engine Oil:	7 quarts

POWER TRAIN

Master Clutch: Dry, single plate
Transmission: Combination sliding and constant mesh

Gear Ratios:	1st 5.000:1	4th 1.00:1
	2nd 3.070:1	reverse 5.830:1
	3rd 1.710:1	

Transfer Case:

Gear Ratios: high 1.00:1 low 1.87:1

Differential:

Gear Ratio: 5.14:1

RUNNING GEAR

Suspension:

Front and Rear: Semi-elliptic leaf spring
4 wheels (2/side)
Combat Tires, 12 ply
Tire Size: 8.25 x 20

Steering: Two front wheels

Type: Cam and twin lever

Brakes: Hydraulic, internal expanding

Operation: Foot pedal

ELECTRICAL SYSTEM

Nominal Voltage: 12 volts DC
Main Generator: (1) 12 volts, 55 amperes, driven by main engine
Auxiliary Generator: None
Battery: (1) 12 volts

COMMUNICATIONS

Radio: SCR 506, 508, or 510

FIRE AND GAS PROTECTION

(1) 2 pound carbon dioxide, portable
(1) 1½ quart decontaminating apparatus M2

PERFORMANCE

Maximum Speed: Level road	50 miles/hour
Maximum Grade:	60 per cent
Maximum Trench:	1.5 feet
Maximum Vertical Wall:	12 inches
Maximum Fording Depth:	28 inches
Minimum Turning Circle: (diameter)	57 feet
Cruising Range: Roads approx.	250 miles

ARMORED CAR T17
(6 wheels, 6 or 4 wheels driven)

GENERAL DATA

Crew:	5 men
Length:	218 inches
Width:	102 inches
Height:	91 inches
Fire Height:	78 inches
Turret Ring Diameter: Inside	54 inches
Tread:	86 inches
Wheelbase: Front to intermediate axle	96 inches
Front to rear axle	146 inches
Ground Clearance:	13.5 inches
Approach Angle:	40 degrees
Departure Angle:	25 degrees
Weight, Combat Loaded:	32,000 pounds
Weight, Unstowed:	28,600 pounds
Power to Weight Ratio: Net	13.8 hp/ton

ARMOR

Type: Turret, cast homogeneous steel; Hull, rolled and cast
homogeneous steel; Welded assembly

Hull Thickness:	Actual	Angle w/Vertical
Front, Upper	0.75 inches (19.1mm)	42 degrees
Middle	0.75 inches (19.1mm)	57 degrees
Lower	0.75 inches (19.1mm)	45 degrees
Sides	0.75 inches (19.1mm)	22 degrees
Rear	0.50 inches (12.7mm)	10 degrees
Top, Front	0.625 inches (15.9mm)	90 degrees
Rear	0.375 inches (9.5mm)	85 degrees
Floor	0.25 inches (6.4mm)	90 degrees
Turret Thickness:		
Gun Shield	1.0 inches (25.4mm)	0 to 52 degrees
Front	1.25 inches (31.8mm)	45 degrees
Sides	1.25 inches (31.8mm)	22 degrees
Rear	1.25 inches (31.8mm)	12 degrees
Top	0.75 inches (19.1mm)	90 degrees

ARMAMENT

Primary: 37mm Gun M6 in Mount M24 in turret

Traverse: Hydraulic and manual	360 degrees
Traverse Rate: (max)	20 seconds/360 degrees
Elevation: Manual	+45 to -10 degrees
Firing Rate: (max)	30 rounds/minute
Loading System:	Manual
Stabilizer System:	Elevation only

Secondary:

(1) .30 caliber MG M1919A4 coaxial w/37mm gun in turret
(1) .30 caliber MG M1919A4 in bow mount
(1) .30 caliber MG M1919A4 flexible AA mount on turret
Provision for (1) .45 caliber SMG M1928A1

AMMUNITION

111 rounds 37mm
450 rounds .45 caliber
4750 rounds .30 caliber
12 hand grenades

FIRE CONTROL AND VISION EQUIPMENT

Primary Weapon: Periscope M4 w/Telescope M40

Vision Devices:	Direct	Indirect
Driver	Door and vision slot	Periscope M6 (2)
Asst. Driver	Door and vision slot	Periscope M6 (1)
Commander	Hatch	Periscope M6 (2)
Gunner	None	Periscope M4 (1) w/Telescope M40
Loader	Hatch	Periscope M6 (1)

Total Periscopes: M4 (1), M6 (6)

ENGINE

Make and Model: Hercules JXD (2)	
Type: 6 cylinder, 4 cycle, in-line (each engine)	
Cooling System: Liquid	Ignition: Battery
Displacement:	320 cubic inches (each engine)
Bore and Stroke:	4.0 x 4.25 inches
Compression Ratio:	6.7:1
Net Horsepower: (max)	220 hp at 3200 rpm (110 hp/engine)
Net Torque: (max)	440 ft-lbs at 1150 rpm (220/engine)
Weight:	1500 pounds, dry (750/engine)
Fuel: 72 octane gasoline	75 gallons
Engine Oil:	14 quarts (7 quarts/engine)

POWER TRAIN

Master Clutch: Dry, single plate
Transmission: Synchromesh, 4 speeds forward, 1 reverse

Gear Ratios:	1st	6.499:1	4th	1.000:1
	2nd	3.543:1	reverse	6.987:1
	3rd	1.752:1		

Transfer Case:

Gear Ratios:	high	1.037:1	low	1.941:1

Differential: Front, intermediate and rear
Gear Ratio: 6.667:1

RUNNING GEAR

Suspension:
Front and Rear: Leaf spring
6 disc wheels (3/side)
Combat Tires: 14 ply
Tire Size: 12.00 x 20
Steering: Two front wheels
Type: Worm and roller
Steering Ratio: 28.4:1
Brakes: Hydraulic, internal expanding
Operation: Foot pedal

ELECTRICAL SYSTEM

Nominal Voltage: 24 volts DC
Main Generator: (2) 24 volts, 50 amperes, driven by each engine
Auxiliary Generator: None
Battery: (2) 12 volts in series

COMMUNICATIONS

Radio: British Number 19
Interphone: 5 stations
Flag Set M238

FIRE AND GAS PROTECTION

(2) 10 pound carbon dioxide, fixed
(1) 4 pounds carbon dioxide, portable
(1) 1½ quart decontaminating apparatus M2

PERFORMANCE

Maximum Speed: Level road	60 miles/hour
Maximum Grade:	60 per cent
Maximum Trench:	1.5 feet
Maximum Vertical Wall:	18 inches
Maximum Fording Depth:	32 inches
Minimum Turning Circle: (diameter)	60 feet
Cruising Range: Roads approx.	250 miles

ARMORED CAR T17E1
(4 wheels, 4 or 2 wheels driven)

GENERAL DATA

Crew:	5 men
Length:	216 inches
Width:	106 inches
Height:	112 inches
Fire Height:	78 inches
Turret Ring Diameter: Inside	54 inches
Tread:	89 inches
Wheelbase:	120 inches
Ground Clearance:	15 inches
Approach Angle:	57 degrees
Departure Angle:	27 degrees
Weight, Combat Loaded:	30,705 pounds
Weight, Unstowed:	27,223 pounds
Power to Weight Ratio: Net	12.6 hp/ton

ARMOR

Type: Turret, cast homogeneous steel; Hull, rolled homogeneous steel; Welded assembly

Hull Thickness:	Actual	Angle/Vertical
Front, Upper	0.875 inches (22.2mm)	30 degrees
Lower	0.625 inches (15.9mm)	45 degrees
Sides	0.75 inches (19.1mm)	13 degrees
Rear	0.375 inches (9.5mm)	30 degrees
Top	0.50 inches (12.7mm)	90 degrees
Floor, Front	0.50 inches (12.7mm)	90 degrees
Rear	0.25 inches (6.4mm)	90 degrees

Turret Thickness:		
Gun Shield	1.00 inches (25.4mm)	0 to 52 degrees
Front	1.75 inches (44.5mm)	45 degrees
Sides	1.25 inches (31.8mm)	22 degrees
Rear	1.25 inches (31.8mm)	12 degrees
Top	0.50 inches (12.7mm)	90 degrees

ARMAMENT

Primary: 37mm Gun M6 in Mount M24A1 in turret

Traverse: Hydraulic and manual	360 degrees
Traverse Rate: (max)	20 seconds/360 degrees
Elevation: Manual	+40 to -7 degrees
Firing Rate: (max)	30 rounds/minute
Loading System:	Manual
Stabilizer System:	*Elevation only

Secondary:

(1) .30 caliber MG M1919A4 coaxial w/37mm gun in turret
(1) .30 caliber MG M1919A4 in bow mount
(1) .30 caliber MG M1919A4 flexible AA mount on turret
(1) 2 inch smoke mortar M3 fixed in turret
Provision for (1) .45 caliber SMG M1928A1

AMMUNITION

103 rounds 37mm
450 rounds .45 caliber
5250 rounds .30 caliber
14 smoke projectiles 2 inch
12 hand grenades

FIRE CONTROL AND VISION EQUIPMENT

Primary Weapon: Periscope M4 w/Telescope M40

Vision Devices:	Direct	Indirect
Driver	Door and vision slot	Periscope M6 (2)
Asst. Driver	Door and vision slot	Periscope M6 (1)
Commander	Hatch	Periscope M6 (2)
Gunner	None	Periscope M4 (1) w/Telescope M40
Loader	Hatch	Periscope M6 (1)

Total Periscopes: M4 (1), M6 (6)

* Stabilizer on early vehicles only

ENGINE

Make and Model: GMC 270 (2)
Type: 6 cylinder, 4 cycle, in-line (each engine)
Cooling System: Liquid   Ignition: Battery

Displacement:	269.5 cubic inches (each engine)
Bore and Stroke:	3.78 x 4.0 inches
Compression Ratio:	6.75:1
Net Horsepower: (max)	194 hp at 3000 rpm (97 hp/engine)
Net Torque: (max)	432.6 ft-lbs at 1000 rpm (216.3/engine)
Weight:	1660 pounds, dry (830/engine)
Fuel: 70 octane gasoline	138 gallons (62 gallon internal tank + two 38 gallon jettison tanks)
Engine Oil:	16 quarts (8/engine)

POWER TRAIN

Transmission: Hydramatic, 4 speeds forward, 1 reverse

Gear Ratios:	1st	4.23:1	4th	1.00:1
	2nd	2.92:1	reverse	5.80:1
	3rd	1.45:1		

Transfer Case: Two speed, constant mesh
  Gear Ratios: high   0.66:1   low   1.52:1
Differential: Front and rear
  Gear Ratio: 9.02:1

RUNNING GEAR

Suspension:
   Front and Rear: Semi-elliptic leaf spring
   4 wheels (2/side)
   Combat Tires: 12 ply
   Tire Size: 14.00 x 20
Steering: Two front wheels
   Type: Recirculating ball w/hydraulic power assist
   Steering Ratio: 26:1
Brakes: Hydraulic, internal expanding
   Operation: Foot pedal

ELECTRICAL SYSTEM

Nominal Voltage: 24 volts DC
Main Generator: (2) 24 volts, 50 amperes, driven by each engine
Auxiliary Generator: None
Battery: (4) 6 volts in series

COMMUNICATIONS

Radio: British Number 19
Interphone: 5 stations
Flag Set M238

FIRE AND GAS PROTECTION

(2) 10 pound carbon dioxide, fixed
(1) 4 pound carbon dioxide, portable
(1) 1½ quart decontaminating apparatus M2

PERFORMANCE

Maximum Speed: Level road	55 miles/hour
Maximum Grade:	57 per cent
Maximum Trench:	1.5 feet
Maximum Vertical Wall:	21 inches
Maximum Fording Depth:	32 inches
Minimum Turning Circle: (diameter)	55 feet
Cruising Range: Roads approx.	450 miles

ARMORED CAR T17E2
(4 wheels, 4 or 2 wheels driven)

GENERAL DATA

Crew:	3 men
Length:	214 inches
Width:	106 inches
Height:	95.38 inches
Fire Height:	80.25 inches
Turret Ring Diameter: Inside	44 inches
Tread:	89 inches
Wheelbase:	120 inches
Ground Clearance :	15 inches
Approach Angle:	57 degrees
Departure Angle:	27 degrees
Weight, Combat Loaded:	26,558 pounds
Weight, Unstowed:	24,097 pounds
Power to Weight Ratio: Net	14.6 hp/ton

ARMOR

Type: Turret, rolled homogeneous steel; Hull, rolled
    homogeneous steel; Welded assembly

Hull Thickness:	Actual	Angle w/Vertical
Front, Upper	0.875 inches (22.2mm)	30 degrees
Lower	0.625 inches (15.9mm)	45 degrees
Sides	0.75 inches (19.1mm)	13 degrees
Rear	0.375 inches (9.5mm)	30 degrees
Top	0.50 inches (12.7mm)	90 degrees
Floor, Front	0.50 inches (12.7mm)	90 degrees
Rear	0.25 inches (6.4mm)	90 degrees

Turret Thickness:		
Gun Shield	1.25 inches (31.8mm)	45 degrees
Front	1.25 inches (31.8mm)	0 degrees
Sides	1.25 inches (31.8mm)	0 degrees
Rear	1.25 inches (31.8mm)	0 degrees

ARMAMENT

    (2) .50 caliber MGHB M2 TT in Fraser-Nash turret mount
    Provision for (1) .45 caliber SMG M1928A1

AMMUNITION

    2610 rounds .50 caliber
    450 rounds .45 caliber

FIRE CONTROL AND VISION EQUIPMENT

Primary Weapons: Navy Mark IX Sight

Vision Devices:	Direct	Indirect
Driver	Door and vision slot	Periscope M6 (2)
Asst. Driver	Door and vision slot	Periscope M6 (1)
Gunner	Open top turret	None

Total Periscopes: M6 (3)

ENGINE

Make and Model: GMC 270 (2)	
Type: 6 cylinder, 4 cycle, in-line (each engine)	
Cooling System: Liquid Ignition: Battery	
Displacement:	269.5 cubic inches (each engine)
Bore and Stroke:	3.78 x 4.0 inches
Compression Ratio:	6.75:1
Net Horsepower: (max)	194 hp at 3000 rpm (97 hp/engine)
Net Torque: (max)	432.6 ft-lbs at 1000 rpm (216.3/engine)
Weight:	1660 pounds, dry (830/engine)
Fuel: 70 octane gasoline	138 gallons (62 gallon internal tank + two 38 gallon jettison tanks)
Engine Oil:	16 quarts (8/engine)

POWER TRAIN

Transmission: Hydramatic, 4 speeds forward, 1 reverse

Gear Ratios:	1st	4.23:1	4th	1.00:1
	2nd	2.92:1	reverse	5.80:1
	3rd	1.45:1		

Transfer Case: Two speed, constant mesh

Gear Ratios:	high	0.66:1	low	1.52:1

Differential: Front and rear
    Gear Ratio: 9.02:1

RUNNING GEAR

Suspension:
    Front and Rear: Semi-elliptic leaf spring
    4 wheels (2/side)
    Combat Tires: 12 ply
    Tire Size: 14.00 x 20

Steering: Two front wheels
    Type: Circulating ball w/hydraulic assist
    Steering Ratio: 26:1

Brakes: Hydraulic, internal expanding
    Operation: Foot pedal

ELECTRICAL SYSTEM

Nominal Voltage: 24 volts DC
Main Generator: (2) 24 volts, 50 amperes, driven by each engine
Auxiliary Generator: None
Battery: (4) 6 volts in series

COMMUNICATIONS

Radio: British Number 19
Interphone: 3 stations
Flag Set M238

FIRE AND GAS PROTECTION

    (2) 10 pound carbon dioxide, fixed
    (1) 4 pound carbon dioxide, portable
    (1) 1½ quart decontaminating apparatus M2

PERFORMANCE

Maximum Speed: Level road	55 miles/hour
Maximum Grade:	57 per cent
Maximum Trench:	1.5 feet
Maximum Vertical Wall:	21 inches
Maximum Fording Depth:	32 inches
Minimum Turning Circle: (diameter)	55 feet
Cruising Range: Roads approx.	450 miles

ARMORED CAR T18E2
(8 wheels, 8 or 4 wheels driven)

GENERAL DATA

Crew:	5 men
Length:	246 inches
Width:	121 inches
Height:	103.25 inches
Fire Height:	84.25 inches
Turret Ring Diameter: Inside	64 inches
Tread:	102.5 inches
Wheelbase: Front to 2nd axle	51 inches
Front to 3rd axle	146 inches
Front to rear axle	197 inches
Ground Clearance:	13.5 inches
Approach Angle:	90 degrees
Departure Angle:	51 degrees
Weight, Combat Loaded:	53,000 pounds
Weight, Unstowed:	49,000 pounds
Power to Weight ratio: Net	9.4 hp/ton

ARMOR

Type: Turret, cast homogeneous steel; Hull, rolled and cast homogeneous steel; Welded assembly

Hull Thickness:	Actual	Angle w/Vertical
Front, Upper	2.0 inches (50.8mm)	15 degrees
Middle	1.25 inches (31.8mm)	18 to 75 degrees
Lower	2.0-1.0 inches (50.8-25.4mm)	0 to 18 degrees
Sides	1.25 inches (31.8mm)	0 degrees
Rear	1.0 inches (25.4mm)	0 degrees
Top, Front	0.75 inches (19.1mm)	90 degrees
Rear	0.50 inches (12.7mm)	82 degrees
Floor	0.375 inches (9.5mm)	90 degrees

Turret Thickness:		
Gun Shield	2.0 inches (50.8mm)	0 to 45 degrees
Front	1.5 inches (38.1mm)	23 degrees
Sides	1.5 inches (38.1mm)	23 degrees
Rear	1.5 inches (38.1mm)	10 degrees
Top	0.75 inches (19.1mm)	90 degrees

ARMAMENT

Primary: 57mm Gun Mark III in Mount T63 in turret

Traverse: Hydraulic and manual	360 degrees
Traverse Rate: (max)	20 seconds/360 degrees
Elevation: Manual	+60 to -10 degrees
Firing Rate: (max)	30 rounds/minute
Loading System:	Manual
Stabilizer System:	Elevation only

Secondary:
(1) .30 caliber MG M1919A4 coaxial w/57mm gun in turret
(1) .30 caliber MG M1919A4 in bow mount
(1) 2 inch smoke mortar M3 fixed in turret
Provision for (1) .45 caliber SMG M1928A1

AMMUNITION
64 rounds 57mm
5000 rounds .30 caliber
480 rounds .45 caliber
14 rounds 2 inch, smoke
12 hand grenades

FIRE CONTROL AND VISION EQUIPMENT

Primary Weapon: Periscope M4 (1) and Telescope M57

Vision Devices:	Direct	Indirect
Driver	Door and vision slot	Periscope M6 (2)
Asst. Driver	Door and vision slot	Periscope M6 (1)
Commander	Hatch	Periscope M6 (2)
Gunner	None	Periscope M4 (1)
Loader	Hatch	Periscope M6 (1)

Total Periscopes: M4 (1), M6 (6)

ENGINE

Make and Model: GMC 329 (2)
Type: 6 cylinder, 4 cycle, in-line (each engine)
Cooling System: Liquid   Ignition: Battery
Displacement: 329 cubic inches (each engine)
Bore and Stroke: 3.94 x 4.5 inches
Compression Ratio: 6.5:1
Net Horsepower: (max)   250 hp at 3000 rpm (125 hp/engine)
Net Torque: (max)   490 ft-lbs at 1000 rpm (245/engine)
Weight: 1750 pounds, dry (875/engine)
Fuel: 74 octane gasoline 140 gallons (90 gallon internal tank + two 25 gallon jettison tanks)
Engine Oil: 24 quarts (12/engine)

POWER TRAIN

Torque Converter: Spicer
    Ratio: 5:1
Transmission: Helical gear, 3 speeds forward, 1 reverse

Gear Ratios:	1st	4.68:1	3rd	1.095:1
	2nd	2.31:1	reverse	4.92:1

Transfer Case: Helical gear, Single speed
    Gear Ratio: 1.075:1
Differential: All four axles
    Gear Ratio: 7.16:1

RUNNING GEAR

Suspension:
    Articulated, leaf spring
    8 disc wheels (4/side) in 2 bogies
    Combat Tires:
    Tire Size: 14.00 x 20
Steering: Four front wheels
    Type: Recirculating ball w/hydraulic power
    Steering Ratio: 26:7
Brakes: Hydraulic, internal expanding
    Operation: Foot pedal

ELECTRICAL SYSTEM

Nominal Voltage: 24 volts DC
Main Generator: (2) 24 volts, 50 amperes, driven by each engine
Auxiliary Generator: None
Battery: (4) 6 volts in series

COMMUNICATIONS:

Radio: British Number 19
Interphone: 5 stations
Flag Set M238

FIRE AND GAS PROTECTION

(2) 10 pounds carbon dioxide, fixed
(1) 4 pound carbon dioxide, portable
(1) 1½ quart decontaminating apparatus M2

PERFORMANCE

Maximum Speed: Level road	50 miles/hour
Maximum Grade:	60 per cent
Maximum Trench:	1.5 feet
Maximum Vertical Wall:	21 inches
Maximum Fording Depth:	40 inches
Minimum Turning Circle: (diameter)	80 feet
Cruising Range: Roads approx.	300 miles

LIGHT ARMORED CAR M8
(6 wheels, 6 or 4 wheels driven)

GENERAL DATA

Crew:	4 men
Length:	197 inches
Width:	100 inches
Height: Overall	88.5 inches
Fire Height:	68.5 inches
Turret Ring Diameter: Inside	54 inches
Tread:	76 inches
Wheelbase: Front to intermediate axle	128 inches
Front to rear axle	80 inches
Ground Clearance:	11.5 inches
Approach Angle:	54 degrees
Departure Angle:	39 degrees
Weight, Combat Loaded:	17,400 pounds
Weight, Unstowed:	14,500 pounds
Power to Weight Ratio: Net	12.6 hp/ton

ARMOR

Type: Turret, rolled and cast homogeneous steel; Hull, rolled homogeneous steel; Welded assembly

Hull Thickness:	Actual	Angle w/Vertical
Front, Upper	0.75 inches (19.1mm)	45 degrees
Middle	0.50 inches (12.7mm)	60 degrees
Lower	0.625 inches (15.9mm)	30 degrees
Sides, Upper	0.375 inches (9.5mm)	22 degrees
Lower	0.375 inches (9.5mm)	22 degrees
Rear	0.375 inches (9.5mm)	0 degrees
Top, Front	0.25 inches (6.4mm)	83 degrees
Rear	0.25 inches (6.4mm)	86 degrees
Floor	0.25 inches (6.4mm)	90 degrees

Turret Thickness:		
Gun Shield	1.0 inches (25.4mm)	0 to 60 degrees
Front	0.75 inches (19.1mm)	15 degrees
Sides	0.75 inches (19.1mm)	18 degrees
Rear	0.75 inches (19.1mm)	17 degrees
Top	0.25 inches (6.4mm)	90 degrees

ARMAMENT

Primary: 37mm Gun M6 in Mount M23A1 in turret

Traverse: Manual	360 degrees
Elevation: Manual	+20 to -10 degrees
Firing Rate: (max)	30 rounds/minute
Loading System:	Manual
Stabilizer System:	None

Secondary:
  (1) .50 caliber MG HB M2 flexible AA mount on turret
  (1) .30 caliber MG M1919A4 coaxial w/37mm gun in turret
  Provision for (4) .30 caliber Carbine M1

AMMUNITION

  80 rounds 37mm *
  400 rounds .50 caliber
  1500 rounds .30 caliber MG
  400 rounds .30 caliber Carbine
  12 hand grenades
  6 antitank mines M1A1
  4 smoke pots M1 or M2

FIRE CONTROL AND VISION EQUIPMENT

Primary Weapon: Telescope M70D

Vision Devices:	Direct	Indirect
Driver	Hatch and vision slots (2)	Protectoscope (1)
Asst. Driver	Hatch vision slots (2)	Protectoscope (1)
Commander	Open top turret	None
Gunner	Open top turret	None

Total Protectoscopes: (2)

ENGINE

Make and Model: Hercules JXD	
Type: 6 cylinder, 4 cycle, in-line	
Cooling System: Liquid Ignition: Battery	
Displacement:	320 cubic inches
Bore and Stroke:	4.0 x 4.25 inches
Compression Ratio	6.7: 1
Net Horsepower: (max)	110 hp at 3200 rpm
Net Torque: (max)	220 ft-lbs at 1150 rpm
Weight:	750 pounds, dry
Fuel: 72 octane gasoline	56 gallons
Engine Oil	7 quarts

POWER TRAIN

Master Clutch: Dry, single plate
Transmission: Synchronized, selective gear

Gear Ratios:	1st	6.499:1	4th	1.000:1
	2nd	3.543:1	reverse	6.987:1
	3rd	1.752:1		

Transfer Case: Constant mesh
  Gear Ratios: high 1.000:1   low 1.956:1
Differential: Front, intermediate and rear
  Gear Ratio: 6.667:1

RUNNING GEAR

Suspension:
  Front and Rear: Semi-elliptic leaf spring
  6 wheels (3/side)
  Combat Tires, 12 ply
  Tire Size: 9.00 x 20
Steering: Two front wheels
  Type: Worm and roller
  Steering Ratio: 24.4:1
Brakes: Hydraulic, internal expanding
  Operation: Foot pedal

ELECTRICAL SYSTEM

Nominal Voltage: 12 volts DC
Main Generator: (1) 12 volts, 55 amperes, driven by main engine
Auxiliary Generator: None
Battery: (1) 12 volts

COMMUNICATIONS

Radio: SCR 506 and/or 508, 510, 608, 610
Interphone: 4 stations
Flag Set M238

FIRE AND GAS PROTECTION

  (1) 4 pound carbon dioxide, portable
  (2) 1½ quart decontaminating apparatus M2

PERFORMANCE

Maximum Speed: Level road		55 miles/hour
Maximum Grade:		60 per cent
Maximum Trench:		1.5 feet
Maximum Vertical Wall:		12 inches
Maximum Fording Depth:		24 inches
Minimum Turning Circle: (diameter)		56 feet
Cruising Range: Roads	approx.	350 miles

* 16 rounds of 37mm in vehicles with two radios

ARMORED UTILITY CAR M20
(6 wheels, 6 or 4 wheels driven)

GENERAL DATA

Crew:	6 men
Length:	197 inches
Width:	100 inches
Height:	91 inches
Tread:	76 inches
Wheelbase: Front to intermediate axle	128 inches
Front to rear axle	80 inches
Ground Clearance:	11.5 inches
Approach Angle:	54 degrees
Departure Angle:	39 degrees
Weight, Combat Loaded:	15,650 pounds
Weight, Unstowed:	12,800 pounds
Power to Weight Ratio: Net	14.1 hp/ton

ARMOR

Type: Rolled homogeneous steel; Welded assembly

Hull Thickness:		Actual	Angle w/Vertical
Front,	Upper	0.75 inches (19.1mm)	45 degrees
	Middle	0.50 inches (12.7mm)	60 degrees
	Lower	0.625 inches (15.9mm)	30 degrees
Sides,	Upper	0.375 inches (9.5mm)	22 degrees
	Lower	0.375 inches (9.5mm)	22 degrees
Rear		0.375 inches (9.5mm)	0 degrees
Top,	Front	0.25 inches (6.4mm)	83 degrees
	Rear	0.25 inches (6.4mm)	86 degrees
Floor		0.25 inches (6.4mm)	90 degrees

ARMAMENT

(1) .50 caliber MG HB M2 on M49 or M66 mount
Provision for (5) .30 caliber Carbine M1
Provision for (1) 2.36 inch Rocket Launcher M9A1

AMMUNITION

1000 rounds .50 caliber
500 rounds .30 caliber Carbine
12 hand grenades
10 2.36 inch antitank rockets M6A3
3 antitank mines M1A1
4 smoke pots M1 or M2

VISION EQUIPMENT

Vision Devices	Direct	Indirect
Driver	Hatch and vision slots (2)	Protectoscope (1)
Asst. Driver	Hatch and vision slots (2)	Protectoscope (1)
Commander and crew	Open top	None

Total Protectoscopes: (2)

ENGINE

Make and Model: Hercules JXD	
Type: 6 cylinder, 4 cycle, in-line	
Cooling System: Liquid	Ignition: Battery
Displacement:	320 cubic inches
Bore and Stroke:	4.0 x 4.25 inches
Compression Ratio:	6.7:1
Net Horsepower: (max)	110 hp at 3200 rpm
Net Torque: (max)	220 ft-lbs at 1150 rpm
Weight:	750 pounds, dry
Fuel: 72 octane gasoline	56 gallons
Engine Oil:	7 quarts

POWER TRAIN

Master Clutch: Dry, single plate
Transmission: Synchronized, selective gear

Gear Ratios:	1st	6.499:1	4th	1.00:1
	2nd	3.543:1	reverse	6.987:1
	3rd	1.752:1		

Transfer Case: Constant mesh
Gear Ratios: high 1.000:1   low 1.956:1
Differential: Front, intermediate and rear
Gear Ratio: 6.66:1

RUNNING GEAR

Suspension:
Front and Rear: Semi-elliptic leaf spring
6 wheels (3/side)
Combat Tires: 12 ply
Tire Size: 9.00 x 20
Steering: Two front wheels
Type: Worm and roller
Steering Ratio: 24.4:1
Brakes: Hydraulic, internal expanding
Operation: Foot pedal

ELECTRICAL SYSTEM

Nominal Voltage: 12 volts DC
Main Generator: (1) 12 volts, 55 amperes, driven by main engine
Auxiliary Generator: None
Battery: (1) 12 volts

COMMUNICATIONS

Radio: SCR 506 and/or 508, 510, 608, 610
Interphone: None
Flag Set M238

FIRE AND GAS PROTECTION

(1) 4 pounds carbon dioxide, portable
(2) 1½ quart decontaminating apparatus M2

PERFORMANCE

Maximum Speed: Level road	55 miles/hour
Maximum Grade:	60 per cent
Maximum Trench:	1.5 feet
Maximum Vertical Wall:	12 inches
Maximum Fording Depth:	24 inches
Minimum Turning Circle: (diameter)	56 feet
Cruising Range: Roads approx.	350 miles

MULTIPLE GUN MOTOR CARRIAGE T69
(6 wheels, 6 or 4 wheels driven)
(Based upon the Light Armored Car M8)

GENERAL DATA

Crew:	3	men
Length:	197	inches
Width:	100	inches
Height: Guns at zero elevation	85	inches
Tread:	76	inches
Wheelbase: Front to intermediate axle	128	inches
Front to rear axle	80	inches
Ground Clearance:	11.5	inches
Approach Angle:	54	degrees
Departure Angle:	39	degrees
Weight, Combat Loaded:	17,140	pounds
Weight, Unstowed:	15,300	pounds
Power to Weight Ratio: Net	12.8	hp/ton

ARMOR

Type: Turret, rolled homogeneous steel; Hull, rolled homogeneous steel; Welded assembly

Hull Thickness:	Actual	Angle w/Vertical
Front, Upper	0.75 inches (19.1mm)	45 degrees
Middle	0.50 inches (12.7mm)	60 degrees
Lower	0.625 inches (15.9mm)	30 degrees
Sides, Upper	0.375 inches (9.5mm)	22 degrees
Lower	0.375 inches (9.5mm)	22 degrees
Rear	0.375 inches (9.5mm)	0 degrees
Top, Front	0.25 inches (6.4mm)	83 degrees
Rear	0.25 inches (6.4mm)	86 degrees
Floor	0.25 inches (6.4mm)	90 degrees

Turret Thickness:

Front	0.375 inches (9.5mm
Sides	0.375 inches (9.5mm)
Rear	0.375 inches (9.5mm)
Top	open

ARMAMENT

Primary: (4) .50 caliber MG HB (TT) on turret mount

Traverse: Manual and electric	360 degrees
Traverse Rate: (max)	60 degrees/second
Elevation: Manual and electric	+85 to -10 degrees
Firing Rate: Each gun	450-575 rounds/minute
Loading System:	Automatic
Stabilizer System:	None

Secondary:
  Provision for (3) .30 caliber Carbine M1

AMMUNITION
  3800 rounds .50 caliber
  300 rounds .30 caliber, carbine

FIRE CONTROL AND VISION EQUIPMENT

Primary Weapon: Navy illuminated Mark IX Sight

Vision Devices:	Direct	Indirect
Driver	Hatch and vision slots (2)	Protectoscope (1)
Asst. Driver	Hatch and vision slots (2)	Protectoscope (1)
Gunner	Open top	None

Total Protectoscopes: (2)

ENGINE

Make and Model: Hercules JXD	
Type: 6 cylinder, 4 cycle, in-line	
Cooling System: Liquid	Ignition: Battery
Displacement:	320 cubic inches
Bore and Stroke;	4.0 x 4.25 inches
Compression Ratio:	6.7:1
Net Horsepower: (max)	110 hp at 3200 rpm
Net Torque: (max)	220 ft-lbs at 1150 rpm
Weight:	750 pounds, dry
Fuel: 72 octane gasoline	56 gallons
Engine Oil:	7 quarts

POWER TRAIN

Master Clutch: Dry, single plate
Transmission: Synchronized, selective gear

Gear Ratios:	1st	6.499:1	4th	1.000:1
	2nd	3.543:1	reverse	6.987:1
	3rd	1.752:1		

Transfer Case: Constant mesh

Gear Ratios:	high	1.000:1	low	1.956:1

Differential: Front, intermediate and rear
  Gear Ratio: 6.667:1

RUNNING GEAR

Suspension:
  Front and Rear: Semi-elliptic leaf spring
  6 wheels (3/side)
  Combat Tires: 12 ply
  Tire Size: 9.00 x 20
Steering: Two front wheels
  Type: Worm and roller
  Steering Ratio: 24.4:1
Brakes: Hydraulic, internal expanding
  Operation: Foot pedal

ELECTRICAL SYSTEM

Nominal Voltage: 24 volts DC
Main Generator: (1) 1500 watts driven by main engine
Auxiliary generator: (1 or 2) experimental installation
Battery: (2) 12 volts in series

COMMUNICATIONS

Radio: SCR 593
Interphone: 3 stations

FIRE AND GAS PROTECTION

  (1) 4 pound carbon dioxide, portable
  (1) 1½ quart decontaminating apparatus M2

PERFORMANCE

Maximum Speed: Level road	55 mile/hour
Maximum Grade:	60 per cent
Maximum Trench:	1.5 feet
Maximum Vertical Wall:	12 inches
Maximum Fording Depth:	24 inches
Minimum Turning Circle: (diameter)	56 feet
Cruising Range: Roads approx.	350 miles

LIGHT ARMORED CAR T27
(8 wheels, 6 wheels driven)

GENERAL DATA

Crew:	4 men
Length:	202 inches
Width:	90 inches
Height:	78 inches
Fire Height:	approx. 70 inches
Turret Ring Diameter: Inside	52 inches
Tread:	78 inches
Wheelbase: Front to 2nd axle	44 inches
Front to 3rd axle	88 inches
Front to rear axle	132 inches
Ground Clearance:	14.25 inches
Approach Angle:	43 degrees
Departure Angle:	57 degrees
Weight, Combat Loaded:	15,200 pounds
Weight, Unstowed:	13,400 pounds
Power to Weight Ratio: Net	14.5 hp/ton

ARMOR

Type: Turret, rolled homogeneous steel; Hull, rolled homogeneous steel; Welded assembly

Hull Thickness:	Actual	Angle w/Vertical
Front, Upper	0.375 inches (9.5mm)	48 degrees
Lower	0.375 inches (9.5mm)	24 degrees
Sides	0.375 inches (9.5mm)	25 degrees
Rear	0.375 inches (9.5mm)	25 degrees
Top, Front	0.25 inches (6.4mm)	86 degrees
Rear	0.25 inches (6.4mm)	82 degrees
Floor	0.125 inches (3.2mm)	90 degrees
Turret Thickness:		
Front	0.75 inches (19.1mm)	14 degrees
Sides	0.375 inches (9.5mm)	27 degrees
Rear	0.375 inches (9.5mm)	27 degrees
Top	open	

ARMAMENT

Primary: 37mm Gun M6 in Mount M23A1 modified, in turret

Traverse: Manual	360 degrees
Elevation: Manual	+20 to -10 degrees
Firing Rate: (max)	30 rounds/minute
Loading System:	Manual
Stabilizer System:	None

Secondary:
(1) .30 caliber MG M1919A4 coaxial w/27mm gun in turret
(1) .30 caliber MG M1919A4 AA mount on turret
Provision for (4) .30 caliber Carbine M1
Provision for (1) Grenade Launcher M8

AMMUNITION

50 rounds 37mm
1500 rounds .30 caliber
500 rounds .30 caliber, carbine
6 rifle grenades
12 hand grenades
4 smoke pots

FIRE CONTROL AND VISION EQUIPMENT

Primary Weapon: Telescope M54

Vision Devices:	Direct	Indirect
Driver	Hatch	Periscope M6 (1)
Asst. Driver	Hatch	Periscope M6 (1)
Commander	Open top turret	None
Gunner	Open top turret	None

Total Periscopes: M6 (2)

ENGINE

Make and Model: Cadillac Series 42	
Type: 8 cylinder, 4 cycle, vee	
Cooling System: Liquid	Ignition: Battery
Displacement:	346 cubic inches
Bore and Stroke:	3.5 x 4.5 inches
Compression Ratio:	7.06:1
Net Horsepower: (max)	110 hp at 3400 rpm
Gross Horsepower: (max)	148 hp at 3200 rpm
Net Torque: (max)	244 ft-lbs at 1200 rpm
Gross torque: (max)	280 ft-lbs at 1200 rpm
Weight:	584 pounds, dry
Fuel: 80 octane gasoline	62 gallons
Engine Oil:	8 quarts

POWER TRAIN

Transmission: Hydramatic, 4 speeds

Gear Ratios:	1st	3.26:1	3rd	1.44:1
	2nd	2.26:1	4th	1.00:1

Transfer Case: 2 speeds forward, 1 reverse
    Gear Ratios: high 1.062:1, low 3.606:1, reverse 2.921:1
Differential: 1st, 2nd and 4th axles
    Gear Ratio: 6.6:1

RUNNING GEAR

Suspension:
    Torsion bar
    8 wheels (4/side)
    Combat Tires
    Tire Size: 9.00 x 16
Steering: Four front wheels
    Type: Mechanical
Brakes: Hydraulic, internal expanding
    Operation: Foot pedal

ELECTRICAL SYSTEM

Nominal Voltage: 24 volts DC
Main Generator: (1) 1500 watts, driven by main engine
Auxiliary Generator: None
Battery: (4) 6 volts in series

COMMUNICATIONS

Radio: SCR 528 or 510 in hull and SCR 506 in hull
Interphone: 4 stations
Flag Set M238

FIRE PROTECTION

(1) 4 pound carbon dioxide, portable

PERFORMANCE

Maximum Speed: Level Road		60 miles/hour
Maximum Grade:		60 per cent
Maximum Trench:		3.7 feet
Maximum Vertical Wall:		16 inches
Maximum Fording Depth:		48 inches
Minimum Turning Circle: (diameter)		60 feet
Cruising Range: Roads	approx.	300 miles

LIGHT ARMORED CAR M38 (T28)
(6 wheels, 6 wheels driven)

GENERAL DATA

Crew: 4 men
Length: 201.25 inches
Width: 96 inches
Height: 78 inches
Fire Height: approx.   70 inches
Turret Ring Diameter: Inside   56 inches
Tread: 80 inches
Wheelbase: Front to intermediate axle   59 inches
              Front to rear axle   118 inches
Ground Clearance: 14.5 inches
Approach Angle: 52 degrees
Departure Angle: 57 degrees
Weight, Combat Loaded: 15,300 pounds
Weight, Unstowed: 13,000 pounds
Power to Weight Ratio: Net   14.3 hp/ton
              Gross   19.3 hp/ton

ARMOR

Type: Turret, rolled homogeneous steel; Hull, rolled
       homogeneous steel; Welded assembly

Hull Thickness: Actual   Angle w/Vertical
    Front   0.375 inches (9.5mm)   22 to 45 degrees
    Sides   0.375 inches (9.5mm)   22 degrees
    Rear   0.375 inches (9.5mm)   36 degrees
    Top   0.25 inches (6.4mm)   90 degrees
    Floor, Front 0.375 inches (9.5mm)   90 degrees
          Rear   0.125 inches (3.2mm)   90 degrees
Turret Thickness:
    Gun Shield   1.0 inches (25.4mm)   0 degrees
    Front   0.50 inches (12.7mm)   27 degrees
    Sides   0.375 inches (9.5mm)   27 degrees
    Rear   0.375 inches (9.5mm)   20 degrees
    Top   open

ARMAMENT

Primary: 37mm Gun M6 in Mount M23A2 in turret
    Traverse: Manual   360 degrees
    Elevation: Manual   +20 to -10 degrees
    Firing Rate: (max)   30 rounds/minute
    Loading System: Manual
    Stabilizer System: None
Secondary:
    (1) .50 caliber MGHB M2 AA mount on turret
    (1) .30 caliber MG M1919A4 coaxial w/37mm gun in turret
    Provision for (4) .30 caliber Carbine M1
    Provision for (1) Grenade Launcher M8

AMMUNITION

    93 rounds 37mm
    440 rounds .50 caliber
    1750 rounds .30 caliber
    500 rounds .30 caliber, carbine
    6 rifle grenades
    12 hand grenades
    4 smoke pots

FIRE CONTROL AND VISION EQUIPMENT

Primary Weapon: Telescope M70D
Vision Devices: Direct   Indirect
    Driver   Hatch   Periscope M6 (1)
    Commander   Open top turret None
    Gunner   Open top turret None
    Loader   Open top turret None
Total Periscopes: M6 (1)
Provision for Observation Telescope M49

ENGINE

Make and Model: Cadillac Series 42
Type: 8 cylinder, 4 cycle, vee
Cooling System: Liquid   Ignition: Battery
Displacement: 346 cubic inches
Bore and Stroke: 3.5 x 4.5 inches
Compression Ratio: 7.06:1
Net Horsepower: (max)   110 hp at 3400 rpm
Gross Horsepower: (max)   148 hp at 3200 rpm
Net Torque: (max)   244 ft-lbs at 1200 rpm
Gross Torque: (max)   280 ft-lbs at 1200 rpm
Weight: 584 pounds/dry
Fuel: 80 octane gasoline   51 gallons
Engine Oil: 8 quarts

POWER TRAIN

Transmission: Hydramatic, 4 speeds forward, 1 reverse

Gear Ratios:	1st	3.92:1	4th	1.00:1
	2nd	2.53:1	reverse	4.167:1
	3rd	1.55:1		

Transfer Case:
    Gear Ratios: 3.44:1 and 1.392:1
Differential: Front, intermediate and rear
    Gear Ratio: 6.667:1

RUNNING GEAR

Suspension:
    Independent, swing arm, coil spring
    6 wheels (3/side)
    Combat Tires
    Tire Size: 12.50 x 20
Steering: Four front wheels
    Type: Recirculating ball w/hydraulic power assist
Brakes: Hydraulic, internal expanding
    Operation: Foot pedal

ELECTRICAL SYSTEM

Nominal Voltage: 12 volts DC
Main Generator: (1) 3000 watts, driven by main engine
Auxiliary Generator: None
Battery: (1) 12 volts

COMMUNICATIONS

Radio: SCR 528 or 510 in hull and SCR 506 in turret
Interphone: 4 stations
Flag Set M238

FIRE PROTECTION

    (1) 4 pound carbon dioxide, portable

PERFORMANCE

Maximum Speed: Level road   60 miles/hour
Maximum Grade: 60 per cent
Maximum Trench: 4.2 feet
Maximum Vertical Wall: 24 inches
Maximum Fording Depth: 48 inches
Minimum Turning Circle: (diameter)   56 feet
Cruising Range: Roads   approx.   300 miles

ARMORED CAR T19E1
(6 wheels, 6 wheels driven)

GENERAL DATA

Crew:	5 men
Length:	220 inches
Width:	120 inches
Height:	89.2 inches
Fire Height:	approx. 79 inches
Turret Ring Diameter: Inside	54.375 inches
Tread:	102 inches
Wheelbase: Front to intermediate axle	63 inches
Front to rear axle	126 inches
Ground Clearance:	16 inches
Approach Angle:	54 degrees
Departure Angle:	47 degrees
Weight, Combat Loaded:	28,500 pounds
Weight, Unstowed:	27,000 pounds
Power to Weight Ratio: Net	15.5 hp/ton

ARMOR

Type: Turret, rolled homogeneous steel; Hull, rolled
homogeneous steel; Welded assembly

Hull Thickness:	Actual	Angle w/Vertical
Front	0.50 inches (12.7mm)	45 to 75 degrees
Sides	0.375 inches (9.5mm)	15 degrees
Rear	0.375 inches (9.5mm)	0 to 60 degrees
Top	0.25 inches (6.4mm)	83 to 90 degrees
Floor	0.25 inches (6.4mm)	90 degrees

Turret Thickness:		
Front	0.50 inches (12.7mm)	22 degrees
Sides	0.375 inches (9.5mm)	22 degrees
Rear	0.375 inches (9.5mm)	22 degrees
Top	0.25 inches (6.4mm)	90 degrees

ARMAMENT

Primary: 37mm Gun M6 in Mount M23A1 in turret

Traverse: Manual	360 degrees
Elevation: Manual	+45 to -10 degrees
Firing Rate: (max)	30 rounds/minute
Loading System:	Manual
Stabilizer System:	None

Secondary:

(1) .30 caliber MG M1919A4 coaxial w/37mm gun in turret
(1) .30 caliber MG M1919A4 in bow mount
Provision for (5) .30 caliber Carbine M1

AMMUNITION

200 rounds 37mm
12,000 rounds .30 caliber
5,000 rounds .30 caliber, carbine
16 hand grenades
6 antitank mines M1A1
4 smoke pots

FIRE CONTROL AND VISION EQUIPMENT

Primary Weapon: Periscope M4 w/Telescope M40
Telescope M54

Vision Devices:	Direct	Indirect
Driver	Hatch	Periscope M6 (2)
Asst. Driver	Hatch	Periscope M6 (1)
Commander	Hatch	Periscope M6 (1)
Gunner	None	Periscope M4 (1)
Loader	Hatch	None

Total Periscopes: M4 (1), M6(4)

ENGINE

Make and Model: Cadillac Series 42 (2)
Type: 8 cylinder, 4cycle, vee

Cooling System: Liquid		Ignition: Battery
Displacement:		346 cubic inches (each engine)
Bore and Stroke:		3.5 x 4.5 inches
Compression Ratio:		7.06:1
Net Horsepower: (max)		220 hp at 3400 rpm (110 hp/engine)
Gross Horsepower: (max)		296 hp at 3200 rpm (148 hp/engine)
Net Torque: (max)		488 ft-lbs at 1200 rpm (244/engine)
Gross torque: (max)		560 ft-lbs at 1200 rpm (280/engine)
Weight:		1168 pounds, dry (584/engine)

Fuel: 80 octane gasoline   106 gallons
Engine Oil: 16 quarts (8/engine)

POWER TRAIN

Transmission: Hydramatic, (2) 4 speeds forward, 1 reverse

Gear Ratios:			
1st	3.658:1	4th	1.000:1
2nd	2.533:1	reverse	4.31:1
3rd	1.444:1		

Transfer Case:
Gear Ratios: 2.7:1 and 1.1:1
Differential: Front, intermediate and rear
Gear Ratio: 9.02:1

RUNNING GEAR

Suspension:
Independent, swing arm, coil spring
6 wheels (3/side)
Combat Tires
Tire Size: 14.00 x 20
Steering: Four front wheels
Type: Hydraulic power
Brakes: Hydraulic, internal expanding
Operation: Foot pedal

ELECTRICAL SYSTEM

Nominal Voltage: 24 volts DC
Main Generator: (2) 24 volts, 3000 watts (1500/each) driven
by main engines
Auxiliary Generator: None
Battery: (4) 6 volts in series

COMMUNICATIONS

Radio: SCR 508 and SCR 506 or 510
Interphone: 5 stations

FIRE PROTECTION

(1) 10 pound carbon dioxide, fixed
(1) 4 pound carbon dioxide, portable

PERFORMANCE

Maximum Speed: level road	60 miles/hour
Maximum Grade:	57 per cent
Maximum Trench:	5.3 feet
Maximum Vertical Wall:	24 inches
Maximum Fording Depth:	32 inches
Minimum Turning Circle: (diameter)	66 feet
Cruising Range: Roads approx.	300 miles

75mm GUN MOTOR CARRIAGE T66
(6 wheels, 6 wheels driven)
(Based upon the Armored Car T19E1)

GENERAL DATA

Crew:	5	men
Length: Over gun	234	inches
Width:	120	inches
Height:	89.2	inches
Fire Height:	approx. 79	inches
Turret Ring Diameter: Inside	60.5	inches
Tread:	102	inches
Wheelbase: Front to intermediate axle	63	inches
Front to rear axle	126	inches
Ground Clearance:	16	inches
Approach Angle:	54	degrees
Departure Angle:	47	degrees
Weight, Combat Loaded:	31,500	pounds
Weight, Unstowed:	28,000	pounds
Power to Weight Ratio: Net	14.0	hp/ton

ARMOR

Type: Turret, rolled homogeneous steel; Hull, rolled
homogeneous steel; Welded assembly

Hull Thickness:	Actual	Angle w/Vertical
Front	0.50 inches (12.7mm)	45 to 75 degrees
Sides	0.375 inches (9.5mm)	15 degrees
Rear	0.375 inches (9.5mm)	0 to 60 degrees
Top	0.25 inches (6.4mm)	83 to 90 degrees
Floor	0.25 inches (6.4mm)	90 degrees
Turret Thickness:		
Gun Shield	1.0 inches (25.4mm)	0 to 45 degrees
Front	0.50 inches (12.7mm)	22 degrees
Sides	0.375 inches (9.5mm)	22 degrees
Rear	0.375 inches (9.5mm)	22 degrees
Top	open	

ARMAMENT

Primary: 75mm Gun M3 in Mount M34 modified in turret

Traverse: Manual	360 degrees
Elevation: Manual	+ 45 to -10 degrees
Firing Rate: (max)	20 rounds/minute
Loading System:	Manual
Stabilizer System:	None

Secondary:
Provision for (5) .30 caliber Carbine M1

AMMUNITION

63 rounds 75mm
500 rounds .30 caliber, carbine
16 hand grenades

FIRE CONTROL AND VISION EQUIPMENT

Primary Weapon: Periscope M4 w/Telescope M40
Telescope M51

Vision Devices:	Direct	Indirect
Driver	Hatch	Periscope M6 (2)
Asst. Driver	Hatch	Periscope M6 (1)
Commander	Open top	None
Gunner	None	Periscope M4 (1)
Loader	Open top	None

Total Periscopes: M4 (1), M6 (3)

ENGINE

Make and Model: Cadillac Series 42 (2)
Type: 8 cylinder, 4 cycle, vee

Cooling System: Liquid	Ignition: Battery
Displacement:	346 cubic inches (each engine)
Bore and Stroke:	3.5 x 4.5 inches
Compression Ratio:	7.06:1
Net Horsepower: (max)	220 hp at 3400 rpm (110 hp/engine)
Gross Horsepower: (max)	296 hp at 3200 rpm (148 hp/engine)
Net Torque: (max)	488 ft-lbs at 1200 rpm (244/engine)
Gross torque: (max)	560 ft-lbs at 1200 rpm (280/engine)
Weight:	1168 pounds, dry (584/engine)
Fuel: 80 octane gasoline	106 gallons
Engine Oil:	16 quarts (8/engine)

POWER TRAIN

Transmission: Hydramatic, (2) 4 speeds forward, 1 reverse

Gear Ratios:	1st	3.658:1	4th	1.000:1
	2nd	2.533:1	reverse	4.31:1
	3rd	1.444:1		

Transfer Case:
Gear Ratios: 2.7:1 and 1.1:1
Differential: Front, intermediate and rear
Gear Ratio: 9.02:1

RUNNING GEAR

Suspension:
Independent, swing arm, coil spring
6 wheels (3/side)
Combat Tires
Tire Size: 14.00 x 20
Steering: Four front wheels
Type: Hydraulic power
Brakes: Hydraulic, internal expanding
Operation: Foot pedal

ELECTRICAL SYSTEM

Nominal Voltage: 24 volts DC
Main Generator: (2) 24 volts, 3000 watts (1500 each) driven
by main engine
Auxiliary Generator: None
Battery: (4) 6 volts in series

COMMUNICATIONS

SCR 506 and SCR 608 or 610
Interphone: 5 stations

FIRE PROTECTION

(1) 10 pound carbon dioxide, fixed
(1) 4 pound carbon dioxide, portable

PERFORMANCE

Maximum Speed:	60 miles/hour
Maximum Grade:	57 per cent
Maximum Trench:	5.3 feet
Maximum Vertical Wall:	24 inches
Maximum Fording Depth:	32 inches
Minimum Turning Circle: (diameter)	66 feet
Cruising Range: Roads	approx. 300 miles

37mm GUN MOTOR CARRIAGE M6
(4 wheels, 4 or 2 wheels driven)

GENERAL DATA

Crew:	4	men
Length:	178	inches
Width:	88	inches
Height:	82.75	inches
Tread:	64.75	inches
Wheelbase:	98	inches
Ground Clearance:	10.63	inches
Approach Angle:	37	degrees
Departure Angle:	31	degrees
Weight, Combat Loaded:	7350	pounds
Weight, Unstowed:	6620	pounds
Power to Weight Ratio: Net	25.0	hp/ton

Winch: 5000 pound capacity on front of vehicle

ARMOR

Gun shield only, 0.25 inches thick

ARMAMENT

Primary: 37mm Gun M3 on pedestal mount M25 or M26

    Traverse: Manual   360 degrees

    Elevation: Manual   +15 to -10 degrees

          Depression limited except to rear

Secondary:

    Provision for (1) .30 caliber Rifle M1903A1

    Provision for (3) .30 caliber Carbine M1

    Provision for (1) Grenade Launcher

AMMUNITION

    80 rounds 37mm

    10 Antitank Rifle Grenades M9A1

    12 hand grenades

FIRE CONTROL AND VISION EQUIPMENT

Primary Weapon: Telescope M6

Vision Devices: Open vehicle

ENGINE

Make and Model: Dodge T-214

Type: 6 cylinder, 4cycle, in-line

Cooling System: Liquid   Ignition: Battery

Displacement:	230.2 cubic inches
Bore and Stroke:	3.25 x 4.625 inches
Compression Ratio:	6.7:1
Net Horsepower: (max)	99 hp at 3300 rpm
Net Torque: (max)	184 ft-lbs at 1400 rpm
Weight:	603 pounds, dry
Fuel: 70 to 72 octane gasoline	30 gallons
Engine Oil:	5 quarts

POWER TRAIN

Transmission: Selective sliding gear, 4 speeds forward, 1 reverse

Gear Ratios:	1st	6.40:1	4th	1.00:1
	2nd	3.09:1	reverse	7.82:1
	3rd	1.69:1		

Transfer Case: For front wheel drive

    Gear Ratio: 1.00:1

Differential: Front and rear

    Gear Ratio: 5.83:1

RUNNING GEAR

Suspension:

    Front and Rear: Semi-elliptic leaf spring

    4 wheels (2/side)

    Combat Tires

    Tire Size: 9.00 x 16

Steering: Two front wheels

    Type: Worm and sector

    Steering Ratio: 23.2:1

Brakes: Hydraulic, internal expanding

    Operation: Foot pedal

ELECTRICAL SYSTEM

Nominal Voltage: 6 volts DC

Main Generator: 6 volts

Auxiliary Generator: None

Battery: (1) 6 volts

COMMUNICATIONS

Radio: SCR 510

Flag Set M238

FIRE AND GAS PROTECTION

    (1) 1 quart carbon tetrachloride, portable

    (1) 1½ quart decontaminating apparatus M2

PERFORMANCE

Maximum Speed: Level road		55 miles/hour
Maximum Grade:		60 per cent
Maximum Trench		1 foot
Maximum Vertical Wall:		12 inches
Maximum Fording Depth:		35 inches
Minimum Turning Circle: (diameter)		44 feet
Cruising Range: Roads	approx.	180 miles

3 inch GUN MOTOR CARRIAGE T55E1
(8 wheels, 8 wheels driven)

GENERAL DATA

Crew:	4 men
Length: Over gun	281 inches
Length: w/o gun	215 inches
Gun Overhang:	66 inches
Width:	105 inches
Height:	73.5 inches
Fire Height:	67.5 inches
Tread:	92 inches
Wheelbase: Front to rear axle	192 inches
Ground Clearance:	17.25 inches
Approach Angel:	40 degrees
Departure Angle:	78 degrees
Weight, Combat Loaded:	30,200 pounds
Weight, Unstowed:	28,000 pounds
Power to Weight Ratio: Net	14.6 hp/ton

ARMOR

Type: Pilot vehicle assembled with mild steel

Hull Thickness:	Actual	Angle w/Vertical
Front	0.25 inches (6.4mm)	0 degrees
Sides	0.25 inches (6.4mm)	0 degrees
Rear, Upper	0.25 inches (6.4mm)	0 degrees
Lower	0.13 inches (3.2mm)	0 degrees
Top, Front	open	
Rear	0.13 inches (3.2mm)	90 degrees
Floor	0.13 inches (3.2mm)	90 degrees

ARMAMENT

Primary: (1) 3 inch Gun M7 in Mount M4 in front hull

Traverse: Manual	40 degrees (20 degrees left or right)
Elevation: Manual	+15 to -10 degrees
Firing Rate: (max)	15 rounds/minute
Loading System:	Manual
Stabilizer System:	None

Secondary:

None on pilot

AMMUNITION

45 rounds 3 inch

FIRE CONTROL AND VISION EQUIPMENT

Primary Weapon: None installed on pilot

Vision Devices: Open top vehicle

ENGINE

Make and Model: Cadillac Series 42 (2)	
Type: 8 cylinder, 4 cycle, vee	
Cooling System: Liquid	Ignition: Battery
Displacement:	346 cubic inches (each engine)
Bore and Stroke:	3.5 x 4.5 inches
Compression Ratio:	7.06:1
Net Horsepower: (max)	220 hp at 3400 rpm (110 hp/engine)
Gross Horsepower: (max)	296 hp at 3200 rpm (148 hp/engine)
Net Torque: (max)	488 ft-lbs at 1200 rpm (244/engine)
Gross Torque: (max)	560 ft-lbs at 1200 rpm (280/engine)
Weight:	1168 pounds, dry (584/engine)
Fuel: 80 octane gasoline	50 gallons
Engine Oil:	16 quarts (8/engine)

POWER TRAIN

Transmission: Hydramatic, (2) 4 speeds forward, 1 reverse

Gear Ratios:	1st	3.658:1	4th	1.000:1
	2nd	2.533:1	reverse	4.31:1
	3rd	1.444:1		

Transfer Case: (2)

Gear Ratios: 2.48:1 and 1.00:1

Differential: Front and rear

Gear Ratios: 4.5:1 and 6.26:1

Chain drive from axle sprocket to the 4 wheels on each bogie

RUNNING GEAR

Suspension

Leaf springs on each 4 wheel bogie

8 wheels (4/side)

Combat Tires

Tire Size: 14.00 x 20

Steering: Front 4 wheel bogie

Type: Cam and lever w/hydraulic boost

Brakes: Hydraulic

Operation: Hand control

ELECTRICAL SYSTEM

Nominal Voltage: 12 volts DC

Main Generator: (2) 12 volts, 375 watts (each) driven by main engine

Auxiliary Generator: None

Battery: (2) 6 volts in series

COMMUNICATIONS

Radio: SCR 610

Interphone: 4 stations

FIRE PROTECTION

(1) 10 pound carbon dioxide, fixed

(1) 4 pound carbon dioxide, portable

PERFORMANCE

Maximum Speed: Level road	50 miles/hour
Maximum Grade:	60 per cent
Maximum Trench:	3 feet
Maximum Vertical Wall:	40 inches
Maximum Fording Depth:	36 inches
Minimum Turning Circle: (diameter)	98.6 feet
Cruising Range: Roads approx.	150 miles

LIGHT ARMORED CARS XM706, M706 (XM706E1) AND XM706E2
(4 wheels, 4 or 2 wheels driven)

GENERAL DATA

Crew:	Up to 11	men
Length: Overall	224	inches
Width: Overall	89	inches
Height: Over turret, XM706, M706	96	inches
Over Parapet, XM706E2	85.75	inches
Fire Height, XM706, M706	approx. 80	inches
Tread:	73.5	inches
Wheelbase:	105	inches
Ground Clearance: Under hull	24	inches
Under differential	16	inches
Approach Angle:	55	degrees
Departure Angle:	53	degrees
Weight, Combat Loaded:	16,250	pounds
Weight Unstowed: XM706, M706	13,800	pounds
XM706E2	13,300	pounds
Power to Weight Ratio: Gross	23.5	hp/ton

ARMOR

Type: Turret (XM706, M706), rolled hard homogeneous steel;
Hull, rolled hard homogeneous steel; Welded assembly

Hull Thickness:		Actual	Angle w/Vertical
Front, Upper	0.375	inches (9.5mm)	30 degrees
Middle	0.25	inches (6.4mm)	75 degrees
Lower	0.25	inches (6.4mm)	35 degrees
Sides, Upper	0.25	inches (6.4mm)	30 degrees
Lower	0.25	inches (6.4mm)	20 degrees
Rear, Upper	0.25	inches (6.4mm)	30 and 37 degrees
Lower	0.25	inches (6.4mm)	37 degrees
Top	0.25	inches (6.4mm)	90 degrees
Floor	0.375	inches (9.5mm)	90 degrees

Turret Thickness:			
Front	0.375	inches (9.5mm)	curved
Sides	0.25	inches (6.4mm)	30 degrees
Rear	0.25	inches (6.4mm)	30 degrees
Top	0.25	inches (6.4mm)	domed

ARMAMENT

XM706, (2) .30 caliber MG M37 or (1) .30 caliber MG M37
  and (1) .50 caliber MG M2 or (2) 7.62mm MG 42
  in turret
M706, (2) 7.62mm MG M73 or M219 in turret

Traverse: Manual	360 degrees
Elevation: Manual	+59 to -14 degrees

XM706E2, Pintle mounts for 7.62mm M60 MG

AMMUNITION

XM706, 9750 rounds .30 caliber or 7.62mm (1000 ready rounds)
  when armed w/ 2 .30 caliber or 7.62mm MGs
M706, 8580 rounds 7.62mm (880 ready rounds)
XM706E2, 5940 rounds 7.62mm (0 ready rounds)

FIRE CONTROL AND VISION EQUIPMENT

M28C Periscope Sight in turret roof (XM706, M706)
(8) vision blocks in turret (XM706, M706)
(10) vision blocks in hull (late XM706, M706, late XM706E2)
(12) vision blocks in hull (early XM706, early XM706E2)
(9) gun ports in hull (late XM706, M706, late XM706E2)
(11) gun ports in hull (early XM706, early XM706E2)

ENGINE

Make and Model: Chrysler Military waterproof version
Type: 8 cylinder, 4 cycle, vee

Cooling System: Liquid	Ignition: Battery

Displacement:	361 cubic inches
Bore and Stroke:	4.125 x 3.375 inches
Compression Ratio:	7.8:1
Gross Horsepower: (max)	191 hp at 4000 rpm
Gross Torque: (max)	325 ft-lbs at 2400 rpm
Weight:	688 pounds, dry
Fuel: 83 octane gasoline	80 gallons
Engine Oil:	10 quarts

POWER TRAIN

Clutch: Single plate
Transmission: Manual, 5 speed, synchronized in speeds 2 to 5

Gear Ratios:	1st	7.24:1	4th	1.59:1
	2nd	4.33:1	5th	1.00:1
	3rd	2.61:1	reverse	7.24:1

Transfer Case: Single speed w/clutch for front wheel drive
  Gear Ratio: 1.32:1
Axles: Beam type, double reduction w/locking differentials
  Gear Ratio: 6.722:1

RUNNING GEAR

Suspension:
  Front and Rear: Semi-elliptic leaf spring
  Direct acting shock absorber at each wheel
  4 wheels (2/side)
  Combat Tires (run-flat): 12 ply
  Tire Size: 14.00 x 20
Steering: Variable ratio power on two front wheels
  Type: Cam and lever
Brakes: Hydraulic, internal expanding
  Operation: Foot pedal w/vacuum assist

ELECTRICAL SYSTEM

Nominal Voltage: 24 volts DC
Alternator: (1) 28 volts, 60 amperes, driven by main engine
Auxiliary Generator: None
Battery: (2) 12 volts in series

COMMUNICATIONS

Radio: AN/GRC 8, AN/VRC 10, AN/VRC 34
Interphone: 4 stations

FIRE PROTECTION

(2) 2 ¾ pound Freon, portable
(3) 5 pound carbon dioxide, fixed

PERFORMANCE

Maximum Speed: Level road	60 miles/hour
Water	3 miles/hour
Maximum Grade:	50 per cent
Maximum Side Slope:	30 per cent
Maximum Trench:	1.5 feet
Maximum Vertical Wall:	24 inches
Maximum Fording Depth:	floats
Minimum Turning Circle: (diameter)	54 feet
Cruising Range: Roads	approx. 400 miles

LIGHT ARMORED VEHICLE LAV-25
(8 wheels, 8 or 4 wheels driven)

GENERAL DATA

Crew:	(3 + 6 troops)	9	men
Length: Overall		252.6	inches
Width: Overall		98.4	inches
Height: Over turret		100.9	inches
Fire Height:	approx.	83	inches
Tread: Front		85.8	inches
Rear		86.8	inches
Wheelbase: Front to 2nd axle		43.3	inches
Front to 3rd axle		95.9	inches
Front to rear axle		136.8	inches
Ground Clearance: Under differential		14.9	inches
Approach Angle:		40	degrees
Departure Angle:		45	degrees
Weight, Combat Loaded:		28,400	pounds
Weight, Unstowed:		24,470	pounds
Power to Weight Ratio:		19.4	hp/ton
Self-Recovery Winch Capacity:		15,000	pounds

ARMOR

Type: Turret, rolled hard homogeneous steel;
    Hull, rolled hard homogeneous steel; Welded assembly
Protection against 7.62mm ball ammunition at point blank range
Protection against 14.5mm ammunition w/applique armor

ARMAMENT

Primary: 25mm automatic gun M242 in turret mount

Traverse: Hydraulic and manual	360 degrees
Traverse Rate: (max)	10 seconds/360 degrees
Elevation: Hydraulic and manual	+60 to -8 degrees
Elevation Rate: (max)	25 degrees/second
Firing Rate:	single shot, 100, 200 rounds/minute
Stabilizer System:	azimuth and elevation

Secondary:
    (1) 7.62mm MG M240 coaxial w/25mm gun in turret
    (1) 7.62mm MG M60 (or M240E1) pintle mount on turret roof
    (2) M257 smoke grenade launchers on turret front

AMMUNITION

Ready:
    210 rounds 25mm
    400 rounds 7.62mm
    8 L8A1 smoke grenades in launchers
Stowed:
    420 rounds 25mm
    1200 rounds 7.62mm
    8 L8A1 smoke grenades
    4050 rounds 5.56mm for M16A1 rifles

FIRE CONTROL AND VISION EQUIPMENT

Primary Weapon: Periscope M36/LAV and Thermal Sight

Vision Devices:	Direct	Indirect
Driver	Hatch	Periscope M17 (3)
		Night vision periscope AN/VVS-2(V)4
Commander	Hatch	Periscope M27 (7)
Gunner	Hatch	Periscope M27 (1)
Troops	Hatch and	None
	Vision Blocks (6)	

Total Periscopes: M17 (3), M27 (8), M36/LAV (1)
    AN/VVS-2(V)4 (1), Thermal Sight (1)

ENGINE

Make and Model: General Motors 6V53T	
Type: 6 cylinder, 2 cycle, vee	
Cooling System: Liquid	Ignition: Compression
Displacement:	318 cubic inches
Bore and Stroke:	3.875 x 4.5 inches
Compression Ratio:	18.0:1
Gross Horsepower: (max)	275 hp at 2800 rpm
Gross Torque: (max)	586 ft-lbs at 2000 rpm
Weight:	1495 pounds, dry
Fuel: diesel oil MIL-VV-F-800	71 gallons
Engine Oil:	22 quarts

POWER TRAIN

Transmission: Allison MT653, 5 speeds forward, 1 reverse
    Single stage, polyphase torque converter
Transfer Case: AG-VST(mod)
    Gear Ratio: 0.5778:1
Differential: AS-DL500
    Gear Ratio: 2.23:1
Wheel Drive Assembly: Planetary hubs
    Gear Ratio: 3.79:1

RUNNING GEAR

Suspension:
    8 wheels (4/side)
    Front 4 wheels, independent, coil springs
    Rear 4 wheels, independent, torsion bars
    Shock absorbers on all 8 wheels
    Tires: Michelin XL w/run-flat inserts
    Tire Size: 11.00 x 16
Steering: Front four wheels
    Type: Hydraulic-mechanical
Brakes: Pneumatic-hydraulic
    Operation: Foot pedal

ELECTRICAL SYSTEM

Nominal Voltage: 24 volts DC
Alternator: 27.5 volts, 220 amperes driven by main engine
Auxiliary Generator: None
Battery: (4) 12 volts, 2 sets of 2 in series connected in parallel

COMMUNICATIONS

Radio: (2) AN/VRC-92A, AN/PRC-104, AN/PRC-68, PLRS
CVC Helmet: 2 in turret, 2 in hull

FIRE PROTECTION

    (2) 9.0 pound Halon, fixed
    (2) 2.75 pound Halon, portable

NBC PROTECTION

NBC System M13A1
    Detection and Warning System: M8A1
        Detection and Warning Device: M43A1
    Precleaner/Particulate Filter Assembly: M1A1-19
    Gas Filter: (2) M18
    Heater, Air/Electric: M3
    Ventilated Face Masks: M25A1

PERFORMANCE

Maximum Speed: Level road		62 miles/hour
Water		6.5 miles/hour
Maximum Grade:		60 per cent
Maximum Side Slope:		30 per cent
Maximum Trench:		5.7 feet
Maximum Vertical Wall:		19.7 inches
Maximum Fording Depth:		Floats
Minimum Turning Circle: (diameter)		50.8 feet
Cruising Range: Roads	approx.	400 miles

LIGHT ARMORED VEHICLE BATTALION COMMAND AND CONTROL LAV-C2
(8 wheels, 8 or 4 wheels driven)

GENERAL DATA

Crew:	7 men
Length: Overall	259.0 inches
Width: Overall	98.4 inches
Height:	110.0 inches
Tread: Front	85.8 inches
Rear	86.8 inches
Wheelbase: Front to 2nd axle	43.3 inches
Front to 3rd axle	95.9 inches
Front to rear axle	136.8 inches
Ground Clearance: Under differential	14.9 inches
Approach Angle:	40 degrees
Departure Angle:	45 degrees
Weight, Combat Loaded:	28,200 pounds
Weight, Unstowed:	23,980 pounds
Power to Weight Ratio:	19.5 hp/ton
Self-Recovery Winch Capacity:	15,000 pounds

ARMOR

Type: Hull, rolled hard homogeneous steel; Welded assembly
Protection against 7.62mm ball ammunition at point blank range
Protection against 14.5mm ammunition w/applique armor

ARMAMENT

    (1) 7.62mm MG on pintle mount
    (2) M257 smoke grenade launchers on sides of upper hull

AMMUNITION

   Ready:
   200 rounds 7.62mm
   8 L8A1 smoke grenades in launchers
   Stowed:
   800 rounds 7.62mm
   8 L8A1 smoke grenades

FIRE CONTROL AND VISION EQUIPMENT

Laser rangefinder: AN/GVS-5 (1)

Vision Devices:	Direct	Indirect
Driver	Hatch	Periscope M17 (3)
		Night vision periscope AN/VVS-2(V)4 (1)
Commander	Hatch	Periscope M17 (5)
		Night vision periscope AN/VVS-2(V)4 (1)
Battalion Commander	Hatch	Periscope M17 (8)
		Night vision periscope AN/VVS-2(V)4
Staff Officer	Vision block (1)	None
Radio Operators	Hatch (2)	Periscope M17 (2)

Total Periscopes: M17 (18), AN/VVS-2(V)4 (3)

ENGINE

Make and Model: General Motors 6V53T
Type: 6 cylinder, 2 cycle, vee

Cooling System: Liquid	Ignition: Compression
Displacement:	318 cubic inches
Bore and Stroke:	3.875 x 4.5 inches
Compression Ratio:	18.0:1
Gross Horsepower: (max)	275 hp at 2800 rpm
Gross Torque: (max)	586 ft-lbs at 2000 rpm
Weight	1495 pounds, dry
Fuel: diesel oil M-VV-F-800	71 gallons
Engine Oil:	22 quarts

POWER TRAIN

Transmission: Allison MT653, 5 speeds forward, 1 reverse
    Single stage, polyphase torque converter
Transfer Case: AG-VST(mod)
   Gear Ratio: 0.5778:1
Differential: AS-DL500
   Gear Ratio: 2.23:1
Wheel Drive Assembly: Planetary hubs
   Gear Ratio: 3.79:1

RUNNING GEAR

Suspension:
   8 wheels (4/side)
   Front four wheels, independent, coil springs
   Rear four wheels, independent, torsion bars
   Shock absorbers on all 8 wheels
   Tires: Michelin XK, w/run-flat inserts
   Tire Size: 11.00 x 16
Steering: Front four wheels
   Type: Hydraulic-mechanical
Brakes: Pneumatic-hydraulic
   Operation: Foot pedal

ELECTRICAL SYSTEM

Nominal Voltage: 24 volts DC
Alternator: 27.5 volts, 220 amperes, driven by main engine
PP-7333 AC/DC Converter
Auxiliary Generator: None
Battery: (4) 12 volts, 2 sets of 2 in series connected in parallel

COMMUNICATIONS

Radio: AN/VRC-92A, AN/VRC-83(V)2, AN/PRC-68, PLRS, AN/GRC-213

FIRE PROTECTION

    (2) 9.0 pound Halon, fixed
    (2) 2.75 pound Halon, portable

NBC PROTECTION

NBC System M13A1
   Detection and Warning System: M8A1
      Detection and Warning Device: M43A1
   Precleaner/Particulate Filter Assembly: M1A1-19
   Gas Filter: (2) M18
   Heater, Air/Electric: M3
   Ventilated Face Masks: M25A1

PERFORMANCE

Maximum Speed: Level road		62 miles/hour
Water		6.5 miles/hour
Maximum Grade:		60 per cent
Maximum Side Slope:		30 per cent
Maximum Trench:		5.7 feet
Maximum Vertical Wall:		19.7 inches
Maximum Fording Depth:		Floats
Minimum Turning Circle:		50.8 feet
Cruising Range: Roads	approx.	400 miles

LIGHT ARMORED VEHICLE, ANTITANK LAV-AT
(8 wheels, 8 or 4 wheels driven)

GENERAL DATA

Crew:	4	men
Length: Overall	251.6	inches
Width: Overall	98.4	inches
Height: Launcher stowed	123.0	inches
Launcher low stow	106.0	inches
Launcher erected	138.5	inches
Fire Height:	approx. 117	inches
Tread: Front	85.8	inches
Rear	86.8	inches
Wheelbase: Front to 2nd axle	43.3	inches
Front to 3rd axle	95.9	inches
Front to rear axle	136.8	inches
Ground Clearance: Under differential	14.9	inches
Approach Angle:	40	degrees
Departure Angle:	45	degrees
Weight, Combat Loaded:	27,650	pounds
Weight, Unstowed:	24,850	pounds
Power to Weight Ratio:	19.9	hp/ton
Self-Recovery Winch Capacity:	15,000	pounds

ARMOR

Type: Hull, rolled hard homogeneous steel; Welded assembly
Protection against 7.62mm ball ammunition at point blank range
Protection against 14.5mm ammunition w/applique armor

ARMAMENT

Primary: TOW 2 missile launcher (2 tube)

Traverse:	360 degrees
Traverse Rate: (max)	10.3 seconds/360 degrees
Elevation:	+35 to -30 degrees
Elevation Rate: (max)	12 degrees/second

Secondary:
    (1) 7.62mm MG on pintle mount
    (2) M257 smoke grenade launchers on hull roof

AMMUNITION

Ready:
2 TOW 2 missiles in launcher
200 rounds 7.62mm
8 L8A1 smoke grenades in launchers
Stowed:
14 TOW 2 missiles
800 rounds 7.62mm
8 L8A1 smoke grenades

FIRE CONTROL AND VISION EQUIPMENT

Primary Weapon: TOW 2 guidance system

Vision Devices:	Direct	Indirect
Driver	Hatch	Periscope M17 (3) Night vision periscope AN/VVS-2(V)4 (1)
Commander	Hatch	Periscope M17 (8) Night vision periscope AN/VVS-2(V)4 (1)
Gunner	Hatch and vision blocks (7)	TOW sight assembly
Loader	Hatch and vision block (1)	

Total Periscopes: M17 (11), AN/VVS-2(V)4 (2)

ENGINE

Make and Model: General Motors 6V53T
Type: 6 cylinder, 2 cycle, vee

Cooling System: Liquid	Ignition: Compression
Displacement:	318 cubic inches
Bore and Stroke:	3.875 x 4.5 inches
Compression Ratio:	18.0:1
Gross Horsepower: (max)	275 hp at 2800 rpm
Gross Torque: (max)	586 ft-lbs at 2000 rpm
Weight:	1495 pounds, dry
Fuel: diesel oil M-VV-F-800	71 gallons
Engine Oil:	22 quarts

POWER TRAIN

Transmission: Allison MT653, 5 speeds forward, 1 reverse
    Single stage, polyphase torque converter
Transfer Case: AG-VST(mod)
    Gear Ratio: 0.5778:1
Differential: AS-DL500
    Gear Ratio: 2.23:1
Wheel Drive Assembly: Planetary hubs
    Gear Ratio: 3.79:1

RUNNING GEAR

Suspension:
    8 wheels (4/side)
    Front 4 wheels, independent, coil springs
    Rear 4 wheels, independent, torsion bars
    Shock absorbers on all 8 wheels
    Tires: Michelin XL w/run-flat inserts
    Tire Size: 11.00 x 16
Steering: Front four wheels
    Type: Hydraulic-mechanical
Brakes: Pneumatic-hydraulic
    Operation: Foot pedal

ELECTRICAL SYSTEM

Nominal Voltage: 24 volts DC
Alternator: 27.5 volts, 220 amperes, driven by main engine
Auxiliary Generator: None
Battery: (4) 12 volts, 2 sets of 2 in series connected in parallel

COMMUNICATIONS

Radio: AN/VRC-92A (2), AN/PRC-104, AN/PRC-68
CVC Helmet: 4

FIRE PROTECTION

    (2) 9.0 pound Halon, fixed
    (2) 2.75 pound Halon, portable

NBC PROTECTION

NBC System: M13A1
    Detection and Warning System: M8A1
        Detection and Warning Device: M43A1
    Precleaner/Particular Filter Assembly: M1A1-19
    Gas Filter: (2) M18
    Heater, Air/Electric: M3
    Ventilated Face Masks: M25A1

PERFORMANCE

Maximum Speed: Level road		62 miles/hour
Water		6.5 miles/hour
Maximum Grade:		60 per cent
Maximum Side Slope:		30 per cent
Maximum Trench:		5.7 feet
Maximum Vertical Wall:		19.7 inches
Maximum Fording Depth:		Floats
Minimum Turning Circle: (diameter)		50.8 feet
Cruising Range Roads:	approx.	400 miles

LIGHT ARMORED VEHICLE, MORTAR LAV-M
(8 wheels, 8 or 4 wheels driven)

GENERAL DATA

Crew:	5 men
Length: Overall	251.6 inches
Width: Overall	98.4 inches
Height:	84.3 inches
Roof Hatch: Length approx.	65 inches
Width approx.	54 inches
Tread: Front	85.8 inches
Rear	86.8 inches
Wheelbase: Front to 2nd axle	43.3 inches
Front to 3rd axle	95.9 inches
Front to rear axle	136.8 inches
Ground Clearance: Under differential	14.9 inches
Approach Angle:	40 degrees
Departure Angle:	45 degrees
Weight, Combat Loaded:	26,720 pounds
Weight, Unstowed:	23,520 pounds
Power to Weight Ratio:	20.6 hp/ton
Self-Recovery Winch Capacity:	15,000 pounds

ARMOR

Type: Hull, rolled hard homogeneous steel; Welded assembly
Protection against 7.62mm ball ammunition at point blank range
Protection against 14.5mm ammunition w/applique armor

ARMAMENT

Primary: 81mm mortar M252 w/360 degree traverse
Secondary:
    (1) 7.62mm MG on pintle mount
    (2) M257 smoke grenade launchers on hull roof

AMMUNITION

    Ready:
    200 rounds 7.62mm
    8 L8A1 smoke grenades in launchers
    Stowed:
    90 rounds 81mm
    800 rounds 7.62mm
    8 L8A1 smoke grenades

FIRE CONTROL AND VISION EQUIPMENT

Primary Weapon:

Vision Devices:	Direct	Indirect
Driver	Hatch	Periscope M17 (3)
		Night vision periscope
		AN/VVS-2(V)4 (1)
Commander	Hatch	Periscope M17 (8)
		Night vision periscope
		AN/VVS-2(V)4 (1)
Mortar Crew	Hatch	None

Total Periscopes: M17 (11), AN/VVS-2(V)4 (2)

ENGINE

Make and Model: General Motors 6V53T	
Type: 6 cylinder, 2 cycle, vee	
Cooling System: Liquid	Ignition: Compression
Displacement:	318 cubic inches
Bore and Stroke:	3.875 x 4.5 inches
Compression Ratio:	18.0:1
Gross Horsepower: (max)	275 hp at 2800 rpm
Gross Torque: (max)	586 ft-lbs at 2000 rpm
Weight:	1495 pounds, dry
Fuel: Diesel oil M-VV-F-800	71 gallons
Engine Oil:	22 quarts

POWER TRAIN

Transmission: Allison MT653, 5 speeds forward, 1 reverse
    Single stage, polyphase torque converter
Transfer Case: AG-VST(mod)
    Gear Ratio: 0.5778:1
Differential: AS-DL500
    Gear Ratio: 2.23:1
Wheel Drive Assembly: Planetary hubs
    Gear Ratio: 3.79:1

RUNNING GEAR

Suspension:
    8 wheels (4/side)
    Front four wheels, independent, coil springs
    Rear four wheels, independent, torsion bars
    Shock absorbers on all 8 wheels
    Tires: Michelin XL w/run-flat inserts
    Tire Size: 11.00 x 16
Steering: Front four wheels
    Type: Hydraulic-mechanical
Brakes: Pneumatic-hydraulic
    Operation: Foot pedal

ELECTRICAL SYSTEM

Nominal Voltage: 24 volts DC
Alternator: 27.5 volts, 220 amperes, driven by main engine
Auxiliary Generator: None
Battery: (4) 12 volts, 2 sets of 2 in series connected in parallel

COMMUNICATIONS

Radio: AN/VRC-92A, AN/PRC-104, AN/PRC-68
CVC Helmet: 3

FIRE PROTECTION

    (2) 9.0 pound Halon, fixed
    (2) 2.75 pound Halon, portable

NBC PROTECTION

NBC System: M13A1
    Detection and Warning System: M8A1
        Detection and Warning Device: M43A1
    Precleaner/Particulate Filter Assembly: M1A1-19
    Gas Filter: (2) M18
    Heater, Air/Electric: M3
    Ventilated Face Masks: M25A1

PERFORMANCE

Maximum Speed: Level road		62 miles/hour
Water		6.5 mile/hour
Maximum Grade:		60 per cent
Maximum Side Slope:		30 per cent
Maximum Trench:		5.7 feet
Maximum Vertical Wall:		19.7 inches
Maximum Fording Depth:		Floats
Minimum Turning Circle: (diameter)		50.8 feet
Cruising Range: Roads	approx.	400 miles

LIGHT ARMORED VEHICLE, RECOVERY LAV-R
(8 wheels, 8 or 4 wheels driven)

GENERAL DATA

Crew:	3 men
Length: Overall, Crane stowed to rear	290.4 inches
Crane stowed to front	256.0 inches
Width: Overall	98.4 inches
Height: Crane stowed to rear	109.0 inches
Crane stowed to front	106.0 inches
Tread: Front	85.8 inches
Rear	86.8 inches
Wheelbase: Front to 2nd axle	43.3 inches
Front to 3rd axle	95.9 inches
Front to rear axle	136.8 inches
Ground Clearance: Under differential	14.9 inches
Approach Angle:	40 degrees
Departure Angle:	45 degrees
Weight, Combat Loaded:	27,920 pounds
Weight, Unstowed:	24,980 pounds
Power to Weight Ratio:	19.7 hp/ton
Self-Recovery Winch Capacity:	15,000 pounds

ARMOR

Type: Hull, rolled hard homogeneous steel; Welded assembly
Protection against 7.62mm ball ammunition at point blank range
Protection against 14.5mm ammunition w/applique armor

ARMAMENT

(1) 7.62mm MG on pintle mount
(2) M257 smoke grenade launchers on hull roof

AMMUNITION

Ready:
200 rounds 7.62mm
8 L8A1 smoke grenades in launchers
Stowed:
800 rounds 7.62mm
8 L8A1 smoke grenades

RECOVERY EQUIPMENT

Rear Mounted Recovery Winch:	
Capacity:	30,000 pounds
Extendable and Rotatable Crane:	
Capacity: Boom fully extended	2,650 pounds
Boom fully retracted	6,600 pounds

Fuel Transfer Sub System:
Portable Auxiliary Power Unit: 10 kilowatt generator

VISION EQUIPMENT

Vision Devices:	Direct	Indirect
Driver	Hatch	Periscope M17 (3)
		Night vision periscope AN/VVS-2(V)4 (1)
Commander	Hatch	Periscope M17 (8)
		Night vision periscope AN/VVS-2(V)4 (1)
Rigger	Hatch and vision block	None

Total Periscopes: M17 (11), AN/VVS-2(V)4 (2)

ENGINE

Make and Model: General Motors 6V53T	
Type: 6 cylinder, 2 cycle, vee	
Cooling System: Liquid	Ignition: Compression
Displacement:	318 cubic inches
Bore and Stroke:	3.875 x 4.5 inches
Compression Ratio:	18.0:1
Gross Horsepower: (max)	275 hp at 2800 rpm
Gross Torque: (max)	586 ft-lbs at 2000 rpm
Weight:	1495 pounds, dry
Fuel: diesel oil M-VV-F-800	71 gallons
Engine Oil:	22 quarts

POWER TRAIN

Transmission: Allison MT653, 5 speeds forward, 1 reverse
Single stage, polyphase torque converter
Transfer Case: AG-VST(mod)
Gear Ratio: 0.5778:1
Differential: AS-DL500
Gear Ratio: 2.23:1
Wheel Drive Assembly: Planetary hubs
Gear Ratio: 3.79:1

RUNNING GEAR

Suspension:
8 wheels (4/side)
Front four wheels, independent, coil springs
Rear four wheels, independent, torsion bars
Shock absorbers on all 8 wheels
Tires: Michelin XL w/run-flat inserts
Tire Size: 11.00 x 16
Steering: Front four wheels
Type: Hydraulic-mechanical
Brakes: Pneumatic-hydraulic
Operation: Foot pedal

ELECTRICAL SYSTEM

Nominal Voltage: 24 volts DC
Alternator: 27.5 volts, 220 amperes, driven by main engine
Auxiliary Generator: None
Battery: (4) 12 volts, 2 sets of 2 in series connected in parallel

COMMUNICATIONS

Radio: AN/VRC-92A, AN/PRC-104, AN/PRC-68
CVC Helmet: 3

FIRE PROTECTION

(2) 9.0 pound Halon, fixed
(2) 2.75 pound Halon, portable

NBC PROTECTION

NBC System: M13A1
Detection and Warning System: M8A1
Detection and Warning Device: M43A1
Precleaner/Particulate Filter Assembly: M1A1-19
Gas Filter: (2) M18
Heater, Air/Electric: M3
Ventilated Face Masks: M25A1

PERFORMANCE

Maximum Speed: Level road		62 miles/hour
Water		6.5 mile/hour
Maximum Grade:		60 per cent
Maximum Side Slope:		30 per cent
Maximum Trench:		5.7 feet
Maximum Vertical Wall:		19.7 inches
Maximum Fording Depth:		Floats
Minimum Turning Circle: (diameter)		50.8 feet
Cruising Range: Roads	approx.	400 miles

LIGHT ARMORED VEHICLE, LOGISTICS LAV-L
(8 wheels, 8 or 4 wheels driven)

GENERAL DATA

Crew:	3	men
Length: Overall	254.6	inches
Width: Overall	98.4	inches
Height:	109.0	inches
Cargo Compartment: Height	54.9	inches
Length	86.0	inches
Width	57.6	inches
Cargo Hatch: Length approx.	65	inches
Width approx.	54	inches
Tread: Front	85.8	inches
Rear	86.8	inches
Wheelbase: Front to 2nd axle	43.3	inches
Front to 3rd axle	95.9	inches
Front to rear axle	136.8	inches
Ground Clearance: Under differential	14.9	inches
Approach Angle:	40	degrees
Departure Angle:	45	degrees
Weight, Combat Loaded:	28,200	pounds
Weight, Unstowed:	22,760	pounds
Power to Weight Ratio:	19.6	hp/ton
Self-Recovery Winch Capacity:	15,000	pounds

ARMOR

Type: Hull, rolled hard homogeneous steel; Welded assembly
Protection against 7.62mm ball ammunition at point blank range
Protection against 14.5mm ammunition w/applique armor

ARMAMENT

    (1) 7.62mm MG on pintle mount
    (2) M257 smoke grenade launchers on hull roof

AMMUNITION

    Ready:
    200 rounds 7.62mm
    8 L8A1 smoke grenades in launchers
    Stowed:
    800 rounds 7.62mm
    8 L8A1 smoke grenades

SPECIAL FEATURES

Telescopic Boom Crane Capacity:	1100 pounds
Chain Hoist Capacity:	2000 pounds

VISION EQUIPMENT

Vision Devices:	Direct	Indirect
Driver	Hatch	Periscope M17 (3)
		Night vision periscope AN/VVS-2(V)4 (1)
Commander	Hatch	Periscope M17 (5) AN/VVS-2(V)4 (1)
Crew	None	None

Total Periscopes: M17 (8), AN/VVS-2(V)4 (2)

ENGINE

Make and Model: General Motors 6V53T
Type: 6 cylinder, 2 cycle, vee

Cooling System: Liquid	Ignition: Compression
Displacement:	318 cubic inches
Bore and Stroke:	3.875 x 4.5 inches
Compression Ratio:	18.0:1
Gross Horsepower: (max)	275 hp at 2800 rpm
Gross Torque: (max)	586 ft-lbs at 2000 rpm
Weight:	1495 pounds, dry
Fuel: diesel oil M-VV-F-800	71 gallons
Engine Oil:	22 quarts

POWER TRAIN

Transmission: Allison MT653, 5 speeds forward, 1 reverse
    Single stage, polyphase torque converter
Transfer Case: AG-VST(mod)
    Gear Ratio: 0.5778:1
Differential: AS-DL500
    Gear Ratio: 2.23:1
Wheel Drive Assembly: Planetary hubs
    Gear ratio: 3.79:1

RUNNING GEAR

Suspension:
    8 wheels (4/side)
    Front four wheels, independent, coil springs
    Rear four wheels, independent, torsion bars
    Shock absorbers on all 8 wheels
    Tires: Michelin XL w/run-flat inserts
    Tire Size: 11.00 x 16
Steering: Front four wheels
    Type: Hydraulic-mechanical
Brakes: Pneumatic-hydraulic
    Operation: Foot pedal

ELECTRICAL SYSTEM

Nominal Voltage: 24 volts DC
Alternator: 27.5 volts, 220 amperes, driven by main engine
Auxiliary Generator: None
Battery: (4) 12 volts, 2 sets of 2 in series connected in parallel

COMMUNICATIONS

Radio: AN/VRC-92A, AN/PRC-104, AN/PRC-68
CVC Helmet: 3

FIRE PROTECTION

    (2) 9.0 pound Halon, fixed
    (2) 2.75 pound Halon, portable

NBC PROTECTION

NBC System: M13A1
    Detection and Warning System: M8A1
        Detection and Warning Device: M43A1
    Precleaner/Particulate Filter Assembly: M1A1-19
    Gas Filter: (2) M18
    Heater, Air/Electric: M3
    Ventilated Face Masks: M25A1

PERFORMANCE

Maximum Speed: Level road		62 miles/hour
Water		6.5 miles/hour
Maximum Grade:		60 per cent
Maximum Side Slope:		30 per cent
Maximum Trench:		5.7 feet
Maximum Vertical Wall:		19.7 inches
Maximum Fording Depth:		Floats
Minimum Turning Circle: (diameter)		50.8 feet
Cruising Range: Roads	approx.	400 miles

ARMORED SECURITY VEHICLE M1117
(4 wheels, 4 or 2 wheels driven)

GENERAL DATA

Crew:	3 men
Passengers:	1 man
Length: Overall	239.0 inches
Width: Overall	101.0 inches
Height: Overall	102 inches
Fire Height:	approx. 86 inches
Tread:	84.3 inches
Wheelbase:	121.25 inches
Ground Clearance: Nominal	18 inches
Approach Angle:	40 degrees
Departure Angle:	40 degrees
Weight, Combat Loaded:	29,500 pounds
Weight, Unstowed:	26,000 pounds
Power to Weight Ratio:	19.0 hp/ton

ARMOR

Type: Turret, rolled hard homogeneous steel;
    Hull, rolled hard homogeneous steel; Welded assembly
    Ceramic composite applique and spall liner
    Protection against 14.5mm ammunition w/applique armor

ARMAMENT

    (1) .50 caliber MG M2HB in turret
    (1) 40mm Mark 19 automatic grenade launcher in turret

Traverse: Powered or manual	360 degrees
Traverse Rate: Powered, max.	45 degrees/second
Elevation: Manual	+45 to -8 degrees

    Provision for (1) 7.62mm MG on turret top

AMMUNITION

    Ready: 100 rounds 40mm
            200 rounds .50 caliber
    Stowed: 500 rounds 40mm
            600 rounds .50 caliber

FIRE CONTROL AND VISION EQUIPMENT

Primary Armament: M36E2 day/night sight in turret

Vision Devices:	Direct	Indirect
Driver	Hatch and (2) vision blocks	AN/VVS 501 night vision
Commander	Hatch and (2) vision blocks	None
Gunner	Hatch	M36E2 sight (7) periscopes
Passenger	(2) vision blocks	None

ENGINE

Make and Model: Cummins 6CTA8.3
Type: 6 cylinder, 4 cycle, turbocharged, in-line

Cooling System: Liquid	Ignition: Compression
Displacement:	504 cubic inches
Bore and Stroke:	4.49 x 5.32 inches
Compression Ratio:	18:1
Gross Horsepower: (max)	276 hp at 1900 rpm
Gross Torque: (max)	858 ft-lbs at 1300 rpm
Weight:	1330 pounds, dry
Fuel: Diesel oil	50 gallons
Engine Oil:	20 quarts

POWER TRAIN

Transmission: Allison MD3560, 6 speed forward, 1 reverse
Transfer Case: Single speed, shift on the move
    Gear Ratio: 0.94:1
Differentials: Meritor double reduction
    Gear Ratio: 3.9:1
Wheel Drives: Reduction gear planetary hub
    Gear Ratio: 2:1

RUNNING GEAR

Suspension:
    4 wheels (2/side)
    Independent coil springs
    Shock absorbers on all 4 wheels
    Tires: Radial tubeless w/run-flat inserts
    Tire Size: 14.00R20
Steering: Front two wheels, TRW Model TAS-65
    Type: Hydraulic-mechanical
Brakes: Hydraulic
    Operation: Foot pedal

ELECTRICAL SYSTEM

Nominal Voltage: 24 volts DC
Alternator: 100 amperes driven by main engine
Auxiliary Generator: None
Battery: (2) 12 volts in series

COMMUNICATIONS

Radio: AN/VRC-91A
Intercom: 4 station, AN/VIC-3

FIRE PROTECTION

    (1) 10 pound FM200, fixed
    (2) 2.5 pound dry chemical, portable

NBC PROTECTION

NBC System: M13A1

PERFORMANCE

Maximum Speed: level road	63 miles/hour
Maximum Grade:	60 per cent
Maximum Side Slope:	30 percent
Maximum Trench:	1.5 feet
Maximum Vertical Wall:	22 inches
Maximum Fording Depth:	60 inches
Minimum Turning Circle: (diameter)	55 feet
Cruising Range: Roads approx.	440 miles

REFERENCES AND SELECTED BIBLIOGRAPHY

Books, Manuscripts and Published Articles

Clarke, Brigadier Dudley, "The Eleventh at War", Michael Joseph Limited, London 1952

Crismon, Fred W., "U. S. Military Wheeled Vehicles", Crestline Publishing Co. Inc., Sarasota, Florida, 1983

Fletcher, David, "War Cars, British Armoured Cars in the First World War", Her Majesty's Stationery Office, London, 1987

Hocking, John G., "A History of United States Armored Cars", Washington National Records Center, Washington, D.C., 1969

Hyatt, First Lieutenant John Alan, "The LAV in the Scout Role", Armor September-October 1991, Volume C number 5, U.S. Army Armor Center, Fort Knox, KY

Green, Michael, "Hummer, The Combat and Development History of the AM General High Mobility Multipurpose Wheeled Vehicle", Motorbooks International Osceola, WI, 1992

Michaels, G. J., "Tip of the Spear, U. S. Marine Light Armor in the Gulf War", Naval Institute Press, Annapolis, MD, 1998

Ong, Peter S. and Ferry, Sergeant David S. USMC, "The Last of the USMC M151 FAVs", Journal of Military Ordnance Volume 11 Number 6, November 2001, Darlington Productions, Inc., Darlington, MD, 2001

Perrett, Bryan and Lord, Anthony, "The Czar's British Squadron", William Kimber & Company, Limited, London 1981

Pitt-Rivers, J. A., "The Story of the Royal Dragoons 1938-1945" Wiliam Clowes & Sons Limited, London

Stewart, P.. F., "The History of the XII Royal Lancers", Oxford University Press, London, 1950.

_____"The Story of the Twenty-Third Hussars 1940-1946", April 1946

Reports and Official Documents

"Field Manual FM23-60 Browning Machine Gun, Caliber .50, HB M2 Ground" War Department, Washington, D.C., 25 September 1940

"Field Manual FM44-57 Service of the Piece Multiple Machine Gun Mounts" War Department, Washington, D.C., 29 January 1945

"Handbook of Artillery" Office Chief of Ordnance, Washington, D.C., May 1920

"Notes on Materiel Heavy Armored Car T18 and T18E2" Yellow Truck & Coach Manufacturing Company, Detroit, Michigan, 15 October 1942

"Notes on Materiel Light Armored Car T23", Fargo Motor Corporation, undated

"Notes on Materiel Light Armored Car T23E1", Fargo Motor Corporation, undated

"Notes on Materiel 37mm Gun Motor Carriage T22", Ford Motor Company, Dearborn, Michigan, undated

"Notes on Materiel T55 3" Gun Motor Carriage", Cook Bros, Los Angles, California, 1 September 1943

"Record of Development of Armored Cars, Half-Tracks, Tank Transporters, Tractors and Motor Transport from 1 September 1942 to 1 September 1944", 28 September 1944

"Record of the Development of Armored Cars, Half-Tracks, Tank Transporters, Trucks and Trailers from 1 September 1944 to 15 May1945 and Record of Development of Motorcycles and Bicycles from 1 September 1942 to 15 May 1945", 28 May 1945

"Technical Manual TM9-303 57mm Gun M1 and Gun Carriages M1, M1A1, and M1A2", War Department, Washington, D.C., 24 February 1943

"Technical Manual TM9-303 57mm Guns M1 and Mk. III (British) and Carriages M1, M1A1, M1A2, M1A3, and M2", War Department, Washington, D.C., 25 April 1944

"Technical Manual TM3-320 Mortar, Chemical, 4.2 inch", War Department, Washington, D.C., 30 June 1945

"Technical Manual TM9-743 Light Armored Car M8 and Armored Utility Car M20", War Department, Washington, D.C., 21 February 1944

"Technical Manual TM9-705 Scout Car M3A1", War Department, Washington, D.C., 26 October 1942

"Technical Manual TM9-741 Medium Armored Car T17E1", War Department, Washington, D.C., 15 December 1942

"Technical Manual TM9-741 Supplement Antiaircraft Turret, Medium Armored Car T17E2" War Department, Washington, D.C., 1 November 1943

"Technical Manual TM9-750A 37mm Gun Motor Carriage M6", War Department, Washington, D.C., 25 November 1942

"Technical Manual TM9-1709 Ordnance Maintenance Chassis and Body for Scout Cars M3A1" War Department, Washington, D.C., 22 September 1942

"Technical Manual TM9-2010 Multiple Caliber .50 Machine Gun Mounts M45, M45C, M45D, and M45F; Multiple Caliber .50 Machine Gun Trailer Mount M55; and Mount Trailer M20", Department of the Army, Washington, D.C., 4 December 1953

"Technical Manual TM9-2200 Small Arms Materiel and Associated Equipment", Department of the Army, Washington, D.C., 9 October 1956

"Technical Manual TM9-2320-245-10 Operator's Manual for Car, Armored, Light: 4x4 (V-100 Commando), XM 706, 2320-999-4370, M706, 2320-168-2620 (Formerly XM706E1), XM706E2, 2320-133-9646", Department of the Army, Washington, D.C.10 August 1972

"U.S. Marine Corps Technical Manual TM 08594A-10/2, Operator's Manual, Light Armored Vehicle LAV-25 (2320-01-123-1602) Automotive Hull", Department of the Navy, HQ USMC, Washington, D.C. December 1993

"U.S. Marine Corps Technical Manual TM 08594A-10/1B, Operator's Manual Light Armored Vehicle LAV-25 (2320-01-123-1602) Turret", Department of the Navy, HQ USMC, Washington, D.C., January 1997

"U.S. Marine Corps Technical Manual TM 08650A-10A Operator's Manual Supplement to TM 08594A-10/2A Light Armored Vehicle, Battalion Command and Control LAV-C²", Department of the Navy, HQ USMC, Washington, D.C., August 1995

"U.S. Marine Corps Technical Manual TM 08655A-10A Operator's Manual Supplement to TM 08594A-10/2A Light Armored Vehicle, Mortar LAV-M", Department of the Navy, HQ USMC, Washington, D.C., May 1995

"U.S. Marine Corps Technical Manual TM 08654A-10A Operator's Manual Supplement to TM 08594A-10/2 Light Armored Vehicle, Logistics LAV-L", Department of the Navy, HQUSMC, Washington, D.C., December 1994

"U.S. Marine Corps Technical Manual TM 08651A-10A Operator's Manual Supplement to TM 08594A-10/2 Light Armored Vehicle Recovery LAV-R" Department of the Navy, HQ USMC, Washington, D.C., April 1995

"U.S. Marine Corps Technical Manual TM 08652A-10/1A Operator's Manual Light Armored Vehicle, Anti-Tamk LAV-AT, Turret", Department of the Navy, HQ USMC, Washington, D.C., August 1993

"U.S. Marine Corps Technical Manual TM 08652A-10/2 Operator's Manual Light Armored Vehicle, Anti-Tank LAV-AT, Automotive Hull" Department of the Navy, HQ USMC, Washington, D.C., July 1993

"Rocket and Underwater Ordnance" Summary Technical Report of Division 3, National Defense Research Committee, Volume 1, Washington, D.C., 1946

"Transportation Equipment and Related Problems" Summary Technical Report of Division 12, National Defense Research Committee, Volume 1, Washington, D.C., 1946